Technical

Communication

THE MACMILLAN COMPANY
NEW YORK · CHICAGO
DALLAS · ATLANTA · SAN FRANCISCO
LONDON · MANILA

IN CANADA
BRETT-MACMILLAN LTD.
GALT, ONTARIO

Technical

Communication

GEORGE C. HARWELL

Duke University

New York

THE MACMILLAN COMPANY

First Printing

Library of Congress catalog card number: 60–5257

The Macmillan Company, New York
Brett-Macmillan Ltd., Galt, Ontario

Printed in the United States of America

Preface

This textbook was written with the engineering student primarily in mind. Actually, however, it can just as well serve as a guide and reference work for the practicing engineer and for persons studying and practicing in several other fields—notably: business, medicine, forestry, and the physical sciences. The basic form and the principles for effective treatment of letters, reports, articles, and speeches in these fields are the same as in engineering. Only the subject matter is different.

The book has three motifs: (1) an immediate and continuous effort to show what good writing really is, (2) an approach that is consistent because it stresses underlying principles instead of a variety of surface practices, and (3) models that are uniform in mechanics and uncomplicated in subject matter.

The text has six general divisions. Chapters 1, 2, and 3 discuss preliminary matters: the qualities of good writing (with particular reference to technical subject matter), the organization of material, and the use of exposition. Chapter 4 takes up the business letter. It seems advisable to make the letter the first specific type of writing to be treated because it is nearest the student's experience and because reference to it facilitates the discussion of reports.

Chapters 5, 6, and 7 are the heart of the book: an extended treatment of reports. Chapters 8 and 9 deal with other forms of communication that a scientific or a technical man should be familiar with—the magazine article and public speaking. Chapter 10 concerns the use and preparation of tables and figures.

The last part of the book is a review of the general principles of composition and a glossary of usage. From one standpoint this review

v

should come first, because everything else in the book assumes a knowledge of what it covers. Still, it would seem somewhat illogical for a book on advanced composition to open with a lengthy discussion of elementary matters; after all, they are included more as a reference manual for the student and as an aid to the teacher in marking papers than as an integral part of the text.

Insofar as it has been feasible, problems concerning the substance and the mechanics involved in a particular type of writing have been treated in the same chapter, so that the chapters are fairly independent of each other. This arrangement saves the student from having to hunt about when he is ready to write a given paper.

The arrangement also adds to the flexibility of the material so that a teacher can take it up in any order he wishes. For instance, the formal report is explained before the informal because the latter is treated as a simplified form of the longer type. Yet they can be taught in the reverse order, for the discussion of the informal report is amply illustrated in itself and has cross references to the preceding chapter.

In the discussion of letters and reports, considerable attention has been given to form, not because it should be an end in itself but because students, and also men well along in their profession, often find that a sense of form crystallizes and integrates their approach to the more substantial things: content and organization.

Throughout the book the term "paper" is used to mean "a piece of writing." It is not a prepossessing word, but it spares both the writer and the reader the recurrent circumlocution of naming the various types of "papers" the student should know something about.

I wish to thank the following people for giving me valuable suggestions and criticism: Professor Ernest Elsevier, Professor E. K. Kraybill, and Dean Walter J. Seeley of the College of Engineering, Duke University; Professor Carl Anderson of the English Department, Duke University; Mr. W. Gillies Brown of the Water and Sewer Department, Durham, N.C.; and Mr. A. Stanley Higgins of the Aircraft Gas Turbine Division of the General Electric Company, Evendale, Ohio.

G.H.

Contents

Technical

Communication

Effective

Writing

THE IMPORTANCE OF CLEAR EXPRESSION

Written and oral expression is an essential part of technical work. Nearly every job is preceded or followed by a report, and often there are reports both before and after. Many engineers estimate that 75% of their time is given not to doing technical work itself but to communicating ideas about that work to other people. No matter what the particular field is, the medium at some point is words.

It follows that the ability to express himself well is a decisive factor in the career of the professional technologist or scientist. He cannot be happy living in the constant dread of being called on to do what he knows he cannot do—namely, write or speak about his work in such a way that others quickly grasp his meaning. On the other hand, the knowledge that he can do it is a source of confidence, and the knowledge that he has done it brings the deep satisfaction that always follows achievement.

A command of clear expression can also lead to more tangible rewards. First, it makes a good impression on a man's superiors by saving them time when they are considering his work. Second, it shows his technical ability to advantage and results in a higher rating of his professional judgment. And third, these things being so, he is given greater responsibility, which leads to promotion and salary increases.

Apropos of the last point is a study conducted some years ago by one of America's largest engineering companies. Its principal finding was that one hundred thousand dollars is the minimum difference in the lifetime earnings of two men who have equal technical ability but of whom one can express himself well and the other cannot.

THE ELEMENTS OF GOOD WRITING

Whether the field is technical or not, the basic elements of good writing are always the same. They do not vary according to the subject matter. The phrases "technical communication" and "technical writing" do not apply to a special way of writing, but pertain to what the writing is about and have little to do with how the writing is done. Even that type of paper most closely associated with technical and scientific fields—the report—is special only in its general make-up, and it is used today in fields not at all technical.

Understanding now that the principal elements of good writing are the same in the technical field as in other fields, let us see what these elements are. We may consider them to be: accuracy, clarity, simplicity, and readability. Naturally they overlap. For instance, accuracy of expression requires clarity; in turn, clarity depends on simplicity, on structure and language that are easy for the reader to follow.

In addition to overlapping each other, these elements will vary in their relative proportions from paper to paper, depending on either the material, the readers the paper is aimed at, or both. For example, no matter who the expected readers may be, data concerning a rudimentary procedure can be set forth in simpler language than data concerning a complex one. Likewise, no matter what its subject, a paper addressed to non-experts should be less technical and therefore less exact than one written for experts, because the need of the non-experts for over-all clarity calls for some sacrifice of detail.

Still, in every case the four elements—accuracy, clarity, simplicity, and readability—must be present if the writing is to have its fullest effect. We shall examine these elements more closely.

Accuracy

For the engineer as well as for the scientist, the first concern is for the accuracy of his material—that is, the correctness and the completeness of his data and the soundness of his evaluation of them. This accuracy will depend on his training and experience, his judgment, and his conscientiousness.

Regardless of how accurate his material may be, however, it becomes worthless if it is communicated inaccurately. Long hours of testing and recording, of computing and evaluating have been wasted if this information is presented so carelessly that the reader misconstrues it and does not act upon it properly. Months of painstaking research and design mean nothing if favorable results are stated so ineffectually that the sponsor of the project fails to extend the financial grant necessary for the engineer to continue his work. In modern industry accuracy in reporting the findings is just as important as the findings themselves. Accordingly, the engineer has completed only half of his job when he has made sure that his data are accurate and his appraisal is sound; it remains for him to write a report that mirrors this accuracy.

Clarity

To be clear should be our constant aim. From the drawing up of the outline down to the choice of the last word in the final draft of the paper, there is no point where we can safely relax in our efforts to be clear. It is true that an idea can be so simple that almost any way of expressing it will be understood by an attentive reader. But there is the rub: we cannot count on all our readers being really attentive—that is, willing to ponder our meaning if our meaning is not apparent at once. For this reason a fixed maxim of composition is: do not write so that you *may* be understood, but write so that you *must* be.

Clear organization of the paper as a whole is prerequisite to its being fully grasped. The major topics and the sub-topics under them should have a logical connection that the reader can easily discern. He should always know where he is. A highly complicated subject can be made intelligible by lucid organization, by our carefully planning what we wish to say before attempting to say it.

This clarity of the whole should carry into the parts—into the paragraphs and the individual sentences. Each paragraph should be built around a central idea, called the topic sentence. Usually this sentence is an actual part of the paragraph. When it is not, it must be distinctly implied. Many other sentences, carrying many other ideas, may also be in the paragraph; but if the paragraph is to have unity, these sentences must bear directly on the topic sentence, their ideas must develop the central idea. Moreover, if the paragraph is to be coherent, these sentences must be so arranged that the connection between them is obvious and the flow from one idea to the next is smooth. The basis, then, of clarity within the paragraph is, first, unification of its content around a central thought and, second, coherence between successive ideas.

The building of clear sentences—sentences constructed grammatically and effectively and punctuated correctly—is a subject so broad and important as to deserve separate treatment (see pages 257-292). Nevertheless, here under the general topic of clarity we should observe that in sentences having more than one idea the writer should take extra pains to achieve clear structure. He should be especially alert for two pitfalls.

One pitfall is neglecting to decide the relative importance of the ideas and thereby failing to indicate to the reader the relative emphasis to be given them. Consider a simple case of two ideas:

a. A new alloy is used in the camshaft.
b. Because of it the camshaft can have a smaller diameter.

There are four possible ways to distribute the emphasis, and it is through sentence structure that the writer indicates which of the four he considers proper under the particular circumstances.

1. If he wants to give the facts equal weight, he should express them in the same kind of construction. Here it would be two independent clauses:*

A new alloy is used in the camshaft; it permits the shaft to have a smaller diameter.

2. If he wishes to retain equal emphasis on the alloy and the smaller diameter but to play down the actual use of the alloy, he should convert the first clause into some type of subordinate construction:

* The grammatical terms used in the following paragraphs, and throughout the text, are defined on pages 313-318.

A new alloy used in the camshaft permits it to have a smaller diameter.

Or he can eliminate the detail about use altogether:

A new alloy permits the camshaft to have a smaller diameter.

3. If he does not regard the two ideas as of equal significance and wants to stress the first one, he should express it as an independent clause and subordinate the second idea to it—that is, word the second idea as a clause or a phrase dependent on the first one:

A new alloy, which permits a smaller diameter, is used in the camshaft. (dependent clause)

A new alloy, permitting a smaller diameter, is used in the camshaft. (phrase)

4. If he wants the stress on the second idea, he reverses the subordination:

Because a new alloy is used, the diameter of the camshaft can be smaller.   (dependent clause)

Through the use of a new alloy the diameter of the camshaft can be smaller.   (phrase)

The other pitfall is failure to arrange the ideas in such a way that the logical connection between them is instantly apparent.

The machine should be dismantled before it is shipped by a competent mechanic.

This says that the machine is to be shipped by a competent mechanic, but the intended meaning is that it should be dismantled by one. Commas before and after the time clause would help, but it is poor practice to resort to punctuation for unscrambling careless construction. A rearrangement of the ideas is the only remedy:

Before the machine is shipped, it should be dismantled by a competent mechanic.

The machine should be dismantled by a competent mechanic before it is shipped.

Another example of a misplaced modifier is:

A small crack in the bottom of the cylinder, which is a result of overheating, is causing the loss in pressure.

The simplest correction is to use two independent clauses:

A small crack, caused by overheating, is in the bottom of the cylinder; the crack explains the loss in pressure.

A small crack in the bottom of the cylinder was caused by overheating; the crack explains the loss in pressure.

The loss in pressure is due to a small crack in the bottom of the cylinder; the crack was caused by overheating.

The passion to be clear should extend down to the choice of the individual words. The general organization, the paragraph development, and the sentence structure of a paper may all be perfectly sound, and yet its effectiveness can be marred or even destroyed by obscure language. The object of all oral and written expression is to set up in another person's mind the same image that is in one's own —or, to put it another way, to induce the same chemical action in another's brain that is taking place in one's own. Since words and the emphasis given them are the primary means of doing this, success is in direct ratio to the appropriateness of the diction.

This is especially true if the mode of expression is writing, for unlike a speaker, a writer is seldom present to clarify his meaning if it is questioned; he has to rely on his original phrasing. If the language is precise, the image he summons up in the reader's mind will be true and sharp; if the language is hazy, the image will be blurred. In short, whether the image is in focus or out of focus, and to what degree, will be determined by the words chosen to evoke it.

Unfortunately, there is no infallible means by which a writer may be sure that what he has put down will be readily understood by all his readers; and excepting most letters and the simplest reports, he will have more than one reader. They will vary in intelligence, in their power to concentrate, and in their knowledge of the field; and he cannot anticipate the needs of each one separately. Still, he can assure himself of maximum success by adopting a simple procedure: writing the first draft and revising it several days before the final draft is prepared.

The first draft should be written from his own standpoint to make certain he is saying what he meant to say. The first revision should be made primarily from the same viewpoint but with some awareness of a cross section of his readers, especially those readers who know least about the subject. The final revision should be entirely from the viewpoint of these readers; and the more time that elapses between the first draft and the final one, the easier it will be for the author to project himself out of his own thinking and read his work as others will read it.

The following sentences may be clear to the writer as he puts them on paper, but he will hardly let them stand if he later reads them from someone else's point of view.

New conduits should be ordered as the old wires are being removed.

This is subject to two interpretations. The first is that the actions are to be simultaneous:

New conduits should be ordered while the old wires are being removed.

The second indicates cause and effect:

New conduits should be ordered because the old wires are to be removed.

Another equivocal sentence is:

Only two days will be needed to fix the generator in the main building.

Does "to fix" have the meaning here of "to repair" or "to install"? Again:

The boiler cannot be used in its present shape.

Does this mean that the customary cylindrical shape of the boiler must be altered if it is to fit into the space allotted for it, or does "shape" have its slang meaning of "condition"? The context would probably indicate the answer, just as it might in the two examples before it. Even so, there is no getting away from the fact that the diction could be, and therefore should be, more precise.

The next sentence illustrates poor choice of structure as well as careless wording:

The walls must be removed with Lolly columns to support the roof.

Only when the reader gets to the end does he see that the writer is not suggesting a new use for Lolly columns—namely, as a means for tearing down walls. The writer brought the suspicion upon himself by carelessly choosing "with" to introduce the second idea. This idea, it turns out, is of equal weight with the first one and therefore should be a parallel construction—here, an independent clause:

The walls must be removed and Lolly columns will be used to support the roof.

Each of the preceding examples of ambiguous diction makes sense as it stands, but merely making sense is not enough. A statement should make the exact sense the writer intends it to make and should be open to no other interpretation. A reader cannot be blamed if he does not take time to grope around until he thinks he has found the correct meaning; the person who should put the most time on a sentence is the writer, not the reader—and he should put enough time on it to ensure that its true meaning not only *may* be understood, but *must* be.

Simplicity

Clearness and simplicity are practically inseparable virtues. That which is clear is usually simple in structure and diction, and that which is simple can nearly always be understood quickly. It is the involved paragraph and the complicated sentence that require more than one reading, and the long, unfamiliar word that causes delay. In view of what has already been said about paragraph and sentence structure and what is to be said about them later, the emphasis here will be on simplicity of language.

The words used to express an idea should be chosen on one basis: to convey that idea as quickly as is practical. With this aim, the words should already be known to the reader or they should be used in such a way that their meaning is obvious. In addition, they should be chosen for conciseness.

Generally speaking, the short word is more forceful than the long one, even when the reader knows both. Yet every day one can observe dozens of instances in which the longer synonym is used. An example prevalent in technical writing is the substitution of the polysyllable "encounter" for the forthright "have" and "find":

> We expect to encounter no trouble.

"Encounter" is a good word. It does mean "to meet with" or "to face" and is known to most people, but it is not as direct in this sentence as its equivalents. And in the following one it is downright wrong because its connotation is wholly ignored:

> During the overhaul we encountered several blown gaskets.

One can encounter an abstract like "trouble" but not that abstract made concrete in "blown gaskets." The habit of the word permits its use with a concrete thing only in referring to people: *to encounter Jones on turning the corner, to encounter one's rival.*

In the following sentence the diction is so heavy and strained as to be almost meaningless:

> Inferior gasoline will induce metallic agitation in the combustion chambers.

In language that every layman understands, this says:

> Inferior gasoline will cause the engine to knock.

Natural wording has also been sacrificed in the next sentence:

We lack the knowledge of why the costs are ascending.

This is a stiff and affected way of saying:

We do not know why the costs are rising.

The aim of simple diction, to repeat, is to convey a thought as quickly as is practical. This means conciseness as well as selectivity. It means that expression can be impeded by too many words as well as by heavy and unfamiliar ones.

The movement of the following sentences is slowed down by super-fluous words; they are just so many pounds of fat hindering the thought:

a. The mechanism can be repaired easily because of the fact that it is constructed very simply.
b. The drum contains a sufficient amount of oil.
c. The frame sprang a leak because of the lack of adequate braces between the sides.

Nowhere is there a downright error; the objection is that each thought is delayed by padding. Compare:

a. The mechanism can be repaired easily because of its simple construction.
b. The drum contains sufficient oil.
c. The frame sprang a leak because the sides lacked adequate braces.

The next example was one of the recommendations in a report describing a possible site for a gasoline terminal. A spur track needed by the terminal would have to cross the property of a brick company, which was willing to grant right of way in exchange for the privilege of using the spur itself. The sentence fairly groans under its burden of fat:

Use of the track to be constructed should be available to the neighboring brick company for any spur desired for its own use at any time requested by it.

The thought is not altered at all if 15 words are deleted:

The proposed track should be available to the neighboring brick company at any time.

One of the easiest circumlocutions to slip into is the impersonal construction in which "there" substitutes for a delayed subject:

a. Sometimes there may be leakage at the second joint.
b. There was a tendency for the coil to overheat.
c. There is only one man in the plant who can operate the press, and that is Garrison.
d. There are extra parts that come with the assembly.

In every instance none of the meaning is lost and considerable strength is added if the expletive construction is removed:

a. Leakage may occur at the second joint.
b. The coil tended to overheat.
c. Garrison is the only man in the plant who can operate the press.
d. Extra parts come with the assembly.

Of course, the expletive use of "there" is not always a fault. Indeed, it is to be preferred when it is less clumsy than an alternative construction or when it gives an idea a desired emphasis:

If there is a better means of distributing the load, we should employ it.

One word can be saved by using "exists," but the saving is hardly worth the less natural reading that results:

If a better means of distributing the load exists, we should employ it.

In the following instance, the expletive gives the first idea an emphasis and the sentence a balance that justify its use:

There are many possibilities, and we intend to study all of them.

To close the discussion of wordiness, the next example seems fit:

> Labor is both abundant and inexpensive, making the over-all conditions conducive to constructing the proposed plant in the city of Centerville.

This sentence violates every principle discussed so far: it is not accurate, it is not clear, and it is not simple. It is not accurate because labor, being a single aspect of the subject, cannot make the over-all conditions favorable; it can affect only one. If the intention is to say that labor, the major factor in locating the plant, is satisfactory, the wording should be changed. The sentence is not clear because the relative importance of the two ideas is not reflected in the structure; instead, it is reversed. The sentence is not simple because the words are both heavier and more numerous than they need be. As an added criticism, they are unpleasantly alliterative. It is not difficult to eliminate all these faults and get a clean statement:

> Because labor, the major consideration, is plentiful and cheap, the plant should be built in Centerville.

Readability

If a piece of writing is accurate, clear, and simple, the chances are strong that it is also readable. When these qualities are missing, reading becomes a chore. Conversely, when they are present, it becomes a pleasure because it is easy. The reader's attention is concentrated on *what* is being said, not distracted by *how* it is being said. In short, accuracy, clearness, and simplicity in themselves make for readability.

Still, the writer should not stop with them. There are other ways to increase the readableness of a paper. One is to diversify the sentence patterns. A series of sentences all built alike can be monotonous and can cause the reader's attention to flag. On the other hand, variation in the length and in the structure of sentences keeps his attention whetted.

The following paragraphs are the introduction of a report on Nualloy cartridge cases. The writer has made it interesting while still observing the requirements of the introduction of a formal report. The writing is accurate, clear, and simple. Yet the author has not relied on these qualities alone to make it readable. He has gone a step more and freely varied the length and the structure of his sentences. The result is an added vitality.

   Recent studies of Belson .22-caliber rimfire ammunition have shown that brass should no longer be used in rimfire cartridge cases because it is not strong enough to withstand the pressure produced by modern high-velocity loads. When loaded for high velocities brass cases have two major faults. The first is excessive expansion of the cases when fired, causing improper functioning of the weapons. The second fault is occasional bursting of the cases. Shrapnel from bursting cases not only damages the guns, but often it injures shooters and bystanders. These two faults occur most often in semiautomatic pistols and rifles.
   An extensive testing and research program has been undertaken by the Belson Arms Company to determine a suitable replacement for brass in rimfire cartridge cases. An acceptable metal must not have the faults of brass, must be easily formed into cartridge cases, and must be reasonably priced; moreover, cartridges made from this metal must have a low rate of misfiring. Since brass is an excellent cartridge case alloy except for the faults previously mentioned, its characteristics are used as standards in judging the alloys which are tested.
   Recently the C. K. Bond Company of Baltimore, Maryland, announced the development of Nualloy, an alloy that it recommends for use in cartridge cases. To determine the advisability of using it as a replacement for brass in rimfire cartridge cases, the Belson Arms Company has tested it. This report covers the following matters: the results of these tests, the availability of Nualloy, its manufacture, and its cost. Special attention is given to the retooling necessary to produce Nualloy cartridge cases and to the firing characteristics of these cases.
   It is recommended that the Belton Arms Company use Nualloy instead of brass as a rimfire cartridge case metal.

The variety in sentence patterns is more evident when it is reproduced in diagram. The horizontal lines below represent independent clauses; the solid diagonal lines, adjective and adverb clauses; the broken diagonal lines, phrases that are not integral parts of clauses.
A reader's enjoyment of a paper is further quickened if this variety in sentence pattern is carried into the very language. Repetition

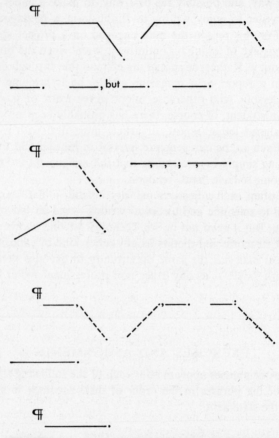

FIGURE 1   Sentence Pattern in Four Paragraphs

of words and the use of clichés blunt the effectiveness of a piece of writing regardless of its excellence in other respects. This does not mean that a writer should altogether avoid repeating a word or using a common idiom. If he does so, he is sure to use language that is artificial and inaccurate. What it does mean is that he should avoid needless repetition by using pronouns and close synonyms and that he should convert clichés—stale, overworked phrases which were once vivid—into fresh wording of his own or into plain, literal wording that never loses its force.

Another way, and possibly the best way, to make a paper readable is for the writer to enjoy writing it. Enthusiasm is contagious; so is boredom. For this reason the man engaged on a project should not make the mistake of letting his enthusiasm wane when the time comes to write about it. Rather, he should understand that through describing his work in a report or a magazine article, he is bringing it to the notice of persons who otherwise might never learn of it. With the composition student, of course, there has probably been no real project; his assigned letter, report, or article must deal with a fictitious situation. Even so, he can generate interest in himself and transmit it to his writing simply by pretending that the assignment is "real" and that he is going to have "real" readers.

All too often such adjectives as "dry," "stiff," "flat," and "dull" are applied to scientific and technical writing—and all too often with justification. But it need not be so. Technical writing allows the same freedom of structure and diction as any other kind of exposition, and the technical man has the same opportunity to exercise versatility— to write with "style"—as any other non-professional writer has.

EXERCISES AND ASSIGNMENTS

A. A series of phrases appears after each of the following statements. Number the phrases in the order of their accuracy in giving the gist of the statement.

1. In a shipment of 2000 transistors, 1806 met specifications.
   - ( ) a majority of the transistors
   - ( ) many of the transistors
   - ( ) most of the transistors
   - ( ) about 90% of the transistors
   - ( ) slightly more than 90% of the transistors
   - ( ) nearly all of the transistors

2. Half of a four-week job has been completed in two weeks.
   - ( ) excellent progress
   - ( ) satisfactory progress

(   ) good progress
(   ) fairly good progress

3. Heat losses were cut from 10% to 2%.
    (   ) reduced considerably
    (   ) reduced appreciably
    (   ) reduced somewhat
    (   ) nearly eliminated

B. Make the following sentences clearer by improving their structure or their diction or both.

1. The first officer following the vice-president is the comptroller.
2. One instance which I recall, an engine change had to be made in sub-zero weather.
3. We are glad you sent us your order and will make every effort to give you our best.
4. Modifications such as multiple carburetion and ignition, high lift cams, superchargers, and increased compression are made on cars as well as radical body designs being employed.
5. Six evenly-spaced ducts should be used on the two longer walls with four on the other two.
6. An emergency source will be provided by a small Diesel engine driven turbogenerator.
7. The minimum gasket thickness should be such that the filler thickness is at least twice the thickness of the combined layer thickness of the jacket.
8. When a bearing has the capacity for a higher thrust on one side than the other, that side will be marked by a red circle.

C. Reword the following sentences so that the language is simpler and more concise.

1. This adjustment will lead to the elimination of the noise problem.
2. There are two major setups which require a change of punches and three minor setups which call for a change in guide-rule lines.
3. The inventory shows that we are in need of spare parts.

4. Our lack of sufficient spare parts could cost us a considerable amount of time.

5. We conducted an examination of the machinery located in the powerhouse and are ready to submit a report on it at the present time.

6. The conductors are of inadequate size to efficiently accommodate the quantity of current that is transmitted.

7. We shall make arrangements to proceed with the beginning in the near future.

8. There are certain precautions which must be taken if the results are to be sound and reliable.

D. Revise the sentence pattern and wording of the following paragraphs to make them more varied and readable.

1. The method of eliminating waste is not adequate to handle the present needs. At the present time the shavings are transported from the cabinet shop by a network of suction pipes. The pipes lead to the different machines. The suction in the pipes is supplied by a 2-ft fan. The fan operates at the end of the cabinet shop. The power of this fan is boosted by a larger fan. This second fan operates in the adjoining room.

2. The reactions proceed in the following manner. Lime is heated with coke. The lime decomposes to calcium oxide. The calcium oxide reacts with the coke to give calcium carbide. The calcium carbide is then reacted with water to yield acetylene and calcium hydroxide. The calcium hydroxide is usually considered waste material. The acetylene is then run into a column. There it is mixed with steam and oxygen. Acetylene is hydrolized to acetaldehyde in the presence of mercuric sulfate. The acetaldehyde is oxidized by the oxygen in the mixture to acetic acid.

Organization of Material

The general arrangement of a body of data is the first thing to decide after we have gathered it. The nature of the material itself, the knowledge and the viewpoint of the people who are to read it, the effect we wish to achieve—these are the factors to consider in choosing a basic approach.

In most cases a set of facts can be presented effectively in more than one way. The problem then is to choose the best way in view of the particular conditions. Many papers gain added force and interest if we depart at points from the basic method of presentation. Consequently, there is the further problem of deciding whether a given paper falls in this class and, if so, where the departures should come —a problem taken up toward the end of the chapter.

First, let us consider the *basic* arrangements for material. Not counting the many possible variations, there are four: Order of Occurrence, Order of Descending Importance, Order of Ascending Importance, and Combination of Orders.

ORDER OF OCCURRENCE

In the Order of Occurrence the data are presented in a sequence that depends on either time or movement. It is a suitable arrangement for material that is of more or less uniform value. In other words, none of the parts are important enough to be treated out of their natural order, the order in which the data occurred or in which they

18

were observed. Usually, but not necessarily, the two orders are the same.

When the sequence is based on time, the time element is important because each thing prepares for what follows it. Instances are the history of a transaction, a report on the development of an object, the description of a problem and its solution, an account involving cause and effect, the procedure for manufacturing or installing equipment, the description of a process from the first stage through the last, the step-by-step account of how a study was conducted, the procedure followed or to be followed in running a test, an analysis, or an experiment.

As an example, let us say that we were called on to improve the efficiency of a manufacturing process by eliminating a certain bottleneck. We solved the problem by adding a new device, and now we are writing a report on it. The main headings are: Design, Manufacture, Installation, Preliminary Test, Adjustments, Final Test. The discussion follows the very sequence that our work did. This is the best arrangement because each stage of our task was dependent on the one before it and the reader can understand each section of the report better if he knows the work that preceded it.

In other cases, although time is still an element in that one thing happened or was observed before another, the fact is not pertinent. The sequence is more directional than temporal; the order is more that of movement than of occurrence. The movement can be from the front to the rear, from the outside to the inside, from the bottom to the top, from east to west, from north to south, and vice versa. It may be from the beginning to the end of a continuous line, as in the routing of a highway or an assembly belt.

To take a concrete illustration, we are writing a quarterly report on the volume of sales of a company product and the conditions that affected that volume. The company has divided the country into five areas, moving from east to west, and has designated them simply as Districts I, II, III, IV, and V. Because sales during the quarter have been about the same in each area, we decide to present the data in its natural sequence and the order of the headings is: District I, District II, District III, District IV, District V.

ORDER OF DESCENDING IMPORTANCE

When material is not of uniform value, it may be organized in the descending order of its importance. The major divisions are arranged so that the most important matter is treated first, the next most important comes second, and so on until the least important is last.

In the last example we postulated that there had been no marked variation in sales among the five districts and therefore discussed them "moving" from east to west. But let us assume differently: sales have varied greatly, being excellent in Districts III and V, normal in II, and badly off in I and IV. Now we should arrange the discussion to reflect these differences, and depending on whether we consider the excellent or the poor records to be more important, our order of headings will be either III, V, II, I, and IV or I, IV, II, III, and V.

As another illustration, in a report on a certain city as the possible location for a new plant, the factors to be taken into account will hardly be of equal weight. The company may be interested in a dozen or more questions, but their relative importance will not be the same under normal conditions. Moreover, it will change if the conditions change.

When a city is considered for the location of a plant, some of the fundamental questions that will affect the survey and, afterward, the organization of the report are: (1) is the factory to be near the source of raw materials? (2) is it to be near the potential market? (3) is it to draw largely on local labor or from the company's other plants? (4) is it to be actually within the city or simply near it?

Suppose we answer these questions as follows: (1) the plant is to be near the source of raw materials, (2) its finished product is intended mainly for a general market rather than the local one, (3) the company will bring in most of the labor, (4) the factory is to be outside the city limits. Under these conditions the order of the main divisions of the report would be:

    I. Supply of raw materials
   II. Transportation facilities
  III. Housing conditions
  IV. Utilities
   V. Local labor

    VI. Local market
   VII. Legal matters

Since, with this particular set of conditions, the chief factor in selecting the city is that it be near the source of raw materials which the plant will use, then the first responsibility of the report writer is to show that the city fulfills this requirement; thus the No. I heading covers raw materials. Almost as important, since the product is intended for the national or at least a sectional market, are the means for and the cost of getting it there; and so transportation is the second consideration.

Because the company is going to bring in most of the labor, housing facilities in and near the city must be adequate; therefore, this factor takes precedence over the supply of local labor (No. V). The question of utilities assumes more importance when the plant is to be outside the city than if it were to be inside because the availability and the cost of power, water, and sewerage could be more of a problem. Local labor and local consumers are relatively unimportant since the company will not depend on them. Because the site is to be beyond the city limits, legal problems should be at a minimum; thus they represent the least important factor.

But let us reverse each of the conditions: (1) the company will ship in most of the raw materials, (2) it will depend wholly on local sale of its product, (3) it will draw most of its labor from the local supply, and (4) the site is to be inside the city. These changes call for a very different organization of the report, not only affecting the order of the sections but eliminating the need for two of them:

     I. Potential market
    II. Labor
   III. Transportation
   IV. Legal matters
    V. Utilities

The chief requirement now is that the city will support the plant— that its size, its buying habits, and the degree of competition promise good sales of the company's product. The first aim of the report now is to establish this fact. Raw materials, which were the No. I consideration in the previous case, are no longer a separate factor in choosing the location because their actual presence is not required. It is only necessary to show that shipping them to the city is feasible, and so they are absorbed into the discussion of transportation.

Labor assumes great importance and becomes the No. II item because the company is going to depend primarily on local help. And for this very reason, that most of the labor is to be local and therefore is already settled, housing conditions require no comment at all, or possibly in connection with the small number of personnel to come from elsewhere, they can be treated as a sub-topic of labor.

Transportation is still of consequence, but with these two differences from the first case: there will be less of it because the plant is to serve a much smaller market, and the schedules and rates of incoming carriers (bringing in the raw materials) are of more interest than those of the outgoing ones (delivering the product to nearby points). The change in the fourth condition, that the plant now is to be inside the city limits, reverses the importance of the two remaining factors. Legal matters are likely to offer more problems than if the site were suburban or rural; ordinances regarding zoning, sewage disposal, smoke regulation, noise, and odors will be stricter and taxes and assessments will be higher. On the other hand, utilities will be less of a problem because their availability is fairly certain and the rates will be lower.

So far we have noticed only the primary sections of a report. As often as not, however, a primary section deals with several matters each of which merits its own heading. When this is true and the main topics are presented in the descending order of their importance, then the sub-topics should be presented in the same way.

To continue the example of locating a plant, let us say that it is to be a large lumber mill and its machinery is to be operated by electricity. Consequently, electricity is the most important utility and our fifth section would be organized in this manner:

V. Utilities
    A. Electricity
    B. Water
    C. Sewerage
    D. Telephone service

But if the machinery is to be steam-driven, water becomes the prime consideration and should be treated as A, electricity moving down to B, C, or D according to its relative importance. Further subdividing should follow the same plan:

V. Utilities
  A. Water
    1. Availability
      a. Present needs
      b. Future needs
    2. Rates

Availability takes precedence over rates because a discussion of cost has no point if the supply is not ample or cannot be made so. Similarly, the immediate requirements of the plant are more important than its possible future ones.

Thus we see that not only may the factors to be discussed in a report have different value but their comparative weight will vary as conditions vary. In such cases the material is usually best presented in the order of its importance.

ORDER OF ASCENDING IMPORTANCE

The Order of Ascending Importance is the reverse of the previous method. The least important material is given first, the next important second, and so on until the most important is reached last. The purpose is to increase dramatic suspense and reach the climax at the end of the paper.

The method is inappropriate for letters and reports. The aim in these is not to create suspense but to say what is to be said as quickly and factually as possible. On the other hand, the method is quite effective in magazine articles, professional society papers, and speeches.

COMBINATION OF ORDERS

A combination of the Order of Occurrence and either the Order of Descending Importance or the Order of Ascending Importance is possible. The latter is infrequent except in papers and speeches where history (order of events) is used as an opening device or is inserted briefly in the dramatic sequence. The combination of the Order of Occurrence and the Order of Descending Importance is fairly common. It is particularly useful in reports that cover a double assignment: (1) the appraisal of a situation or an object as it is at the time of writing and (2) recommended changes to improve it or to convert it to a new use.

As an illustration, an engineer has been asked to inspect a ventilating system that was installed in a large building some years ago. It is now inadequate not only because of wear but also because of extensive enlargement of the building. On the basis of his inspection he is to recommend the repairs and the expansion needed to restore the efficiency of the system.

The first part of his report will give his findings; it will describe the arrangement and the condition of the system as it is now. The description will follow the order of his inspection, which was probably the route of the air from the intake point to its exit point. Hence the organization of this first section will be based on the sequence of his movement:

   I. Induction units
  II. Blowers
 III. Starters
  IV. Ductwork
   V. Grilles

It would be the purest coincidence, however, if the order of the importance of these parts turned out to be identical to the order in which they were examined. On the contrary, it is quite likely the inspection revealed that the repair and rerouting of the old ducts and the installation of new ones will be the biggest task and the most costly item. Accordingly, the recommendations concerning the ductwork will be the most important ones the engineer makes. Let us assume further that he found the starters in great need of repair and the blowers in only fair condition but the intake units and the grilles will involve little expense other than installing additional ones for the expanded system.

Now the sequence in which these parts were inspected is beside the point. What matters is their relative importance, and that largely from the financial standpoint because costs usually reflect the size and difficulty of a job. Therefore, the second part of the report, containing the suggestions for an altered and expanded ventilating system, should follow the Order of Descending Importance and the main headings will be:

   I. Ductwork
  II. Starters
 III. Blowers
 IV. Induction units
  V. Grilles

DEPARTURE FROM THE BASIC METHOD

It is to be emphasized that these four ways of presenting material are *basic* arrangements. They are *general* patterns, and we can depart from them wherever we think departure will add to the total effectiveness of the paper. Exactly where these departures should come is largely a matter of judgment, and the answer will turn on the same conditions that dictate our choice of the basic plan: the nature of the material itself, the knowledge and the special interests of our readers, and the effect we wish to get.

It would be difficult and fruitless to list all the reasons why we might deviate from the basic plan. Nevertheless, four recur so often that they need comment:

1. To show the importance of the subject
2. To satisfy the reader's natural curiosity
3. To preserve the organic unity of the paper
4. To put costs in perspective

The first exception is made to let the reader see from the beginning the significance of the paper—to let him understand at once why the paper has been written and why he ought to read it. For example, it may be a report outlining a new procedure for testing certain chemicals. If the steps are presented in the order of their occurrence, as would be most likely, it will not be until the end of the report that the reader appreciates the superiority of the new procedure over the old and hence realizes the importance of the subject. But if he had been aware of its importance from the start, he probably would have been a more attentive reader.

When we deviate from the basic plan in order to explain the importance of the subject, we can put the explanation in either of two places. If there is not much of it and we wish to give it no particular emphasis, it can be a paragraph or two added to the introduction. But if it is lengthy or we wish to emphasize it, it should be treated as the first section of the discussion and have its own heading if headings are used elsewhere.

The second reason for departing from the general plan stems from courtesy to the reader. We should satisfy his natural curiosity about the over-all subject of a report before asking him to study the details. If the report concerns a city, as in one of our previous instances, and we are not positive that all of our potential readers are familiar with that city, we should describe it briefly before analyzing the factors that bear more directly on its choice as a location. Otherwise, the reader's full attention may not be on what we have to say, simply because we have never let him "see" the city and so orient himself. Before learning of its labor supply and its transportation facilities, he wants to learn something about the city as a city—its exact location, its history, its area and population, its features. These matters may not be important in evaluating the city as a location for a plant; yet they should be presented first if the reader's full interest in the rest of the report is to be assured.

The same is true of a report on a new type of lathe, or motor, or dredge—its appearance may have nothing to do with its performance and still the reader will want to have a picture of it in his mind while he reads of its operating principles. Again, we give him this picture either in a supplement to the introduction or in a special section at the beginning of the discussion.

The third reason for shifting from the fundamental pattern comes up most often in connection with reports organized according to the Order of Descending Importance. Adherence to this method should not be so rigid as to impair the unity of the whole. Quite frequently one aspect of a subject may be of such import as to demand early treatment, whereas another aspect may have little significance and therefore, by strict standards, belong toward the end of the discussion. As an instance let us again consider the report on the location of a lumber mill.

The question of labor has high priority because the company intends to rely on the local supply. Yet the different types of help do not have the same importance. In the operation of a lumber mill semi-skilled and unskilled workers are much more numerous than skilled and clerical help, and their pay is a critical item in the budget. As a result, the available supply and the prevailing wage rates of these people demand that labor be treated early in the report—as a matter of fact, second only to the potential market.

But skilled and clerical help, because of their small number, are not important enough to be discussed before transportation, legal matters, and utilities. Should we, then, split the section on labor, having one part follow Local Market and the other come at the end of the discussion? The answer is no, for this would violate the overall unity of the report. We would be separating related material, splitting subheadings that have a common superior heading. Thus section II, complete and logically arranged, would be:

II. Labor
   A. Semi-skilled workers
   B. Unskilled workers
   C. Skilled workers
   D. Clerical help

The treatment of costs is our fourth exception. Often, of course, they are no problem. They are simply discussed along with the other factors. In a report on the purchase of equipment we might present all the data about each piece, including costs, before proceeding to the next piece. Or if the readers have a general knowledge of the other factors, we can begin with a discussion of costs and then take up the remaining matters. In neither instance have we varied from the basic order.

There are times, however, when we are forced to vary. Costs can be the prime consideration and yet we cannot discuss them first. In the example just given, we may find it necessary to describe the need for each piece of equipment and compare the performances of competing makes before examining costs because the significance of costs can be seen only in the light of the other data. Thus, in spite of their importance they are the last section of the discussion.

OUTLINING

Except for short papers an outline should be written out and not left floating around elusively in the back of the mind. Writing it may take time but it will prove a sound investment. For each minute we give to careful outlining, we are well repaid when we undertake the actual writing. We are repaid in quantitative measure by saving time; we do not have to rearrange material and rewrite passages. And we are repaid in a qualitative way; our finished paper has a smoothness and a compactness it might not have otherwise.

The first step is to set down the purpose of the paper and work out the thesis. The thesis is a precisely worded statement of the central idea the paper is to convey; it is the magnet that holds the paper together. It may be the same as the purpose, or it may not be.

In reports they are usually the same, though there might be some difference in wording. The purpose of a certain report, let us say, is to show that the Zenith Transportation Company should replace its present streetcar system with buses. The thesis would be fundamentally the same: in order to operate more economically, to give faster service and broader coverage of the city, and to increase the good will of the public, the Zenith Transportation Company should replace its streetcar system with buses. On the other hand, the purpose of a magazine article might be to persuade young men to enter the field of jet propulsion, whereas its thesis might be that the field of jet propulsion offers young men a chance for excitement, excellent pay, and rapid advancement hardly equaled elsewhere.

The first draft of the outline is likely to be only the primary and secondary headings. Let us assume we are to write a report on the needs of the company library. Our original outline could be this:

    I. Stacks
      A. Books
      B. Magazine files
      C. Newspaper files

  II. Reading rooms
    A. Research
    B. Entertainment

As we study our notes and sort them according to these general headings, we see that the outline will be a better guide if it is more explicit. We further subdivide and have our final working outline:

The Company Library

Purpose: to show the needs of the library.
Thesis: The only pressing need of the company library is additional stacks for the regular-size books.
  I. Stacks
    A. Books
      1. Regular-size volumes
        a. Technical subjects
        b. History and biography
        c. Fiction
      2. Oversize volumes
    B. Magazine files
    C. Newspaper files
  II. Reading rooms
    A. Research
      1. General reference works
      2. Magazine indexes
    B. Entertainment

For most purposes the topic outline, illustrated above, is superior to other types. Each part is listed as a word or phrase that indicates the topics in the order they are to be discussed. These headings are usually nouns or noun phrases, preceded by a number or a letter. Headings of equal degree are given the same indention.

For other points that apply to logical outlining see "Topic Headings," pages 120-125.

EXERCISES AND ASSIGNMENTS

A. Suppose that you are explaining how to play the game of bridge or hearts or rummy. Arrange the following topics in the proper order: the bidding, the scoring, the number of players, the play, the card deck.

B. Let us change the conditions on page 20 to read thus: (1) the plant is to be located in northern California and serve as an assembly point for equipment manufactured in Ohio, (2) the equipment is intended for the Pacific Coast market, (3) the company will depend slightly more on local labor than on that which it will send from its other plants, and (4) the plant is to be outside the city. List in their proper order the main topics that would be treated in the report.

C. The headings listed below are from a report on an irrigation system for a farm. The data are presented in the order of their importance, but the outline has three errors. Point them out and correct them.

Materials
   Pumps
      Secondary Pumps
      Main Pump
   Plumbing
      Connections
      Sprinklers
      Piping
Installation
Costs
Description of the Farm

D. You are planning a talk in which you are going to tell how your company finally solved a problem that had cost them heavily in the past. Arrange in the most effective order the following topics that you intend to cover: partial successes, cost of solving the problem, selection of special personnel to work on the problem, future savings as a result of solving the problem, complete success, the problem, early failures.

E. Make a topic outline of the information in the following sentences. The sentences contain or suggest the various headings and subheadings. The title of the paper will be "Fuels for Steaming Purposes."

1. The second step is to analyze the sample of coal.
2. An ultimate analysis of coal covers total carbon, hydrogen, nitrogen, and oxygen.
3. The chief characteristics of hogged fuels are high moisture, high volatile matter, and high oxygen content.
4. The important properties of fuel oil are specific gravity, heating value, viscosity, flash point, fire point, sulphur content, and ash content.
5. Refinery gas is a byproduct of certain refining processes.
6. Refinery gas is used to generate steam at the refinery or in plants near the refinery.
7. The principal fuels for steam generation are coal, oil, natural gas, refinery gas, and wood.
8. Common hogged fuels are California redwood, Western hemlock, Douglas fir, and pine sawdust.
9. There are four types of coal: anthracite, bituminous, lignite, and peat.
10. The only disadvantage of natural gas is that it cannot be stored.
11. Two coal analysis methods are in general use: the proximate and the ultimate.
12. A proximate analysis of coal covers volatile matter, fixed carbon, ash, sulphur, and heating value.
13. Wood as fuel can be divided into four categories: hogged fuels (also called wood waste), bark, residue from turpentine extraction process, and bagasse.
14. The first step is to sample the coal.
15. The advantages of natural gas are its cleanliness and convenience to plants located near the source of supply.

Methods of
Exposition

In its broadest sense, exposition is the setting forth of facts. Nearly all communication on a scientific or technical subject is exposition. It may be handled in any of four ways: as explication, description, definition, or narration.

Before examining these methods separately, let us understand two things. First, it is rare that a piece of writing of any length is treated in just one of these ways; usually a writer employs them in combination, two or more methods often appearing in a single paragraph. Second, the distinction between the types is often obscure and, to both the writer and the reader, unimportant. For instance, the account of a process, classified below as explication, could just as logically be regarded as description; and the description of equipment, treated below as description, nearly always involves mention of its operation (explication) and often an account of its development (narration).

EXPLICATION

Explication is used to explain something. Of the four methods it is most common in technical discourse because it deals with the vast realm of abstract ideas, or mental concepts, that dominate the scientific and the technical man's work: principles; theories; natural laws and phenomena; physical properties; operating characteristics; opinions; problems and their causes, effects, and solutions; advantages and disadvantages; interpretation of data; and reasons why something should or should not be done.

Quite often explication takes the form of persuasion because we wish to stress the reasons for doing or not doing a thing. To be successful, we must sound sincere and reasonable, making our conviction clear but at the same time showing that we realize there may be good arguments against what we are proposing.

Regardless of the particular subject, effective explication rests on an analysis of the reader. We begin by determining what he needs to know—in other words, by deciding how elementary and detailed our explanation should be. The second step is to arrange the information in the order he will grasp it most quickly. Finally we choose the language with him in mind, taking care to avoid terminology that might be over his head.

Below are two selections explicating abstract topics. The first explains the characteristics of electromotive force produced by the piezoelectric effect; the explanation is aimed at electrical engineering students.

In 1880 Pierre and Jacques Curie performed experiments on crystalline substances such as quartz, tourmaline, and Rochelle salts with astounding results. They found that these crystalline substances produced an electromotive force between opposite sides when mechanical force was applied along certain optical axes. They also found the converse to be true—that when an electromotive force was applied to these crystals in a certain fashion, an internal mechanical stress developed.

The most active piezoelectric substance is Rochelle salt, used in piezoelectric microphones, loudspeakers, and phonograph pickups. Quartz, although exhibiting the piezoelectric effect to a much smaller degree than Rochelle salt, is employed to advantage for frequency control in oscillators because of its permanence, low-temperature coefficient, and low frictional losses. Tourmaline is similar to quartz, but is not used as much because of its high cost. Recently a Swiss electric equipment manufacturer employed crystals of potassium hydrophosphate as a substitute for natural quartz in radio transmitters. Another possible substitute, reported lately from England, is lithium tartrate. In this country crystals of ethylene diamine tartrate were developed during World War II to relieve a critical shortage of quartz supply.

The piezoelectric effect is particularly useful in high-frequency vibration research. It has been used with great success, for example, in studies of the vibrations of turbines and of internal combustion engines. Fairly high emf's can be produced by piezoelectric action, but the energy available from any one crystal is so small that it would be quite impractical to connect a number sufficient to produce the large amounts of electric energy required for general use. However, in some of the applications mentioned above, amplification makes available additional energy.[1]

The second example is from a magazine read by both engineering students and professional engineers. Note that it states a problem and its causes and points out the advantages of the solution offered in the article, of which the excerpt is only the introductory paragraphs.

In recent years the analog computer has become available to a large number of design and development engineers. It is not difficult for an engineer to become proficient in the use of the analog computer, but one problem which confronts all who use it is that of scaling: How many volts represent one inch? Three popular scaling methods are: (1) the "actual equation-machine equation method," (2) the "per-unit method," and (3) the "direct analogy method." The first method is better suited to the mathematician than to the engineer because it deals with equations of the system being studied. The system equations are rewritten in terms of computer voltages and are then called "machine equations." This tends to cause the engineer to think in terms of the computer rather than to retain a physical picture of the actual equipment he is developing. The other two methods are better in this respect since the thinking tends to be more in terms of actual physical variables. However, when using either of these two methods, many engineers feel that the tie between actual and computer variables is not firm or concrete and that the probability of making a mistake is high enough to introduce uncertainty, especially when integrators or differentiators are involved.

The scaling method presented here has the advantage that it does provide a firm tie between actual and computer variables (by using an equation for scaling) while encouraging the engineer to think in terms of variables and components in the actual equipment. A second ad-

[1] E. K. Kraybill, *Electric Circuits for Engineers*, pp. 11-13. Copyright, 1951, by The Macmillan Company. Reprinted by permission of The Macmillan Company.

vantage is that the scaling equation provides an inherent alarm if a mistake is made. A third advantage is that loop gains may be evaluated to provide an independent check on results.[2]

Explication is also used to explain how something is done or should be done or how it operates. It details such things as a process, a test procedure, a method, a plan, or a set of instructions—things that involve action.

These subjects are usually treated in the order of occurrence, but if the discussion is long it should begin with a statement of the purpose of the thing being explained, any theory involved, and a listing of the main steps in the sequence in which they will be treated. These steps should represent completed stages in the process, not arbitrary divisions by the writer. The part each step contributes to the whole should be pointed out, preferably before the step is explained. It is imperative that transition between steps be marked plainly and that when two operations go on simultaneously the fact be emphasized. An explanation of a process, a plan, or a test procedure is of small value if it turns out to be a maze of overlapping details to the reader. In explanations of procedure or instructions to be followed by someone else, extra care should be given the wording; and if the steps are numerous, each should be numbered or lettered and made a separate paragraph, regardless of its brevity.

Whether the explanation is long or short, three points should be observed. First, the amount of detail offered is governed by whether the reader is to do the thing or simply understand it; if he is to perform the action, he will need fuller explanation than if he is only seeking information for itself.

Second, we should decide beforehand whether the operation or the operator is more important and focus attention accordingly. Sometimes the worker is incidental. For instance, in the performance of automatic machinery the worker has no part except to start and stop the machines and see to their maintenance. On the other hand, an operation may demand considerable skill and the primary interest is in the operator's training and duties.

[2] L. Jubin Lane, "A Method of Scaling and Checking Computer Circuits," *Applications and Industry*, May 1958, p. 67. Reprinted by permission of the American Institute of Electrical Engineers.

Third, we should not switch the point of view between steps. This is more liable to occur in explaining procedure or drawing up instructions than in other forms of explication. The following paragraph is weakened because of the shifting between second and third person.

Use only wood tamping tools that have no metallic parts except nonsparking metal connectors for the sectional poles. Tamping should be no harder than is necessary to insure firm loading. Never tamp the primer. Explosives should be confined to the bore hole with sand or clay or some other noncumbustible material.

The excerpts given below are not particularly long, but they are typical of explication that tells how something is or should be done or how it works. The first one sketches a procedure.

A planning engineer first takes an ordinary blueprint of the part to be produced, and lists dimensions and the proper sequence of machining operations on a simplified planning sheet. A typist next transcribes the planning sheet data on punched tape, using a special keyboard. The completed tape is inserted in a tapereader in the controls, and the information fed into the computing "brain" of the system. Using the taped information, the controls give measuring, positioning, and cutting orders to machine tools on the automated line. In the prototype system demonstrated at the press conference the human operator needs only to place unmachined castings on the line and remove finished parts, but even this operation can easily be made automatic.

The second example concerns safety measures.

Some type of glove should be worn by almost all construction workers, the exception being those who operate or work around drill or punch presses, lathes, and other revolving machinery.
Canvas gloves are satisfactory for light handling jobs. Leather offers greater resistance to abrasion, sparks or molten metal. Asbestos gloves should be used for protection against excessive heat, such as welding. Rubber gloves should be worn by electricians handling live wires.
Neoprene and plastic-coated canvas gloves are also used extensively for light material handling jobs since they offer very good resistance to abrasion, thus increasing the life of the canvas glove and also providing resistance to water and chemicals.
Metal mesh or steel reinforced gloves should not be worn where

there is danger of the wearer coming in contact with electric current. Long, loose gauntlets should be avoided.

The next selection explains an operating principle.

There are two general methods of using ice to cool stored articles: the direct and the indirect. The old-fashioned icebox employs the direct method, and the modern electric refrigerator is based on a variation of it.

In the direct method the ice is placed in the same space as the articles to be cooled. The space is divided into compartments between which there is free circulation of air. The ice is in an upper compartment. The cooling effect throughout the space is achieved by the air circulating alternately over the ice and through the other compartments. As the ice chills the air in contact with it, the density of the air increases and the air descends to the compartment below. There it displaces warmer air, which rises toward the ice. The cool air itself becomes warmer as it moves through the storage units and eventually returns to the ice compartment. Thus the circuit is completed and a new one begins.

The indirect method is more suitable for large plants. In this method the ice is kept separate from the storage space, and cooling is brought about through a medium such as brine. The brine is in tubes arranged vertically in a compartment filled with chopped ice. When chilled the brine circulates through the storage space and returns to the ice chamber. The circulation may be effected by the difference that occurs in the density of the brine when it is cooled or by a small pump. The storage units can be held at any desired temperature above the minimum by controlling the amount of brine passing through each unit.

For a longer example of explication see the magazine article on pages 191-200.

DESCRIPTION

Technical description deals with the concerete and the tangible. It tells how a thing affects the senses—how it looks, sounds, feels, smells, or even tastes. Most description, however, is concerned with appearance. It is a word-picture of something: an apparatus, a structure, a place, a condition, or a person.

The description can be based on first-hand experience; for example, we might describe an apparatus we ourselves have made or a condition we have helped to bring about. Or it can be based entirely on observation; that is, we describe equipment made by somebody else or a condition brought about by others. Furthermore, the subject matter can be general or specific. On one occasion we might describe the construction of modern suspension bridges in general and cite particular ones to illustrate how certain details were handled; on another occasion we might center the description around a single bridge, showing that in most of its details it is typical.

In technical description we should make no attempt to stimulate an emotional response, as a novelist or short-story writer does. The aim should be simply to supply intelligence. This intelligence should be conveyed in language that produces a clear picture. Adjectives and adverbs like *few, large, small, warm, close, slightly,* and *nearly* are usually unsatisfactory because their connotation varies among people. The following sentence lacks the exactness necessary for technical description to be instructive:

A small coil may be seen several feet to the left of the big wheel and slightly to the rear of it.

Compare:

An 8-in. coil is located 4 ft to the left of the main drive wheel and 1 ft behind it.

Short descriptive passages raise no special technical problems, but longer ones do. Our familiarity with the subject can blind us to the reader's needs and interest. If the thing being described has many parts, we should begin with a picture of the whole, list the order in which we are going to take up the parts, and when we get to each part, show its relationship to the whole. Such a procedure lessens the chance of the reader getting lost.

Details should be selected solely for their objective importance. Even though our enthusiasm for certain features may be greater than for others, we should treat them in their proper proportion. Nor should we let our enthusiasm for the whole lead us into giving superfluous details, details that would only bore the reader and delay him in getting to what really interests him.

Comparison and visual aids are valuable in clarifying description.

If we are writing about something new or unfamiliar, we can help our reader see it more quickly and vividly if we compare it with something already known to him. We point out the similarities first and then proceed to the dissimilarities, showing exactly what the differences are. Drawings, maps, and photographs, explained and illustrated in Chapter 10, re-enforce the word-picture and make it easier for the reader to visualize the subject.

The technical descriptions given below are representative. The first concerns a specific apparatus.

A huge inductance coil designed and built at Westinghouse Electric Corporation's transformer division, Sharon, Pa., is now being used to supply energy to an electric-arc tunnel for testing missiles.

The coil is similar to that used on a current-limiting reactor, except for the vast difference in size. Whereas a normal current-limiting reactor is wound with two or three 500-mcm cables, this coil is wound with thirty-six 850-mcm cables in parallel. The huge coil measures 119 inches in diameter, as compared to approximately 35 inches for a current-limiting reactor.

Energy is stored in the coil when its field is built up by a d-c source; the arc chamber circuit is closed at this time. Contacts in series with the coil are then opened. An arc is produced in the chamber by the instantaneous collapse of the strong magnetic field in the coil. This heats the air in the arc chamber to 40,000 F and raises the pressure to 30,000 psi. The plastic seal vaporizes, releasing a blast of hot gas which rushes through the test section into the vacuum chamber at the incredible speed of 32,400 mph.

The coil, the largest ever built, is part of Tunnel Hotshot II in the Gas Dynamics Facility at the Arnold Engineering Development Center near Tullahoma, Tennessee. Hotshot II will permit advanced research into many areas of aerodynamics and astronautics heretofore restricted in scope, such as the problem of re-entry into the atmosphere of a missile's earthward plunge from space.[3]

The following paragraphs describe a structure. Note that they concern a general type of building rather than any particular one.

Cost control through engineering in the textile industry as well as in other industries may be achieved by careful attention to detail. Like-

[3] "Missile Testing Inductance Coil," *Electrical Engineering*, June 1958, p. 458. Reprinted by permission of the American Institute of Electrical Engineers.

wise, the modern industrial plant or mill must be planned with careful attention to location, size, shape, and design, in order to achieve most economical and efficient operation.

The trend today is toward one-story construction of the mill. This decreases the need for pillar support and provides more space for arranging batteries of machines, allowing increased production, efficient flow of materials, reduction of handling, and, finally, lower cost per pound. Accurate regulation of moisture content and temperature for each room of the mill improves the quality of the product and the environment for employees. High-speed modern equipment makes it necessary to consider noise control. Dust control and improved lighting must also be noted in planning for the mills of today and tomorrow. Windowless construction, made possible by air-conditioning and indirect lighting, appears to characterize the modern mill.

Mechanical handling is another characteristic feature of the modern mill which contributes to cost control in the textile industry. Lift and platform trucks; truck towlines; wheel and roller, belt and live roller, pallet, and overhead conveyers—all are available and can find application in the modern textile plant. A component and systems approach to the design of a mechanical-handling system allows efficient selection of the over-all materials-handling scheme which contributes to cost control by replacing time-consuming and expensive manual moving.[4]

Description of people in technical writing seldom pertains to actual persons but rather to types of workers whose qualifications and duties are described. Such a subject almost inevitably requires a blend of description and explication, as in the following paragraphs.

Mining engineers take over a project once it's decided an ore or coal deposit has commercial value. They choose a mining method such as open pit for deposits near the surface, or sink shafts into the earth for deep-lying minerals. Machinery must be selected and installed. After a plant is built, mining engineers manage it.

Mining engineers must make designs that take the skills of civil, mechanical, electrical, and chemical engineers. They use mechanical and electrical machinery of all kinds—like a transportation system, and special ventilating equipment for underground work. The more remote the mine location, the more diversified the work a mining engineer does. He may travel extensively, even live abroad for years at a time.

[4] "The Plant," *Mechanical Engineering,* May 1958, p. 143. Reprinted by permission of the American Society of Mechanical Engineers.

Though mining camps may be far from large cities, they usually have comfortable housing and excellent recreational facilities, schools and hospitals—all at nominal cost. Mining engineers especially need traits of adaptability and resourcefulness.

For an example of extended description see pages 172-173.

DEFINITION

Definition is really inseparable from description. In fact, a sentence definition is often the heart of a descriptive passage; conversely, a definition that requires a full paragraph or more of elucidation is one of the purest forms of description. Nevertheless, because definition requires special treatment, we shall consider it separately.

Definitions are classified as informal and formal. Scarcely a day passes that we do not define something informally. For example, concerning golf we might say:

Novices rarely shoot an eagle, which is scoring a hole in two less than par.

The "which" clause is an informal definition. It is characterized by being a subordinate idea in the sentence; the emphasis is not on it but on the first idea. And as so often true of informal definitions, this one is worded too loosely to be quite accurate.

In scientific and technical work, where new terms are being continually coined and old ones given new meanings, the informal definition is unsatisfactory. More emphasis on the definition and more precision in its wording are desirable; therefore, in technical writing the formal definition is preferred to the informal.

The formal definition is a sentence in itself and is carefully worded for complete accuracy. Cast as a formal definition, the preceding example would read:

An eagle is a score of two less than par on any hole having a par over three.

A formal definition has four parts: the term, the verb, the class, and the differentia.

The *term* is what is being defined; in our case it is "eagle." A *simple term* is a single word having a special meaning in a certain context. The word itself can, and usually does, have other meanings, but when we speak of it as a term we are thinking of only one of them. A *compound term* is two or more words combined to have a special meaning. Sometimes this meaning is simply the aggregate of the meanings of the separate words, as in "three-point landing" and "circular saw." Sometimes it has little or no connection with the meaning of the components, as in "Texas leaguer" and "Portuguese man-of-war."

The *verb* connects the term and the class. Usually it is some form of "to be."

The *class,* or genus, is the group in which we put the term. In our golf example, the class is "score."

The *differentia* is the part of the definition that separates the term from all other members of the class. It literally differentiates, and it includes everything in the sentence except the term, the verb, the class, and the articles that modify the term and the class. All of it may follow the class, as in our example. Or all of it may precede the class, as in the next example, where the term is indicated by one line, the verb by two, the class by three, and the differentia by four:

A pillbox is an enclosed concrete-and-steel gun emplacement.

Or it may be split:

A pork pie is a man's soft hat having a round, flat crown.

In constructing a definition we should be on guard against certain faults that can impair its usefulness.

Probably the most serious one, and the one most natural to commit, is attempting to define the term in some form of itself. Subconsciously we are assuming the reader already knows the term in one form but not in another, something not likely to be true. If we say, "An engineer is a person engaged in the profession of engineering," we have moved in a circle and are back to the term, though it is in a different form. The same is true of "A mower is a machine used to mow grain or grass." This sort of definition is valid, of course, if we have already defined the term in its second form—in our cases, "engineering" and "to mow"—for we have established the basic meaning of the term and now need to explain only the particular form.

With compound terms repetition is permissible when one of the components is known to the reader and it is only the other one which needs defining. For example,

> A pontoon bridge is a temporary bridge supported on flat-bottomed boats or hollow cylinders, called pontoons.

We have repeated part of the term, "bridge"—not only repeated it but made it the class—because we assume that this is not the part that will cause difficulty. We can even repeat all the parts if we know that each is familiar separately and it is only their combined meaning which needs clarification. For instance,

> A three-point landing is a landing by an airplane in which it touches the ground simultaneously at three points—the two main wheels and the tail wheel or skid stick.

If there is any question about the reader's knowledge, however, we should avoid repetition altogether.

A second fault is to choose an inappropriate class. When we do this we evoke the wrong image and bring into the reader's mind associations that the differentia cannot entirely dispel. One extreme is to make the class too broad. If we say that a watch is a machine, we are putting it in a category that includes too many things unlike a watch, such as automobiles and typewriters.

We can go to the other extreme and pick a class so narrow that in effect we eliminate our own term. We do this if we say that a watch is a gadget, for "gadget" today suggests a thing of superfluous value and therefore does not describe a watch. A particularly bad form of this error is to make the class a word that really is another term in the class—for example, to say that a watch is a clock. Both "watch" and "clock" are terms in the class "timepiece" or, if "timepiece" seems too specific, "device."

The same mistakes can be made in the differentia. It can be too broad or too narrow. When it is too broad, all other terms in the class are not eliminated. If we say that a watch is a means of measuring time, we have not eliminated clocks, sundials, hourglasses, and calendars. On the other hand, when the differentia is too restrictive, it excludes the term we are trying to define. If we say that a watch is a device used for keeping time and designed to be worn on the wrist, we have defined only one type of watch.

A mistake that does not destroy the validity of a definition but reduces its effectiveness is lack of grammatical parallelism. The first place that this mistake is liable to occur is in the class. The class should be parallel with the term. If the term is a noun, a gerund, or an infinitive, the class should be the same. Thus:

A *fence* is a *person* who makes part or all of his livelihood by buying and selling stolen goods.

Shucking is *removing* the husk from the grain of corn.

To shuck is *to remove* the husk from the grain of corn.

In compound terms this need for parallelism does not require that the class be compound too, though it may happen to be. Compare:

A *flying saucer* is an unidentified *object* flying, or capable of flying, at great speed and at a great height.

Russian roulette is a *form of gambling* in which a person, to win a bet, spins the cylinder of a pistol containing one bullet, aims the barrel at his head, and pulls the trigger.

Parallelism should also exist between parts of the differentia that come after the class. The following definition fails in this respect:

A chair is a movable seat with four legs and a back and designed for one person.

Two of the details that follow the class are expressed as a prepositional phrase and the last one as a participial phrase. The sentence should read:

A chair is a movable seat having four legs and a back and designed for one person.

Now all three details are expressed in participial phrases. True, one phrase is introduced by a present participle, "having," and the other by a past participle, "designed," but tense does not affect parallelism.

Quite often the formal definition, being a single sentence, is not enough by itself. This can be true because we have used terms that require explanation themselves or because we need to prove the validity of the definition.

Our first definition above is an instance of terms being used that require clarification themselves:

An eagle is a score of two less than par on any hole having a par over three.

If the definition is intended to enlighten non-golfers—and it must be, for we can assume that golfers know what an eagle is—then we should also define "par" and "hole." When we do this we extend the definition into a *paragraph of definition*. The following paragraph opens with a formal definition of "automation" and proceeds to enlarge upon it.

Automation is a new concept rooted in the idea that the ultimate efficiency in a business is achieved when the business is organized, engineered, and operated as an integrated organic system, centrally and automatically controlled. The newness of automation is thus twofold. It recognizes that only system integration makes it possible to take efficient advantage of automatic control techniques. For example, maximum automatic control of warehouse operations—and therefore maximum efficiency—is achieved only when the flow of materials within the warehouse is integrated with production scheduling, paper work, and sales policy. Conversely, it is the new use of available communications and control techniques that makes it feasible to achieve levels of integration never before possible. Carried to its logical conclusion, automation sets as a new goal for business the complete integration of all functions of the business—purchasing, production, sales, distribution, accounting—into one balanced flow under the control of a single, central automatic control.

When we face the second problem, that of showing that the definition is valid, we usually need several paragraphs and accordingly write an *essay of definition*. We show that the definition is sound by illustrating the term, tracing its derivation, or comparing it with other terms in the same class, or by combining these methods.

NARRATION

Narration is the easiest form of exposition. We relate a thing just as it happened. The selection of details is almost automatic, and proportioning them offers little or no difficulty. Unlike fiction, technical narration makes no effort to create suspense.

It may concern personal activity, such as the conduct of an interview or the tour of a mine. It may recount an event, such as the ceremonies upon the opening of a laboratory. Most often, however, it pertains to subjects of larger scope—in short, history. It can be the history of a company or a project, or a stage-by-stage account of the development of a product, a piece of equipment, or a plan.

When narration concerns the development of something, explication and description are usually interwoven with it, as in the following selection.

The internal combustion engine is relatively new. The earliest attempts to build such an engine were based on the use of gunpowder. Barsanti and Matteucci built a free-piston engine in 1857, which operated as follows: An explosion drove a piston vertically upward. As it started down under the action of gravity, it engaged a ratchet which was so connected as to turn the shaft. Such a clumsy machine was doomed to failure, although Otto and Langen successfully marketed a number of free-piston engines about 1867. In 1860, Lenoir proposed and built an engine without compression. This engine drew in a charge of gas and air at atmospheric pressure for half a stroke, at which point the mixture was burned. The resulting rise in pressure provided the motive force to complete this stroke, return the piston to the end of the next stroke to exhaust the burned gases, and to bring the piston again to the point of the burning of the new charge. While this engine was used for a while, its efficiency was too low for it to be an economic source of power.

Although Beau de Rochas, a Frenchman, worked out the theory and gave the conditions for high efficiency in 1862, it remained for Nicholas A. Otto (1832-1891) to build a successful engine in 1876 after he had independently invented the same cycle. This engine was called the silent Otto engine, but the word "silent" should not be taken in a literal sense. Otto was born in Holzhausen, Germany, and was a partner in a gas-engine manufacturing plant at the time of his famous invention.

To circumvent Otto's patents, Sir Dugald Clerk, born in Glasgow in 1854, invented the two-stroke-cycle engine, which was first exhibited in 1881. In these early stages of the internal combustion engine, rotative speeds of the order of 200 rpm were typical. The German Gottlieb Daimler (1834-1899) was the first to conceive of small, relatively high-speed engines for greater power from a particular size, say 1000 rpm (vs. 4000 rpm and more for today's automotive engines), and he made them work by improved hot-bulb ignition. The "high-speed" engine made the automobile a practicable idea.[5]

EXERCISES AND ASSIGNMENTS

A. Write one or more paragraphs of explication on one of the following topics:

1. The multiplication procedure on a slide rule
2. The scoring system in football
3. Your reasons for choosing the profession for which you are preparing
4. The advantages and disadvantages of living in a dormitory instead of a private home
5. The procedure for driving an automobile

B. Write one or more paragraphs of description on one of the following topics:

1. The type of supervisor under whom you would like to work
2. A recreation room for company employees
3. A mechanical apparatus that interests you
4. A small sports car
5. The structural features of a building you admire

C. Compose a formal definition of five of the following terms:

[5] V. M. Faires, *Thermodynamics*, pp. 185-186. © V. M. Faires, 1957. 3rd edition of *Applied Thermodynamics*. Reprinted by permission of The Macmillan Company.

air compressor   hot rod
anechoic laboratory   plumb bob
blowtorch   thermodynamics
friction   transit
ham (in radio)   Wheatstone bridge

D. Write one or more paragraphs of narration on one of the following topics:

1. The history of your alma mater
2. The entertainment provided between halves at a recent football game
3. The evolution of your interest in a hobby
4. The history of a company for which you have worked
5. The development of a machine or apparatus with which you are familiar

Business

Letters

CONTENTS

General Treatment

The typical business letter has three divisions: an introduction, a discussion, and a conclusion.

The introduction is a single paragraph of two or three sentences and often of only one. Its primary function is to state the business that the letter concerns. If previous correspondence on the subject has to be referred to—and usually it does not—the reference should follow rather than precede the statement of the business.

The discussion takes up the business. It gives information either directly requested by the addressee or needed for him to act on when the business originates with the writer. This section, the main part of the letter, will vary from one paragraph to several.

The conclusion is a single paragraph that most often has the simple function of giving the letter a friendly ending.

If the discussion has been rather lengthy and the writer suspects that the central object of the letter may have become obscured by details, he may restate it in the conclusion. Likewise, if he wishes to urge prompt action, he may do so here as well as in the discussion. Both the restatement of purpose and the request for action should precede the friendly gesture so that the letter will end, as we like our

49

conversations and interviews to end, on a pleasant and informal note.

In letters having little discussion the introduction, discussion, and conclusion can be combined in one paragraph, though the practice is recommended only when the whole letter is going to have no more than four or five sentences.

In business letters paragraphs and sentences tend to be shorter than in other kinds of writing. One reason is that in short paragraphs and sentences there is less risk of making errors in composition—an important point because most business letters are dictated by people who seldom have time to proofread them. Another reason is that short paragraphs and sentences are grasped more readily by the person taking dictation and by the recipient of the letter, who may be under time pressure himself. A good practice is to use a new sentence for each idea and a new paragraph for each aspect of the topic.

Tone

> Life is not so short but there is
> always time enough for courtesy.
>   Emerson

Applied to letter-writing, Emerson's observation means that no writer should let himself be in such a hurry that he does not take the time to be polite. Courtesy is the keynote of modern business, and every successful firm insists on its employees observing it as carefully in their correspondence as in their over-the-counter dealings.

Because a letter is addressed directly to the person who reads it, his emotional response to it is much quicker and deeper than to a book or an article, or any other kind of writing addressed to people in general. In most instances the relationship between the writer of a letter and the recipient is no less intimate than it would be if the writer were actually speaking and the recipient were actually listening. Consequently, a courteous tone is just as important in a letter as in a conversation—perhaps in one respect more so, for a lapse in speaking can be corrected at once because we are there to note its effect, whereas this is not true if we are guilty of a lapse in writing.

It is this intensely personal element about a letter and the necessity of being constantly tactful that have led to the great stress that business firms put on the "You attitude." The phrase means that while writing the letter the sender bears in mind the interests of the receiver. It implies no obsequiousness or forfeiting of the writer's own interests but simply a recognition of the fact that a business transaction is a two-way affair. Accordingly, it is to be viewed from the other person's standpoint as well as his own.

Besides being the fair position to take, the You attitude is likely to get a favorable reaction to the letter. When the recipient is made to feel that we have considered the matter from his viewpoint, he is more willing to do what we ask of him—whether it is to supply information, carry out instructions, adjust a complaint, bear no ill will when we reject his complaint, write a report, or pay an overdue bill. The result is going to turn primarily on the tone we use, and the tone is strongly affected by whether the letter is written from the I and We standpoint or the You one.

Language

Tone depends as much on the phrasing we use as it does on our basic attitude. For instance, "we are willing to" suggests that a reluctant concession is about to be made; compare "we are glad to," "we are pleased to," "it will be a pleasure to" or, if these phrases exaggerate our company's attitude, "we can arrange to" or "we are ready to."

"I shall expect to receive" and "please send me" say practically the same thing, but one sounds like a command whereas the other sounds like what it is—a request. "It is our policy not to refund" suggests a callous inflexibility on the part of the company. "Usually we do not refund unless" shows that the company does make adjustments under certain conditions and invites the complainant to establish one of these conditions.

"You allege" and "you claim" suggest disbelief on the writer's part; "you write" or simply the quiet "you say" brings up the recipient's point for discussion without antagonizing him. Other antagonizing expressions are "we maintain," "we contend," and "we take the position that." They have an uncompromising ring. "We think," "we believe," and "it is our opinion" are more amenable without implying any lack of conviction. "You have failed to send us" suggests neglect on the addressee's part; "so far we have not received" suggests an oversight on the addressee's part or a delay on the carrier's part.

In choosing the language for a letter we should weigh it for more than its effect on the tone. We should choose it also on the basis of simplicity and freshness. A good deal has been said in Chapter 1 about the virtue of simple diction in general. Therefore, we shall notice here only those pretentious expressions that are found in letters more than in other forms of writing, probably because letters do not go through the hands of professional editors.

First, there is the problem of *I* versus *we*. This should really be no problem at all, and the only reason it is lies in the fact that some people consider the use of *I* a sign of egotism. Certainly the needless and recurrent use of *I* does give that impression, but the needless and recurrent avoidance of it by saying *the writer, the author,* or *we* suggests presumptuousness, a more acute form of egotism. *We* is correct if the writer is speaking for or about his company or his associates. *I* is correct if he is offering a personal opinion or referring to a personal act. The following example shows the difference:

> A shortage of materials has made it necessary for us to postpone ship-ment of your order. We are now working overtime, and I understand that your order will be completed by November 8th.

A construction that is finally dying out, but that is dreadfully late in doing so, is the participial ending for the letter: "Hoping for an early reply," "Looking forward to seeing you," "Thanking you in advance," and so on. Such expressions were customary in Lord Chesterfield's day and for a hundred years after, and they were fol-lowed by a complimentary close that read "I remain / Your most humble and obedient servant" or something equally stilted. But modern business has streamlined the ending to a direct and simple statement: "I shall appreciate an early reply," "I am looking for-ward to seeing you," "I should like to thank you now for."

Below is a list of cumbersome words and phrases. In the right column are their simple equivalents.

the aforesaid plan	this plan
the aforementioned incident	this incident
the above-mentioned men	these men

with reference to	about
during the course of	during
if we succeed in (making)	if we (make)
at an early date	soon
at the present time	now
in the event that	if
with a view to (improving)	to (improve)
for the purpose of (improving)	to (improve)
inasmuch as	since, because
endeavor	try
along the lines of	like
am of the opinion	believe, think
due to the fact that	because, since
information that we have in our files	our information
capable of (lifting)	can (lift)
if it is possible for me	if I can
in a position to	can
it is our understanding	we understand
prior to	before
I am writing to ask that you send me	please send me
we must ask you to (refund)	please (refund)
we should like to have the benefit of	we should appreciate

Clichés are even more pernicious than wordiness because, in addition to often being wordy themselves, they make stale, monotonous reading. They take the life out of any letter, burying its message under a mass of old phrases that have long since lost their power to stimulate thought. And of course they put the writer in a bad light because they expose his inability to lift his language out of a rut worn by others.

Clichés and their inseparable cousin, jargon, are to be found in all kinds of writing and in all lines of work, each vocation spawning its own. Some of the more common ones seen in business correspondence have been included in the preceding list of circumlocutions. Others and their more natural equivalents follow.

you will find enclosed herewith	enclosed is a copy
	a copy is enclosed
I beg leave to	I should like to
contents duly noted	(Superfluous. We would not be answering his letter if we had not read it.)
your favor of the sixth	your letter of March 6
in lieu of	instead of, in place of
kindly read same	please read it
I should like to take this opportunity to say	I should like to say (or just say it)
acknowledge receipt of your letter	I have received your letter (or simply nothing. Again, we would not be answering his letter if we had not received it.)
advise	(Correct only if we are going to give advice. Otherwise:) say, tell, inform
under separate cover	I am mailing you our latest catalogue (The fact it is not enclosed tells him it is arriving separately.)
pursuant to your request	as you requested
in receipt of	we have received
allow me to say	(We should simply say it. By the time he reads it, he cannot stop us if he wants to.)

TYPES

The contents and the detailed treatment of a business letter are governed by its particular aim. The types explained and illustrated in this chapter are those that engineers write most frequently.[1]

Letter of Inquiry (or Request)

The principal thing to remember about a letter of inquiry is that it is a request. We are asking a favor, and the letter should be built around a recognition of the fact. It should be written in such a way

---

[1] The sales letter is omitted because engineers are rarely called on to write it. It requires special training and is nearly always handled by a special department in the company or by an advertising agency.

as to require the least possible time of the recipient in answering it. This means we should:

1. Make the inquiry at once (in the first paragraph).
2. Word it so clearly that the reader will lose no time in wondering just what we do want.
3. Explain why we want the information so that he can decide (a) whether he can let us have it and (b) whether sending it to us is worth his time.
4. Arrange the points vertically if there are many, and number or letter them.
5. Word them, if we can, so that he can answer them "yes" or "no."
6. Ask for no more details than we really need.

A letter of inquiry follows.

Northwest Electronics
1720 Park Avenue
Vancouver, Washington

June 25, 1959

Mr. A. S. Parker
Sales Representative
Heath Company
Benton Harbor, Mich.

Dear Mr. Parker: Subject: VFO Model VF-1

I should like certain information about the VFO Model VF-1.

A customer plans to purchase these VFOs for a fleet of tugboats if they will meet his requirements. Answers to the following questions are needed:

1. Can a frequency of 3096 kc plus or minus 2% be set from the calibrated dial?
2. Will this frequency be maintained within 2%?
3. At an ambient temperature of 10 F, what is the recommended warm-up time?

I will appreciate an early reply.

Sincerely yours,
Leslie E. Cabe
Leslie E. Cabe

LEC:jc

Answer to an Inquiry (or Request)

If we have to refuse a request, we should take extra care to be tactful in order to keep the good will of the inquirer. The usual procedure is (a) to express appreciation for the inquiry, (b) to give the reasons why the request cannot be granted, (c) to refuse the request, and (d) to suggest some alternative that may be of help. This is one of the few letters in which the business is not stated at the very beginning. Since the business is to refuse something, the refusal should be prepared for; if it comes first it may strike the reader as rudely abrupt and the reasons, coming after, may look like trumped-up excuses.

The job of granting a request is much easier. We simply give the information that has been asked for. If the inquirer has tabulated his points, we use the same numbers or letters he used and answer them in the same order. If he has not tabulated his questions and we must cover several points, we shall do well to itemize them anyway, as an aid to ourselves in being sure to cover them all and to him in grasping them.

An answer to an inquiry follows.

ACE CAMERA CORPORATION
1641 West Street
Onandato, Tennessee
October 18, 1959

Mr. James Hedrick
34 Ardmore Drive
Cheney, Wisconsin

Dear Mr. Hedrick:

We are glad that you have requested our recommendations for eliminating the "oily" appearance of glass-bound color transparencies.

The difficulties you mention result from the formation of Newton rings, which are caused by close contact between the glass and the film.

To eliminate the rings, either of the following procedures may be employed:

1. Place the glass-mounted slides in the projector with the projection lamp on, and allow the slide to be exposed to the heat of the lamp for a minimum of three minutes to a maximum of five minutes.
2. Pre-heat the oven of a kitchen stove to 300 F. Put all glass-mounted slides into the oven for four minutes minimum, six minutes maximum.

If you desire further information about any matter related to the photographic field, we shall be happy to assist you.

Very truly yours,
John M. Gorlow
John M. Gorlow

JMG:p

Letter of Instruction

The letter of instruction may give directions to a customer who has asked for them (in which case it is also an answer to an inquiry). The directions may tell him how to adjust equipment for a new purpose or for greater efficiency, or how to check the equipment in order to locate the source of trouble he is having. The letter may instruct a subordinate about work he is to do, or it may list specifications that are to be met or standards that are to be followed.

In every case the prime emphasis is on clarity—on making sure that the directions, the specifications, or the standards cannot possibly be misinterpreted; for if they can be, they will be. Such things are best understood, remembered, and followed if the general reason for them is explained first and the specific reason for each step is given with it.

When there is a time sequence, as there usually is, it should be observed. Further, the points will be clearer if they are presented vertically and are designated by numerals or letters or, in the case of sub-points, both. Questions should be anticipated and answered.

A letter of instruction follows.

CANNOY AND WESSEL
Printers
Losantiville, Ohio

June 23, 1959

Mr. Richard Roe
Jonas Printery
215 Fairmont Drive
Canton 6, Ohio

Dear Mr. Roe: Subject: Handbook Production

I am happy to supply you with the information you requested concerning the production of maintenance and operating handbooks for government contracts.

Since the work we have been doing for the past few years has been under government contract and your production facilities are similar to ours, I feel that the experience we have gained will be of value to you.

I shall describe the progress of a handbook from the engineer's rough drafts and sketches to the completed handbook.

1. The engineers give their rough drafts and sketches to the editing group. This group edits the material on the basis of good grammar, clarity, conciseness, prescribed specifications, contractual requirements, and technical approval of the engineers. The sketches are turned over to the art department for conversion into reproducible form. The text is then typed in final form. Mock-up pages are prepared, the illustrations being cut into the text at the proper place.

2. The necessary title page, table of contents, list of illustrations, appendixes, and index are prepared and assembled with the mock-up pages. This material is sent to the photographic laboratory to be processed as printer's negatives.

3. On return from the photographic laboratory, the negatives are inspected for imperfections and mounted on yellow mats to printer's specifications.

4. The mounted negatives are sent to the printer for offset printing. The printer returns page proofs for our inspection and ap-

proval or disapproval. If the quality of the printing is poor, directions are given for re-running. If the proofs are acceptable, the material is collated and bound in appropriate covers.

5. The final step is the distribution of the completed books to authorized internal personnel and cognizant government agencies.

The meeting of contractual deadlines will dictate the scheduling of your work load. After all data have been assembled, at least eight weeks should be allotted for editing, typing, proofreading, printing, and distribution of an individual book.

If, after you get into your work, questions arise that I have not covered, do not hesitate to write me again. If I can answer the questions, I shall be happy to do so.

Very truly yours,
N.W. Cannoy
N.W. Cannoy

NWC:jd

Claim Letter

A claim letter, or letter of complaint, expresses dissatisfaction with the goods or the service of the addressee or his company. It might concern faulty equipment or its installation, a delayed or damaged shipment, an incomplete order, an error in a bill or a discount, or a mistake in credit terms.

Whatever its particular subject is, we should write it on the premise that the fault was unintentional on the part of the addressee. Courtesy should still be the keynote, and not just because it is good manners: it has a practical value too. It is much more likely to get a quick and satisfactory response than an angry or sarcastic letter. Further, if the trouble turns out to be the fault of our own company—for instance, the receiving department or the bookkeeping department—our position will be less embarrassing and it will be much easier for us to apologize.

A good claim letter should:

1. State the nature of the complaint.
2. Give the history of the transaction, citing previous correspondence on the subject.

3. Be exact about dates, sums of money, quantities, order numbers, and other figures.
4. Indicate the adjustment expected.

The following is an example of a claim letter.

BOOTH AND BROTHERS
184 West St.
Norfolk 4, Virginia

April 7, 1958

Shipping Department
Apex Equipment Company
1001 Main Street
Baltimore, Maryland

Attention: Mr. J.V. Davis

Gentlemen:

The generator received from you today was not accompanied by the maintenance tools.

Your 1957 catalogue states that a set of maintenance tools is supplied with each generator. This equipment was purchased on our order GA-50371 and shipped by Railway Express on Bill of Lading 6274.

I am sure that the failure to include these tools was an oversight. We do, however, need the tools as soon as possible for installation and adjustment of the equipment and would appreciate it if you would send them immediately. Thank you very much.

Yours truly,
E.H. Spainhour
E.H. Spainhour

EHS:lm

Adjustment Letter

The adjustment letter is the answer to a claim letter. It may reject the claim, grant part of it, or grant all of it, depending on the extent to which our company considers itself at fault.

If we are refusing to make any adjustment or are granting only part of the one asked for, we give the grounds for refusing before the refusal itself, just as in the letter declining a request and for the same reasons. We stress that our company appreciates the claimant's position and has studied his complaint with an open mind. If he gets the impression that we resent his complaint and are rejecting it perfunctorily, we shall lose his good will and probably that of his friends too.

A letter granting the adjustment asked for is much simpler to write. A satisfactory one would:

1. State that the claim is to be honored and say when.
2. Explain how the error was made.
3. Express regret that the error occurred and that the addressee was inconvenienced.

Two adjustment letters follow. The first rejects the claim; the second grants it.

FLETCHER AND GRAHAM
CRANE MANUFACTURERS
Drawer 6
San Francisco 2, Cal.

20 July 1958

William Allard and Son
483 Manning Street
Spokane, Washington

Gentlemen: Subject: <u>Heavy-duty</u> <u>Hoist</u>, <u>Model</u> <u>G</u>

Our engineers have completed their report on the hoist that we installed in your plant in November 1956 and that failed on the eighth of this month. I am enclosing a copy of their report.

Their inspection revealed no defect in material and no fault in the way the hoist was installed. There was some indication that the hoist had been regularly overloaded. You were kind enough to permit our men to study your weigh sheets, and the records confirmed the visual evidence.

Although Model G is a heavy-duty hoist, it is the smallest in this class and was designed to handle an average load of 2 tons and a maximum of 2½ tons. Your weigh sheets show that during several long periods since its installation the hoist raised an average load of 3.1 tons.

Since this overloading is the cause of the breakdown and our operating instructions and markings on the hoist make its capacity clear, we cannot accept any responsibility for the failure. I regret that this must be our position. We do find, however, that it will not be necessary for you to buy a new outfit, and we shall be pleased to submit a detailed cost estimate if you should like us to repair your present equipment.

Yours sincerely,
T.H. Graham
T.H. Graham

THG:r
Enc.

JAMISON ELECTRIC COMPANY
684 West 10th St.
Houston, Texas

February 24, 1959

Acme Machine Co.
1007 Broad St.
Philadelphia, Pa.

Attention: Mr. John Peters

Gentlemen:

We shall gladly honor your request for the replacement of four defective amplifiers shipped to you on purchase order GSX-49056. These new units will be shipped not later than June 27 by air express.

After your order was shipped, we discovered that the apparatus used in testing the amplifiers was not performing consistently. Some of the tests were reliable; others were not. Apparently the four defective amplifiers sent to you were among those that the machine failed to detect. We are sorry if the mistake has inconvenienced you.

Very truly yours,

H.A. Weaver

H.A. Weaver

HAW:aw

Letter of Transmittal

A letter of transmittal officially turns a report over to whomever the report is intended for; literally it transmits the report from the writer to the reader.

It may be mailed separately, but usually it is put at the beginning of the report. In the latter instance it does not list the report as an enclosure, for actually the situation is the reverse: the letter is enclosed in the report. It is addressed to the person or the group for whom the report was written. The subject line consists of the words "Report on" plus the title of the report as given on the title page.

The body states the authorization if the report were specifically requested, the purpose of the report, and its thesis. If there were no specific authorization, the author gives any other reason that the report was written.

The letter also contains any special matters that are not important enough to be included in the report itself, though bearing on it. Such matters may be the time covered by the study, suggestions for further study, the need for prompt action on the report, the personal benefit the author feels he derived from the work, and (alas) an explanation of why the report is late or incomplete.

Acknowledgments constitute the last paragraph before the one containing the gesture of good will. These acknowledgments list the persons and the organizations that aided the writer in preparing the report; often they indicate the nature of the aid. If the list is long it should not be included in the letter but should be put on the following page under the heading ACKNOWLEDGMENTS.

A letter of transmittal follows.

VALENTINE MOLD & MACHINE CO.

Plant 4   1924 Glenmount Ave.   Ext. 260
                            Akron 19, Ohio
                                                    April 16, 1958
Mr. Eugene J. Valentine, President
Valentine Mold & Machine Co.
1924 Glenmount Ave.
Akron 19, Ohio

Dear Mr. Valentine: Report on Increasing Efficiency
                                        of Producing Cup Molds

In accordance with the instructions you gave me in our conference
on April 6, I have investigated the methods of producing multicavity
cup molds. As you suggested, I have limited my report to include
only the processes from selection of the steel to the tapping of the
mold.

The general conclusion of this report on methods to increase efficiency is that the methods now used are sound but outdated, and can
be easily modernized at little or no added expense.

Mr. H.J. Stratton, superintendent of Plant 4, gave me every help
in my investigation and materially speeded the work by his suggestions.

                                        Sincerely yours,
                                        Heath E. Valentine
                                        Heath E. Valentine
                                        Production Engineer
HEV:he

Letter of Application

A letter of application is easier to write when it is accompanied by
a Personal Record than when it is not. A Personal Record is a page
or two on which the applicant lists facts about himself; it will be
explained later. When it accompanies the letter, the letter usually
can be held to one page and the pronoun *I* does not have to appear

often. The following discussion assumes that such a record will be enclosed in the letter.

In the opening paragraph the applicant, first of all, tries to create a special interest in his application. He may do this in any of several ways:

1. By indicating at whose suggestion he is writing—a company official, the company recruiter who has interviewed him, or a mutual acquaintance.
2. By stating that he is answering a certain advertisement by the company.
3. By saying why he is interested in working for that particular company.
4. By stating his general qualifications.

Next he indicates the specific work he prefers to do. He should not hesitate to do this, for companies want to know an applicant's preferences. They have learned that the good workers are happy workers and happy workers are those who are doing the work they prefer. Moreover, he can indicate his willingness to accept any other position if there is no opening in the departments he has mentioned. The paragraph ends with a statement of when he can report for work should he be made an offer.

The discussion is one or two paragraphs. It has a double function: to call attention to points in the Personal Record that seem to give the writer special qualifications for the job he is seeking; and to explain any items in the Personal Record that on the surface appear unfavorable.

The last paragraph tells when he will be available for an interview if the addressee wishes one, indicates where he can be reached in the meantime, and concludes with the gesture of good will.

If he has a copy of the company's personal data form, he fills it out and encloses it. If he has to make his own form, the models on pages 67 and 70 are adequate. The information is divided into four general categories: data about the applicant as a person, data about his education, data about his work experience, and the names of people who can be referred to for additional information.

In a letter written by an inexperienced person, such as the average student, the sections describing his special interests and his college work and activities should be rather full because he must be judged largely by them. Under experience, however, he should list all jobs that he has held for any appreciable length of time, no matter how remote they might be from the type of work he is applying for. They will show what experience he has had in working with others, in dealing with the public, and in taking orders.

With an older person the emphasis reverses. College grades and activities assume less importance as his experience increases, and only the work he has done since college will interest a prospective employer.

Below are two letters of application and two Personal Records. The first letter and record pertain to a college senior applying for his first permanent job. The second letter and record pertain to a practicing engineer who has been out of college 15 years.

> 630 W. Beaver Avenue
> State College, Pa.
> February 18, 1958

Mr. Richard B. Olafson
Personnel Director
Western Aircraft Corp.
Ludlow, Illinois

Dear Mr. Olafson:

At the conclusion of our interview yesterday Mr. T.T. Clyde, your recruiter in this area, suggested that I write you directly concerning employment. I am especially interested in air frame design, although I am sure I would enjoy working in other fields too. I graduate on June 3 and can report to you any time after that date if you have an opening for me.

As you will see on the enclosed data sheet, my senior project was the designing of a workable model of a sport plane. The construction of the craft gave me valuable experience in actual designing, and writing the thesis showed me the importance of taking notes as

I worked and putting them in a form that other people can understand. You will also notice that my grades have been above average but that I have found time for extracurricular activities.

Six years will have elapsed between my graduation from high school and my graduation from college. This is explained by my being in service two years. After finishing high school I was not sure what I wanted my lifework to be, and decided that by enlisting in the army I could think things through before entering college, as well as avoid interrupting my education once it was resumed. The decision turned out to be a good one, for I have worked in college with a seriousness of purpose that I lacked in high school.

If you would like me to come to Ludlow for an interview, I can do so between March 22 and March 30, which is our spring vacation, or on any Saturday or Monday provided I know far enough in advance to make arrangements about my school work. Meanwhile you can reach me at my State College address. I shall appreciate your consideration.

Yours truly,
Harvey N. Smith
Harvey N. Smith

HNS:hs

Personal Record
of
Harvey Neal Smith
February 18, 1958

Personal Information

Present address: 630 West Beaver Avenue, State College, Pa.
Permanent address: 1170 Club Boulevard, Terre Haute, Ind.
Age: 23   Marital status: single
Birthplace: Terre Haute, Ind.   Military status: 2 years in U.S.
                                                      Army

Height: 5 ft, 10 in.   Health: Excellent
Weight   170 lb   Physical defects: none

Education

High school: Terre Haute High School—graduated June 1952
College: Pennsylvania State University—to receive B.S. degree in
            Aeronautical Engineering June, 1958
Academic average: 2.78 (3 is A, 2 is B)
Senior thesis: Design of a Sport Plane
Honors: Tau Beta Pi
           Phi Beta Kappa
Extracurricular activities:
    Associate editor of campus magazine, the Penn State Engineer,
        during senior year
    Reporter on campus newspaper, the Daily Collegian, during fresh-
        man and sophomore years
    Student member of the Institute of Aeronautical Sciences
    Intramural football and basketball

Experience

Summer 1957, 1956—draftsman, Louis Stoddard and Co., General
    Contractors, Terre Haute, Ind.
July 1952—August 1954—U.S. Army. Had attained rank of ser-
    geant when honorably discharged.
Summer and Christmas 1951, 1950—clerk, Giant Food Store, Terre
    Haute, Ind.

References

Prof. J.V. Dale   Rev. John T. Malone
Department of Aeronautical Engineering   Grace Methodist Church
Pennsylvania State College   Terre Haute, Indiana
State College, Pennsylvania

            Mr. Louis Stoddard, Jr.
            Vice-president
            Louis Stoddard, General Contractors
            43 Walker Street
            Terre Haute, Indiana

125 Colonial Drive
Wilmington, N.C.
June 20, 1958

Mr. Theodore L. Cobb
Shields Locomotive Works
Shields Building
Philadelphia 2, Pa.

Dear Mr. Cobb:

Mr. J.N. Van Fossen, chief engineer of your Atlanta plant, has informed me that he will retire at the end of the current year and that you do not plan to replace him by a member of your own company. I should like you to consider this as a formal application for the position. If offered the job I can report by September 1, in time to have the benefit of Mr. Van Fossen's guidance for four months.

As the accompanying record shows, I have had 12 years' experience in railroad work. I have enjoyed it and shall regret leaving the Atlantic Coast Line, but under the circumstances I feel I should leave if given the opportunity for advancement that your Atlanta position would be. Advancement with my present employers is bound to be slow. The other assistants to the chief engineer are comparatively young men, have seniority, and are quite capable. I have discussed the situation with my superior, Mr. B.L. Kennan, and I am writing you with his knowledge.

I believe that my experience with the Atlantic Coast Line especially qualifies me for the Atlanta position. Both here and previously in Rocky Mount I have been in direct charge of the repair shop.

Mr. Kennan has told me that, with a week's notice, I can have a few days off at any time convenient to you, if you want me to come to Philadelphia or if you want me to visit the Atlanta works. You can reach me by letter or phone at either my home or my business address.

If you wish any information in addition to what is in this letter and the enclosed record, I shall be glad to supply it.

Sincerely yours,
John D. Robbins, Jr.
John D. Robbins, Jr.

JDR, Jr:jc

Personal Record
of
John Davis Robbins, Jr.
June 20, 1958

Personal Information

Home address: 125 Colonial Drive, Wilmington, North Carolina
Business address: 642 Front Street, Wilmington, North Carolina
Home phone: Roger 2-4011   Business phone: Roger 2-6819
Age: 37   Marital status: married, 2 children
Birthplace: New York City   Health: good
Height: 5 ft, 9½ in.   Physical defects: none
Weight: 160

Education

Graduated in upper quarter of class, Georgia Institute of Technology, 1943. Bachelor of Science in Mechanical Engineering.

Experience

1953 to date—assistant to the Chief Engineer, Atlantic Coast Line Railroad (Wilmington, N.C.)
1946-1953—assistant to the Division Engineer, Atlantic Coast Line Railroad (Rocky Mount, N.C.)
1943-1946—Army Corps of Engineers, Fort Belvoir, Va.

References

Mr. B. Lawrence Kennan   Mr. T.L. Utley
Chief Engineer   Division Engineer
Atlantic Coast Line Railroad   Atlantic Coast Line Railroad
642 Front Street   Adams Building
Wilmington, N.C.   Rocky Mount, N.C.

Col. John James Rousseau
Army Corps of Engineers
Sprague Building
Fort Belvoir, Va.

MECHANICS

Form

Practically all business firms today employ some variation of the block style as the basic form of their letters. The block style is so called because each unit of the letter appears as a neat block of typing. This is effected by having every line in each unit begin flush under the one above it and by using abbreviations or avoiding them to have the lines come out fairly even on the right side. Here is an inside address in block form:

> Mr. John L. Martin
> Supervisor, Shipping Dept.
> Ronwell Machine Company
> 1831 River Street
> Pittsburgh 8, Pennsylvania

Note also that with the block style open punctuation is used; that is, the lines are followed by no marks of punctuation except where an abbreviation calls for a period.[2]

Three variations of the block form are currently popular: the balanced block, the semiblock, and the full block.

The *balanced block style* has the inside address, the salutation, the first line of the paragraphs (as well as the succeeding lines), and the identification line against the left margin. The date is against the right margin, and the complimentary close and the two signatures begin in the center of the page or slightly to the right of center. The general effect is that of balance.

---

[2] In the older form, seldom seen today, each line is indented appreciably more than the one above it and is followed by punctuation, a comma after each line but the last and a period after the last. The example above would appear thus:

> Mr. John L. Martin,
> Supervisor, Shipping Department,
> Ronwell Machine Company,
> 1831 River Street,
> Pittsburgh 8, Pennsylvania.

Letterhead

_____

_____

_____

Date _____

Inside address _____

_____

_____

Salutation _____

Body _____

_____

_____

_____

_____

_____

_____

_____

Complimentary close _____

Written signature _____

Typed signature _____

Identification line

_____

Actual examples of this form can be seen on pages 55, 56, 60, and 62.

The *semiblock style* differs from the balanced block in only one detail: the first line of each paragraph is indented. This indentation is commonly 5 to 7 spaces but can be as many as 10 if the writer chooses. The semiblock and the balanced block forms are about equal in popularity. Examples of the semiblock form appear on pages 58, 61, 64, 66, and 69.

In the *full block style* every unit begins at the left margin, including the date, the complimentary close, and the signatures.

Letterhead
_____

Date _____

Inside address _____

_____

Salutation _____

Body _____

_____

_____

_____

_____

_____

_____

Complimentary close

Written signature
Typed signature

Identification line

This form was slow to gain wide acceptance because of its one-sided appearance, but in the last few years many firms have adopted it because it saves a stenographer's time. Most of these firms confine its use to internal correspondence (that is, letters going to another part of the same firm) and employ the balanced block or semiblock form in letters going outside the company. Of those firms that use it for external correspondence, many counteract the unbalanced effect by using stationery that has the letterhead in the upper right corner and a company slogan, emblem, or picture in the lower right one.

Regardless of which style is followed, the general practice is to double-space between the different parts of the letter (with certain exceptions to be noted later) and between paragraphs, and to single-space within the parts and within the paragraphs. Whenever a short letter must be put on regulation-size paper, however, the spacing within paragraphs is made double and that between paragraphs triple to keep the letter from looking lost in a vast expanse of white.

Margins should be ample: an inch and a half to two inches on the left and at the top (if there is no letterhead, as on a second page); one to one and a half inches on the right and at the bottom. When a letter does not fill a page, it should be approximately centered, a bit more of it above the middle than below it.

Erasures, blots, scratch-outs, clogged typewriter keys, a faded or worn ribbon—all hurt the appearance of a letter. In turn, appearance can hurt its effectiveness. We suspect the reliability of untidy people; so it is with untidy letters, for we assume that they reflect the traits of the writer.

Parts

ESSENTIAL PARTS. In addition to the body a business letter should have five parts: the heading, the inside address, the salutation, the complimentary close, and the handwritten and typed signatures. A sixth one, the identification line, is so common today that it may well be included among the essential parts.

HEADING: If the stationery does not have a letterhead, the writer's address and the date are given in the upper right corner.[3] The writer's name should not appear here, an error sometimes made by persons who confuse the straight business letter with the memorandum and the memorandum report. The address should be com-

---

[3] For simplification, the position described for the various parts of the letter is that characteristic of the balanced block and semiblock styles. Other details about the parts are equally true of the full block form.

plete, giving the house number and street—or the post office box—
on line 1 and the city, the postal zone if there is one, and the state
on line 2. The date is line 3; it may be written in the American style
(May 6, 1960) or the European style, in which case the comma is
no longer needed (6 May 1960). When a box number is part of the
address, four lines may at times give more of the block effect than
three. Both of the following arrangements are good:

P.O. Box 438   Post Office Box 3117
Darien, Pa.   East Riding Station
August 14, 1960   Wilmington 7, Del.
                                      14 August 1960

The use of abbreviations depends on whether they will add to or
detract from the block impression. Permissible ones are *St.* (street),
Ave. (avenue), *Blvd.* (boulevard), and *P.O.* (post office).[4] *Rd.*
(road) and *Bx.* (box) are purposeless because the space saved is
negligible, and *Sta.* (station) has for some reason not been widely
adopted. The name of the month and the city should not be abbreviated, but that of the state may be.

When the stationery has a letterhead, it replaces all of the typed
heading except the date line. This line may remain in its usual position against the right margin, or it may be typed directly under the
letterhead. In either position it is at least two spaces below the last
line of the letterhead, the exact distance depending on what will best
serve the appearance of the page.

INSIDE ADDRESS: The conventional place for the name and the
address of the recipient of the letter is three spaces below the date
line and flush with the left margin. Today, however, one occasionally
sees it at the very end of the letter, still against the left margin but
below the other parts.

The recipient may be one person or a group, such as a company,
a department, or an organization. If it is one person and he is addressed by name, rather than by his position, the name should be
preceded by a courtesy title, such as Mr., Dr., Dean, or Captain.

---

[4] The italics (or in typing, the underline) do not appear in the letter. They are
used here in conformity with the rule that a term used as a term is designated
as such by italics or quotation marks.

The number of lines in the address depends on the particular case, but usually it ranges from three to six. Typical are the following:

Mr. John R. White
127 West 14th St.
Dayton, Colorado

_____

Shipping Department
Benson Machine Tool Co.
Fourth and Packard Streets
Lancingville, Nebraska

Mr. J. Carl Elliott
Director of Research
Turbine Division
Electric Products Corp.
34 Shannon Avenue
Bedford, New York

Just as in the heading, the use of abbreviations depends on how they affect the block impression we are trying to achieve, and again certain ones have the sanction of good usage and others do not. Here, however, courtesy affects practice in two ways. First, if we know the addressee's way of signing his name, we should observe it, using initials or full first and second names as he does. Second, we should follow a company's own practice in abbreviating or writing out *company, corporation,* and *incorporated* and using the word *and* in preference to &.

When a company's name is extremely long, it can be divided between two lines for the sake of appearance. The second line is indented three or four spaces so that it will not be mistaken for a separate detail in the address. An example:

Chief Design Engineer
New Wellington Shipbuilding
and Drydock Company
171 Myrtle Road
New Wellington, Alabama

SALUTATION: The salutation is placed two spaces below the address and against the left margin. It is a formal greeting of the addressee, and its precise wording is governed by the first line of the address.

If we have called the person by name there, we owe him the respect to repeat it here instead of writing *Dear Sir*. With the first and third sample addresses given on page 76 the salutation should be "Dear Mr. White" and "Dear Mr. Elliott" respectively. When we do not know the recipient's name and have to address him by title alone, as in the example immediately above, then *Dear Sir* is acceptable.

When the first line of the inside address includes a group of people such as a company, an organization, or a section of either, as in the second illustration on page 76, the salutation is *Gentlemen,* not *Dear Sirs.* If the group is composed entirely of women, *Ladies* or *Mesdames* is correct. If it is a mixed group but the fact is of no significance, as in the case of a bookkeeping department, *Gentlemen* is sufficient. If it is a mixed group and the fact should be recognized, as in the case of a school board, then *Ladies and Gentlemen* is in order.

For most business letters, in which only moderate formality is wanted, the best forms for the salutation are *Dear Mr. X, Dear Miss X, Dear Sir, Dear Madam,* the last being proper for either a married woman or an unmarried woman. When more formality is desired, these forms become *My dear Mr. X, My dear Miss X, My dear Sir,* and *My dear Madam.* The use of the recipient's first name or nickname in the salutation, *Dear Ralph* or *Dear Bob,* is acceptable when the relationship between addressee and writer is so close that a more formal greeting would seem artificial.

Every word in the salutation is capitalized except *dear* when it follows *My.* The usual practice is to put a colon after the salutation. When the greeting is informal, such as *Dear Ralph* or *Dear Bob,* the colon is still preferable to the comma (used in friendly letters) if the letter pertains mostly to business. Some firms, however, have adopted open punctuation—that is, no mark is placed after the salutation—to make this part consistent with the heading and the address.

COMPLIMENTARY CLOSE: The complimentary close is a polite way of ending the letter. It is put two spaces beneath the last line of the text and begins midway between the side margins or just to the right of midway. Only the first word is capitalized. A comma follows the last word if a colon or a comma has been used after the salutation; otherwise, there is no punctuation.

Under ordinary circumstances the most common forms are *Yours*

truly, Yours very truly, and *Very truly yours.* If something less formal
is wanted, *Sincerely yours, Yours sincerely,* and *Sincerely* are good.
Cordially yours and *Yours cordially* are reserved for letters in which
real cordiality exists between the writer and the recipient. *Respectfully
yours* and *Yours respectfully* are best when the addressee is a superior
in position, a special customer, or an older person—in short, any
person deserving special respect from the writer. *Respectfully submitted* is common in letter-reports and letters transmitting formal
reports.

SIGNATURES: A business letter has two signatures, a handwritten
one and a typed one. The first is preferably in the writer's own hand,
but sometimes promptness in getting the letter mailed makes it advisable for his secretary to sign his name. In this case her written initials
are put under the last few letters of his name. The object of the handwritten signature is to give the letter a personal touch and in some
instances to validate it legally; the object of the typed one is to ensure there will be no doubt about the written one. The typed signature
is placed three, four, or five spaces below the complimentary close—
far enough to prevent any crowding of the written one, which will be
placed between it and the closing. Both should begin flush with the
first word of the complimentary close.

Yours very truly,   Yours sincerely,
R.D. Porter   *R.D. Porter*
R.D. Porter   *C.M.*
                                               R.D. Porter

When the writer's title is included in the signature, it is typed one
space below the typed signature and flush with it.

Very truly yours,
R.D. Porter
R.D. Porter
Drafting Supervisor

When a company's name is included in the signature, it is typed two
spaces beneath the complimentary close and above the written signature; it begins even with the other details.

Sincerely yours,
Connecticut Wire & Cable Co.
R.D. Porter

IDENTIFICATION LINE: The identification line is the initials of the person who dictated the letter and the initials of the typist. Ordinarily these persons are the man who signs the letter and his secretary, but not invariably. Sometimes a letter is sent out over the name of one man when a subordinate has been given the responsibility of composing it; and often in large offices several typists are under the authority of a secretary, who distributes among them the less important correspondence.

The initials are placed two spaces below the signature and against the left margin, those of the dictator first. The most common practice is to write his in all-capitals and the typist's in small letters, no periods or spacing in either. The two sets may be separated by a colon, a slanting line, or a dash. Usually all of the initials of the dictator are given, but only the first and last ones of the typist—frequently, in small offices, just the last one. Here are a few examples:

RDP:cm   RDP/cm   RDP-cm   RDP:m   rdp:cm

ADDITIONAL PARTS. Besides the basic parts, several others can be useful. They will be taken up in the order of their appearance in the letter rather than in the order of their importance or the frequency of their occurrence.

REFERENCE LINE: A reference line can serve in either of two ways. It can facilitate the filing of the letter in the writer's office, in which case it is simply a code number; or it can aid the addressee by indicating to whom further correspondence should be addressed. It is placed two spaces below the date line. Examples of both types follow:

January 4, 1956

C47Y3

January 4, 1956

In replying please
address Mr. T.L. Thomas,
Purchasing Office

CLASSIFICATION LINE: If a letter should be read only by the addressee or by him and a restricted group, the degree of restriction is indicated in the lower left corner of the envelope and again on the first page. On the first page the line is flush with the left margin and three spaces below whatever is last on the right margin (the date or reference line, as the case may be) and three or four spaces above the address. It may read *Personal, Confidential, Proprietary,* or *Secret* and may be underlined, written in all-capitals, or both.

ATTENTION LINE: The purpose of an attention line is to direct the letter to a certain person in a group when it has been addressed to the group. It is not addressed to the particular person in the first place because the writer does not want the business to go unattended for an indefinite period in case that person is absent. Yet if he is present, the writer prefers that he handle the matter which the letter concerns.

An attention line should have no effect on the salutation. Since the letter is addressed to a group, it is that group who should be greeted. To aid stenographers, however, in filing all correspondence with a given firm in one place, a few companies disregard this rule. They address the letter to the firm, use an attention line to route it to the person they wish to deal with, and direct the salutation to him; but the practice is of dubious value and, so far, rather limited.

The line, which may take any one of several forms, is placed in the lower left corner of the envelope and in any one of several positions on page 1. The most common forms and positions are:

Kennedy and Company
1281 Main Street
Richmond 4, Virginia

Attention: Mr. L.D. Bradshaw
          General Manager

Gentlemen:

Kennedy and Company
1281 Main Street
Richmond 4, Virginia

Attention of Mr. L.D. Bradshaw

Gentlemen:

Kennedy and Company
1281 Main Street
Richmond 4, Virginia

       Attention: Mr. L.D. Bradshaw, General Manager

Gentlemen:

Kennedy and Company
1281 Main Street
Richmond, Virginia

Gentlemen:

Attention: General Manager

The wording and form are not affected by the position. They are varied in the examples above for illustrative purposes.

SUBJECT LINE: The subject line indicates what the letter is about; it is a brief title of the letter. It serves a double purpose: it enables the recipient to see at a glance what precedence the letter should be given in the day's work, and it simplifies filing in the sender's office if correspondence is filed according to subject matter.

It should be worded accurately and concisely. The word *Subject* may be used to introduce it or may be omitted. The older expressions *In re* and *Re* seem to be losing favor. *Subject* is followed by a colon, and the words constituting the subject should be capitalized as a literary title is (see page 281). Underlining is optional. If open punctuation is used in the heading and the address, no period follows the subject line unless it ends with an abbreviation.

Its most frequent position is on the same line with the salutation. It is spaced so that it will end against the right margin; for good appearance it should not begin within an inch and a half of the salutation. Rather than give a crowded effect to the line, it should be divided and carried to a second line. Below are two examples:

Gentlemen: Subject: Delayed Shipment of Fuses

_____

Dear Mr. Wallace: Subject: Estimated Cost of
                                        Renovating Steam Plant

_____

It may also be centered between the side margins and placed either between the address and the salutation or between the salutation and the text:

Mr. J.L. Gaines
Superintendent
Acme Bag Factory
17 East Fourth St.
Acme, Indiana

Subject: Redecoration of Main Office Building
‾‾‾‾‾‾‾‾‾‾‾‾‾‾‾‾‾‾‾ ‾‾‾ ‾‾‾‾ ‾‾‾‾‾‾‾‾

Dear Mr. Gaines:

‾‾‾‾‾‾‾‾‾‾‾‾‾‾‾‾‾‾‾‾‾‾

Dear Mr. Gaines:

Subject: Redecoration of Main Office Building
‾‾‾‾‾‾‾

The estimated cost of redecorating your main office building totals $3200. This, of course, does not include the reception room, which was redecorated only a year ago.

‾‾‾‾‾‾‾‾‾‾‾‾‾‾‾‾‾‾‾‾‾‾

CONTINUATION DATA: The average business letter is one page or less in length because businessmen feel that a single letter should concern a single topic. If more topics need to be discussed, they are taken up in separate letters because, first, in all likelihood they will be handled by different people or even different departments and, second, lumped together in one letter the separate matters lose some of their separate importance.

Still, there are times when a matter is so complicated or the necessary details are so numerous that even a letter on a single topic requires two or more pages. These additional pages, called second sheets, do not have a letterhead; consequently, they need some marking so that the letter can be reassembled if they become separated from the first page or from each other. Further, they have an unfinished look if they begin abruptly with a resumption of the text. For these two reasons it is customary to put continuation data at the top of them.

These data are placed an inch and a half to two inches from the top and three spaces above the text. They consist of the first line of the inside address, the new page number, and the date. The neatest arrangement centers the page number between the other two details:

Mr. John C. Dallas   -2-   April 12, 1958

Another arrangement is:

Mr. John C. Dallas, page 2, April 12, 1958

If little text is to go on the page and the writer wishes to avoid a top-heavy look, the upper margin and the spacing between the continuation line and the text may be increased slightly and the data may be arranged vertically:

Purchasing Division
7 August 1957
Page 2

ENCLOSURES: Anything to be included in the same envelope with the letter is referred to in the text and noted at the end of the letter. This second citation is to remind the reader to look for the enclosure in case it has become separated from the letter. The notation is flush with the left margin and is one or two spaces below the identification line. If more than one item is being enclosed, a figure indicating the number is added. The nature of the enclosure, already stated in the text, is not repeated unless the enclosure is a check or a money order. A few of the possible forms are:

Enclosure   Enclosures 2
Enc. Money order   Enc.
Encs. 1. Check No. 4321   Encls. 2
       2. Copy of original order
       3. Bill of lading

In the third case all enclosures are listed because the first one, being a check, should be. If the writer wishes the enclosure to be returned, the notation reads:

Enc. (to be returned)

Notice of an attachment, something clipped or pinned to the letter, is treated exactly like the notice of an enclosure except that the notation reads "Attachment" or "Attached: Check No. 4321."

CARBON COPIES: If a copy of the letter is being sent to anyone other than the addressee, the fact is indicated at the end of the letter, one or two spaces below the identification line or, if it is present, the enclosure line. Usually it is necessary to give only the name of this third person because either the addressee knows his position or the writer has identified him in the text. If neither is true, then he is identified in the notation.

PNR:sc
cc Mr. James D. Tillman

PNR:sc

c Mr. James D. Tillman
   Adjustor, Maybank Insurance Agency

When the number of copies is more than one, all are listed:

PNR:sc

cc 1. Mr. James D. Tillman
   2. Mr. K.C. Ward
   3. Captain J.R. Whitman

The copy made for the writer's files is not included.

EXERCISES AND ASSIGNMENTS

A. Indicate which of the following phrases and sentences are faulty because of their wording and tell why they are faulty.

   1. Please permit us to point out
   2. If what you say is true

3. You must not have read the instructions correctly.
4. If you will consult page 23 of our catalogue
5. We are sorry that we do not now have in stock
6. You should have known
7. We shall fill your order as soon as possible.
8. Please advise me whether the shipment has left.
9. I hope that I have not taken up too much of your time.
10. With reference to your complaint dated November 23

B.   With X mark each error in the skeletal letters given below.

M.V. Winters
2034 Pershing St.
Memphis, Tenn.

June 11, 1957

J.N. Wells and Sons
178 Market Street
Nashville, Tennessee

Gentlemen: Ordering Accessories for Steam
                                    Press

_____

_____

_____

_____

_____

_____

Yours truly,
M.V. Winters
M.V. Winters

mw

JACKSON AND KELLMAN
Architects
1409-1411 Vines Building
San Pedro, California

17 Oct., 1959

Randall, Moore & Co.
419 Stevens Street
San Pedro, California

Attention: Mr. C.C. Randall
President

My Dear Mr. Randall,   Subject —Preliminary Design

_____
_____
_____

_____
_____
_____
_____

_____
_____

                                        Yours respectively,
                                        Charles C. Kellman
                                        C.C. Kellman

C.C.K.:mg
Enc. Sketch of proposed building
cc Office file

C. Compose a letter that incorporates the following data:

You are chief engineer of the Robinson Construction Company.
The company's address is 402 Independence Avenue, Worleyton,
    Wisconsin.
The letter is going to the Fremont Steel Corporation.

The steel company's address is 2302 Chatham Road, Camersville, Illinois.

The object of the letter is to report that I-beams ordered from the steel company are a week overdue and to urge immediate shipment.

Your order number for the beams is S-1283.

Your complaint is directed to the attention of Mr. J.O. Price.

You are sending a copy of the letter to your superior, Mr. Wallace T. Robinson, president of your company.

Your typist is Roberta Smith.

You have instructed her to enclose a copy of the original order.

D.   Write a letter that would fit one of the following conditions:

1. You, a college senior, are asking a company for information about one of its products because you wish to use the information in your senior thesis.

2. As a representative of the company, you are refusing the request because the information is classified as proprietary.

3. You are instructing someone who has asked for help in finding the source of trouble he is having with equipment bought from your company five years ago.

4. You are granting the full claim of a customer.

5. You are a college senior applying for your first permanent job. You know no one connected with the company and do not know whether the company has advertised openings. Your interest in the company has been stimulated by a recent visit to one of its plants with other members of your class.

6. You are an engineer with three years' experience with one company and are applying to another company without knowing whether the position you want is open.

Reports:
General Matters

DEFINITION

We come now to the very heart of scientific and technical writing —the report. And we should begin by settling a basic question: exactly what is a report?

Loosely, any communication about conditions—conditions that did exist, that do exist, or that are likely to exist—is a report. When a student writes home about his grades or his finances, he is writing about actual or probable conditions and so he is writing a report. When an instructor lists the names of those students who have been absent from class during the week and sends the list to the recorder's office, he is sending a report. When a worker fills out a form showing the reading of various gauges at prescribed times during his eight-hour shift, he is filling out a type of report. When in January the President of the United States goes before Congress and tells what the government has done during the preceding year and recommends what should be done during the coming one, he is delivering a report.

None of these, however, is quite the kind of report that we are interested in here, for none is the type that an engineer would ordinarily be called on to deliver. The student's and the instructor's reports are not on technical subjects, the worker's report requires no composition except possibly a sentence or two at the end under *Remarks,* and the President's report concerns both non-technical and heterogenous matters.

An engineer's report, on the other hand, almost invariably pertains to a technical subject, is mostly or entirely the product of careful composition, and is homogeneous in subject matter. Its function is to convey data that were compiled for the purpose of showing either what has been done or what should be done or both; and its forms have become more or less conventional because experience has proved them practical. It is this particular kind of report—most often called the technical report—that we are to examine in this and the next two chapters.

DISTRIBUTION

Reports may move in any of four channels. They can be directed outside the company to customers, in which case they concern a product or a service sold by the writer's company. Within the company they can move upward to superiors and concern either an actual job performed by the writer or an investigation he conducted in order to aid his superiors in forming an opinion. Within the company they can move downward to the men under the writer's authority and concern policy to be observed or work to be undertaken. And within the company they can move horizontally from one division to another, from one plant to another, from one department to another, or from the writer to a colleague in the same department.

Although a report is usually directed into only one of these channels, there are times when it is directed into more. For example, it

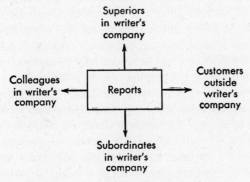

FIGURE 2   The Movement of Reports

may be needed by the writer's superior as well as by a customer, or by the men working under the writer's supervision and by other departments that are to co-operate with them on a project.

TYPES ACCORDING TO CONTENTS

Companies have their own ways of designating their reports. These ways of designating reports are numerous and they can be special to a particular company; a report bearing one name in Company A can have different ones in Companies B and C. Some of the more common names are: inspection reports, periodic reports, test reports, performance reports, costs reports, field reports, research reports, service reports, recommendation reports, and specification reports. A complete list would be several times longer than this one, but from the standpoint of the student it would probably be more bewildering than helpful.

The best approach for a student is to learn the few generic types and the general function of each. Then, when he gets into actual practice and is called on for a certain report, he can recognize its type, recall what it is supposed to do, and write it creditably regardless of what name it goes under in his company.

In the following discussion the names given the reports have been preferred to other possibilities because they seem most descriptive of the contents and the function of the various types. The two main categories are work reports and examination reports.

Work Reports

A work report concerns work that has been done. The job is beyond the speculative stage because some part or all of it has been finished.

A work report can be more definitely typed as either a progress report, a completion report, or an instruction report.

PROGRESS REPORT. A progress report concerns work that is being done, and as its name tells us, it describes the progress that has been made up to the time of its writing. Such reports are called for when a project must be spread over a long period and management needs interim checks on how the job is proceeding. The reports may be submitted at regular time intervals or at the end of the various stages of work.

COMPLETION REPORT. A completion report deals with a job that has been completed at the time it is written. It might be a *final progress report,* the last in a series of reports on the same subject. In this case it may summarize the reports that preceded it or simply describe the final phase of work, the work done since the last progress report. Just as often, however, it is a *special completion report,* an independent report dealing with a limited assignment, such as the installation of a boiler or the overhauling of a transformer—any job that did not require enough time to warrant a progress report.

INSTRUCTION REPORT. An instruction report also concerns work that has been completed. But the work here is either the final plans for a project or a record of practical experience that is to guide others.

In the first instance the writer is forwarding plans that other people are to carry out. The report is directed from a superior to his subordinates or from a project engineer (the man directly responsible for a job) to his associates in the task. The report allocates the work among those engaged in it and describes the procedures to be followed. Thus its effect is to co-ordinate the separate efforts of those participating in a job, whether they are in the same department or in different ones.

The report describing experience is directed to a person who is concerned about work that he is unfamiliar with, work similar to that done previously by the writer. By recounting his own experience the writer hopes to lessen the problems faced by the recipient.

Examination Reports

An examination report deals with a job that is still in the speculative stage. It presents data that were gathered during an examination made to determine whether work should be done, or how it should be done, or both.

It is intended to aid the reader in making a choice. The choice may be between competitive products, between ways of improving a service, between methods of installing equipment, and so forth. Quite often the choice is simply between not taking action and doing so—for instance, whether or not to expand facilities or to change a specification.

Frequently a problem requires more than one report. The first one is called a *preliminary examination report.* It pertains to some question that holds the key to further procedure and that must be settled before a more detailed and costly investigation is undertaken. It might be the question of how to proceed, of deciding between alternate ways of carrying on the main study—for example, which of several methods of testing a fuel is likely to give the best results.

Or it might be the question of whether to proceed at all—whether a detailed study is worth while. A company investigating several cities as the location for a new plant would establish in preliminary reports which cities could not meet its essential needs and were therefore not worth further study. The others would be examined thoroughly and the final choice would be based on these second reports. Once such basic questions are answered, the main study can be undertaken, and the results are incorporated in a *final examination report.*

Preliminary reports do not always concern procedure, nor is their number limited to one. Sometimes several basic questions must be answered before the final, detailed investigation is practicable, and they must be answered in sequence because the second depends on the first and the third on the second, etc. To illustrate, a state highway department makes a survey to determine whether a by-pass around a city is needed for east-west traffic. The findings are Preliminary Report No. 1. Assuming the conclusion to be affirmative, the question arises: will it be better to route the by-pass north of the city or south of it? A second study is conducted, and its data and the resultant recommendation that the route be south of the city constitute Preliminary Report No. 2.

The problem now comes up of whether the by-pass should have limited accessibility, and Preliminary Report No. 3 presents evidence that it should. With these matters settled the department is ready for the final investigation to decide on the exact route and its requirements, and these results and recommendations are incorporated in the Final Report.

Examination reports, both preliminary and final, are of two kinds: analytic and advisory.

ANALYTIC REPORT.   An analytic report presents material collected during an investigation and analyzes it to show its significance. Essentially, of course, all examination reports do this. Yet, in the effort to employ self-descriptive names for the types of reports, it seems well to reserve the term "analytic reports" for those reports that stop with the analysis, that do not go beyond drawing conclusions from the data. Such reports are also called "evaluative reports" and "appraisal reports."

ADVISORY REPORT. An advisory report offers recommendations. It presents the facts, draws conclusions from them, and, on the basis of these conclusions, advises what action should be taken. It may advise only a general course and offer no more than one recommendation; or it may advise in detail and offer many recommendations. These reports are widely known also as "recommendation reports."

The subject of classifying reports by their contents and function can be summarized in a diagram showing their relationship to each other.

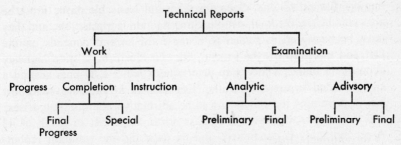

FIGURE 3   Reports Classified by Contents and Function

TYPES ACCORDING TO FORM

Reports are also classified on the basis of their make-up and general treatment. They are called "formal" and "informal," and any of the types described in the preceding section can also be placed in either of these categories. Whereas there is considerable difference in the nomenclature based on content, the designation of reports as "formal" and "informal" (or "nonformal") is rather general.

The sub-classifications and their inter-relationship may be seen in the diagram below. A detailed explanation of them is given in Chapters 6 and 7.

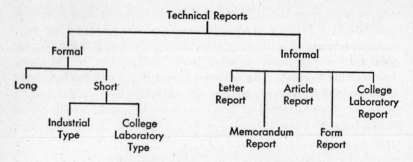

FIGURE 4   Reports Classified by Form

ARRANGEMENT OF THE ESSENTIAL PARTS

Regardless of its type, there are three indispensable parts to a report: the introduction, the discussion, and the terminal section. In the specific treatment of each part, the formal report varies a good deal from the informal, and these differences will be covered in the next two chapters. Here, however, where we are noting what is common to the two types, we might examine the arrangement of these basic parts.

Conventional Order

Until lately the normal arrangement of these parts was accepted as:

> Introduction
> Discussion
> Terminal section

This order is still more customary than its alternative and probably will remain so. Its strength is that it is perfectly logical. It supplies information to the reader in the order that most of us are used to receiving it in. The subject is introduced and its importance is indicated; then the blocks of data are presented, each to itself and at face value; and finally they are correlated and, usually, evaluated for the reader to accept or reject. There has been a logical progress from a beginning, through a middle, to an end.

Modified Order

In recent years a different arrangement has become steadily popular until today it is regarded as being just as "normal" as the older one. It brings the terminal section forward so that it immediately follows the introduction and precedes the body proper:

> Introduction
> Terminal section[1]
> Discussion

This order has two virtues. One is that it permits a hurried reader to see the main points in a report quickly, without having to read the discussion until a more convenient time. Nor does he have to bother with finding the terminal section, for he has it before him. The other virtue is that it allows a person to grasp the import of the discussion at once because, having already read the terminal section, he has seen what the data lead to.

Much can be said for both the conventional and the modified arrangements. One caution, however: no matter which may be the order of presentation, the order of writing should be the former. To write the terminal section before the discussion is dangerous because the data can be unconsciously "weighted" to support a conclusion or a recommendation to which the writer feels he has committed himself. When the data are set forth first, this risk is minimized.

GENERAL TREATMENT OF THE BODY

Viewpoint

A report should be written from a completely objective point of view. It should not be colored by the writer's wishes or slanted to make a conclusion or a recommendation look more valid. The bad features should be given as well as the good, the cons as well as the pros, what does not support a conclusion or a recommendation as well

---

[1] Of course this section is no longer the terminal one in the sense of being last positionally. Even so, "terminal section" seems to be the best term because it is brief and yet comprehensive (embracing all specific types of report endings without the prolixity of naming them) and the section still represents the end-product of the writer's work.

as what does. No information should be withheld because it is counter to the writer's over-all opinion on a point.

Nor should he try to persuade the reader to his opinion through arguing. The tool of the report writer is exposition, not argumentation. This does not mean that he should suppress his views. On the contrary, he should be quite frank in voicing them, for the reader expects him to be. But once he gives them and cites the grounds for them, his task is done. If the contents and the composition of the report are what they should be, the report will do the persuading and the reader will accept the writer's judgments.

Tone

The tone of a report can have a good deal to do with whether it succeeds in winning a reader's confidence. If it sounds amateurish, it is not likely to inspire trust; if it sounds professional, it will probably sound reliable.

The effect of a report is weakened by a tone that is too casual. It is true that an informal report should not be stiff in its phrasing; it should have a definite personal quality. Still, it remains a business document and this personal touch should not have the casualness of everyday conversation. Consider this sentence:

> I had a look at the place and figure it will do all right if you change a few little things.

The idea is reasonably clear, but as the thesis for a report the sentence will cause us to suspect the writer's attitude toward his work. We cannot be blamed for assuming that he conducted the examination in the same breezy manner in which he wrote this sentence, and probably the rest of the report. The following revision suggests a more conscientious person and still the tone is informal:

> I inspected the building and believe it will serve your purpose if you make a few minor alterations.

The professional air of a report is also weakened by the inclusion of petty details. Even when such details are related to the subject because they are part of the description or the procedure, their presence clutters the reading and obscures what is really significant. For instance, in the description of a refinery gas burner, details about the color and weight of the various parts would be superfluous, for color and weight have nothing to do with the operating efficiency of the burner.

Notice in the following paragraph how the trivia dim the important points:

> I learned from the Weston Realty Company that the land is owned by Mr. John V. Warren. I telephoned Mr. Warren on the morning of May 3 and made an appointment to see him that afternoon. I met him at the site at three o'clock, and he said that there are five acres in the tract and he will sell it for $1500 an acre.

The man who is thinking about buying this land will be interested in two, possibly three, points in this account—the size of the tract, its price, and possibly the name of the owner. Therefore, the paragraph can be reduced to:

> The tract, owned by Mr. John V. Warren, contains five acres and can be purchased for $7500.

Tone also requires tact in referring to a point already known to the reader. Sometimes this can pose a dilemma, for the writer feels the reference is necesary to put another remark in the proper light and yet he does not want to offend the reader by seeming to assume the reader is ignorant on the point. A simple solution is to cushion the reference with a parenthetical phrase such as "as you know," "as you recall," "as we all realize," "according to our past experience," "in keeping with the company's policy." For example:

> Since all the heavy machinery, as you know, is to be on the first two floors, no special bracing will be necessary for the upper stories.

Tense

The tense of the verbs in reports is subject to the same laws that govern tense in general. Nevertheless, it may be pointed out that since progress reports and completion reports tell of work that has been finished at the time of writing, the tense is predominantly or entirely past. Instruction reports detailing plans use the present or the future tense; those relating experience that is to be a guide in similar work are written in the past or the present tense (for an example of the latter see pages 163-165).

Examination reports use the past tense as long as details of the examination itself are being discussed, but the present tense is proper in speaking of a condition that still exists at the time of writing. Compare:

A. I found that two voltmeters needed to be regulated.
B. I found that two voltmeters need to be regulated.

"Found" is correct in both sentences because it refers to the examination itself, which is in the past at the time the report is being written. But "needed" in sentence A is correct only if the meters have been regulated since inspection; otherwise, the reading should be that of sentence B.

PROCEDURE OF PREPARATION

In studying report preparation we should constantly bear in mind that reports follow no fixed, inviolable rules. Up to a point all of them have something in common; up to another point those of a given type have still more in common. But after this point they must reflect the special circumstances out of which they grow, and artificial standards cannot be imposed on them. They become individualistic and refuse to conform any further; to force on them absolute conformity to a preconceived pattern would compromise their identity and their usefulness. Every report, in the final stage, must be tailored to fit:

a. the material it is to embody,
b. the purpose it is intended to serve, and
c. the particular readers it is meant to inform and help.

What follows in this chapter and the next two chapters is offered, not as a casehardened template, but as a suggested practical approach —a frame of reference in which the student or the practicing engineer can find help in solving problems in substance and form.

Most of this book concerns, in one degree or another, the writing of reports. But the writing is the final stage, and the author's success depends just as much on how well he lays the groundwork for the writing as on how he actually does it.

The procedure for compiling a work report differs from that of compiling an examination report. The difference is due to the unlike circumstances out of which the two types grow. Still, the difference is not great and lies wholly in the fact that the work report is simpler and its preparation therefore requires fewer steps.

Work Report

Step 1:   Collect the data.

Since the work report describes work that has been done, no preparation for gathering the data is required. The data accumulate as the job proceeds and it simply remains for us to record them. The best way to ensure completeness and accuracy is to take notes as the job progresses—stage by stage or day by day, as the nature of the work suggests. With progress and completion reports, the notes record what is actually happening. With the instruction report, the notes record each detail of the plan as it is decided on or each detail of experience as it is recalled.

Step 2:   Determine who will read the report.

The person for whom a report is intended has a great deal more to do with its preparation than most of us realize. The success or failure of a report—and therefore our success or failure—will be in direct proportion to how thoroughly he understands it. This means that at all times we should remain aware of how much he knows and how much he does not know about the subject, and write the report accordingly.

Perhaps he is our immediate superior, in which case he knows the field as well as we do, and probably better. A report on our particular work, therefore, can be confined to specific details, and its language and data can be highly technical. The case may be the very opposite: the report is intended for a customer who has only a superficial knowledge of the field and virtually none of the work to be discussed. Accordingly, general principles must be explained for him to grasp the details of the work, and the language and data must not baffle him. Or the report may be going to a person whose knowledge is somewhere in between these extremes, and so it must be written in a different key.

As we have seen, a report is frequently directed to more than one person. When this is so, it should be written at the level of the person least familiar with its subject matter. For example, it may be going to our immediate superior, who is the subsection manager; then to the section manager; then to the plant manager; and finally to the division manager. Of these four men the one farthest from the particular work, and so least familiar with it, is the division manager; therefore, the report should be written at the level he will understand. Or it may be an instruction report going the other way, down to our subordinates, in which case it should be composed with the least experienced one in mind.

No matter how many or how few people are to read the report or which channel it is to take, we should never forget that we are writing for another person's information, not our own. Hence, we must regard and interpret the material from somebody else's standpoint. This is not always easy to do, especially when weeks of contact with a project have made its details almost second nature to us.

Step 3:   Organize the material.

Having gathered the data and having decided how detailed and how technical the report should be, we are ready to organize it. Since organization was discussed in Chapter 2, we need only a reminder here.

a. Compose the thesis first. The easiest way to ascertain exactly what this should be is to write down the words "The object of this report is to show that . . ." and then finish the sentence. The first nine words should bring into sharp focus the central idea that the report is to convey.

b. Select the method of organization that will be most effective for the particular material and readers.

c. Draw up the outline.

Step 4: Write the report.

A logical order in which to write the various parts is:

a. Introduction
b. Discussion
c. Terminal section
d. Abstract
e. Supplementary parts

By composing the introduction first we not only are starting at the natural beginning but are reminding ourselves of the circumstances that called the report into being; and so our perspective should be keener during the writing. Next come the presentation of the data recorded in our notebook and any remarks that throw light on them. After this we are ready for the main job: correlating the facts and pointing out their significance. This is the sole function of the terminal section. If the report is to have an abstract at the beginning, it is written now—when the body is complete. Last come the extra parts if there are to be any. The informal report generally omits them as well as the abstract.

Examination Report

Step 1: Fix in mind the exact purpose of the examination.

Since the examination report calls for an investigation, the early steps in preparing it have to do with planning a study that is to yield the required data. The first of these steps is to make absolutely sure we know what is wanted so that there will be no false starts. We should review the authorization and then compose a thesis sentence for the examination. Again the wording will come more rapidly and precisely if we begin the sentence with a formula; this time: "The purpose of this examination is to find out . . ." This thesis that is to guide the investigation is not to be confused with the thesis in Step 7 that is to guide the writing.

Step 2: Make certain that the scope of the examination is clear.

In beginning a study we should be certain that we understand how much ground it is to cover, exactly what the limits are within which we are to work. This is called the scope of the examination, and it provides the criterion by which we determine the factors to be included in the report and those to be omitted.

Usually the scope is clear in the authorization. If the authorization does not particularize, we can generally assume that there are no restrictions on the subject and that the investigation is to include every factor which has a bearing on it.

Suppose we were asked to test a new alloy to discover all its possible applications. We would have a blanket authorization as to scope, and the tests would cover a wide range: brittleness, fatigue, ultimate strength, modulus of elasticity, thermal behavior, heat conductivity, electric conductivity, corrosiveness, density, and others. But if the authorization stated that we were to find out whether the alloy is practical for use in window frames, the scope would be reduced considerably and the tests would be limited in range: ultimate strength, thermal behavior, corrosiveness, and density.

Sometimes, however, the authorization for a study may fail to specify what its scope is to be, not because the scope is unlimited but because the person asking for the report has assumed we understand what its limits should be. In connection with preliminary reports we had the example of a highway department routing a by-pass. The authorization for the final report may have stated simply that it was to recommend the exact route for the by-pass and to indicate the requirements of that route. Yet the scope of the final study was affected drastically by two reports that preceded it—those which specified that the road was to pass south of the city and that it was to have limited accessibility. Thus we can see that in determining the scope of an investigation we must be familiar with any work that has gone before it.

It is also necessary to take company policies into account, for often they bear on the scope of a study and yet are not mentioned in the authorization because of the very obviousness of their importance. A simple illustration is that of a study made to decide the feasibility of buying new machinery. One of the factors to be examined would be the initial costs—the purchase price, the transportation charge, and the expense of installation. Let us suppose, however, that it is the policy of the company to have no outstanding bills but to pay for its purchases immediately in order to receive the benefit of discounts. Then this study of costs is not complete; it must include the discount period and the rates offered by the supplier.

So far we have noticed situations in which there was explicit authorization for a report, whether it indicated scope or not. Frequently, however, there is no specific authorization. It exists, of course, but it is tacit. It lies in the general responsibility we have been given, and investigation of certain kinds of problems is part of the normal routine of our work. When this is true, then we must rely on past experience and common sense in working out the scope of an examination. In situations of this kind, where scope is neither stated nor implied, we should take extra precautions to ensure its accuracy. Carelessness in ascertaining beforehand what the coverage of a study should be can lead either to a report including irrelevant matters or to its omitting important ones.

Step 3: Determine the general order of investigation.

With the purpose and the scope before us as guides, we are ready to plan our approach to the problem. Or, more precisely, we are ready to work out the procedure for collecting the data. What factors are of fundamental importance and therefore should be examined first? These vital questions are given first priority because on their answers depends whether there is any point in continuing the study.

In testing the alloy mentioned above to learn whether it can be used in window frames, the critical test would be the one to determine its ultimate strength. This, then, should be the first test. But suppose we made the mistake of running less important tests before this basic one and the results in every case were satisfactory. It would be only so many days wasted if, when we finally tested for strength, we found that the alloy bent under the pressure of a strong wind. We see, then, that by outlining a study before beginning it we stand to save incalculable time.

After determining what the vital factors are and putting them at the head of the list, we decide which matters are of next importance and should be investigated second and add them to the list. We continue until we have a complete chart to work by. This written procedure for gathering the data is a general outline for the report itself. Usually, however, it has to be filled in, and sometimes rearranged, before it is entirely satisfactory as a guide for the writing.

Step 4:   Decide where the examination is to be conducted and which techniques will be needed.

Sometimes an investigation does not require us to leave the office in which we customarily work. Sometimes it requires the use of the laboratory, the testing cells, or the library. Sometimes it necessitates our going into the field—to another unit of the company or to a customer. And sometimes we may need to do parts of the study in two or more of these places. We should settle this question of locale before setting out to gather the data. If we do not, we may lose time by doubling back on ourselves or by working where the facilities are less adequate than those elsewhere.

There are several techniques for gathering data. Probably the most common one is inspection—the inspection of equipment, structures, or conditions. Almost as common is testing—the testing of equipment, materials, or theories. Often we may gather the information by reading magazine articles, books, or other reports. Occasionally we may get it through personal interviews or through written questionnaires. Of the last two the interview is usually more fruitful, but if the number of people to be questioned is large or they are widely scattered, the questionnaire is more practical. Sometimes the situation calls for our combining two or more techniques, just as it may call for our working in more than one place.

The planning of the investigation is now complete. The rest of the procedure for preparing an examination report is the same as that for preparing a work report.

Step 5:   Collect the data.
Step 6:   Determine who will read the report.
Step 7:   Organize the material.
Step 8:   Write the report.

Reports:

Formal

The formal report is preferred to the informal if any one of the following conditions is true: the material is lengthy, the report is to be read by many people, it is to be filed for reference over a long period of time.

It is distinguished from the informal report in that (a) it nearly always has supplementary components—that is, parts besides the basic ones of the body; (b) the text is double-spaced unless the report is very short; (c) the style of writing is impersonal; and (d) in keeping with this detached style, general practice still favors using pronouns of only the third person except in the letter of transmittal. Occasionally, however, one does see a good formal report that disregards this last convention.

THE LONG REPORT

Essential Parts

INTRODUCTION. The introduction of a formal report is extremely important; yet it is the part most frequently neglected. Reports that are excellent in every other way are often marred by weak beginnings, apparently because the writers do not understand the function of an introduction.

This function is, first, to put the whole report in its true perspective and, second, to provide a smooth, sound opening for it. To do this, the introduction must include the following matters:

a. The *background* of the report. This is a concise account of what led up to the report. It might be two or three paragraphs that trace the history of the subject, the development of an object, or the growth in a company's business; or they may summarize other reports on the subject. Again, it may be only a sentence or two pointing out the need for something that the report describes or outlining a problem that it attempts to solve. Like so much else in a report, the amount of detail actually given depends on the knowledge of the reader least familiar with the subject.

b. The *purpose* for which the report is written. This is the natural culmination of the background. It briefly states the exact nature of the work or of the examination that the report concerns.

c. The *scope* of the report if it is not evident from the title.

d. The *thesis* of the report. This is the general conclusion or the general recommendation, or it may be a combination of the two. Sometimes it is very explicit: "The report shows that a new bridge is needed over Pawnee Creek and recommends that it be built just west of the present one." Sometimes the thesis may consist of two or three conclusions or recommendations because the study covered more than one aspect of the subject. For example: "It is recommended that the new bridge be built just west of the present one, that it be of the cantilever type, and that it have four traffic lanes." Sometimes a thesis has to be rather broad because it must embrace many details, no one of which is outstanding: "If the recommendations offered on the following pages are adopted, production should be increased at least 20%."

e. The *method* of conducting the study if the report is on a little-known or a controversial subject. In such cases the procedure used in gathering the data needs to be explained to establish their validity. If the reader does not know how the problem was investigated, he will not know how much faith to place in the solution.

Even when the report is on a "safe" subject, the manner in which the data were collected may be described, for we lose nothing by showing the reliability of our data. There are also times when a study has raised such unusual problems that the reader will be interested in learning how they were solved.

If the method of conducting the study requires more than one or two paragraphs, it is better treated as a separate section at the beginning of the discussion rather than as a part of the introduction.

In addition to these five matters, the introduction may include any of the following:

a. *Special information.* As pointed out in Chapter 2, the introduction may include material that belongs in the report but would not be appropriate under any of the headings in the discussion and is not important enough to be given a separate heading.

b. The *authorization.* Since the authorization is given in the letter of transmittal, which precedes the introduction, it need not be repeated here. At times, however, we may wish to restate certain details because they throw light on the background, the purpose, or the scope of the report.

c. The *time* covered by the study. Ordinarily this is stated in the letter of transmittal, but if it is of sufficient importance it can be given in the introduction instead.

d. The *general plan* of the discussion. This is reflected, of course, by the primary heads in the table of contents; but if we want to make sure that the reader understands it before beginning the discussion, we can summarize it in the introduction. Usually it is best at the end, where it can serve as a natural step into the body proper. Below is an illustration.

The report is divided into four parts: the present streetcar routes, the present distribution of the city's population, the condition of the cars and the rail system, and a comparison of the costs of operating streetcars and buses.

The following paragraphs are the introduction of a report entitled *Effects of the Ernhardt Incentive Program on Employee Morale.* The notes in brackets and italics indicate the function of the preceding sentence or sentences. These notes do not actually appear, though introductions frequently have subheads that serve the same purpose.

Production costs rose an average of 32% on the company's products during the 10 years between 1946 and 1956. Since most of this increase was due to the sharp rise in the wage scale, management became concerned with the problem of increasing production per man-hour and requested that Mr. E.N. Ernhardt, Director of Employee Relations, study the possibilities of an incentive program. In November 1956 he submitted a comprehensive plan designed to stimulate output per capita by offering various incentives to the employees for meeting and exceeding quotas. The plan was adopted without modification by the Board of Directors on December 8, 1956. At the same meeting the Board asked that the employees' reactions to the program be learned after it had been in effect six months. [*Background*]

The present report gives the results of a study made to determine the employees' attitude and response to the program. [*Purpose*] The study was limited to the Breton Park Works, where the plan was initiated and where it has been in operation long enough to yield significant results. [*Scope*] As suggested by the Board, the investigation did not include personnel on straight salaries or employees who had not been with the company at least one year before the program began. [*Scope as restricted by authorization*]

The central finding of the report is that all features of the plan are popular except the requirement that a worker must take any grievance to the subforeman immediately above him before going to his general foreman. [*Thesis: basic conclusion*]

The study was made by the Department of Employee Relations during the five weeks between August 17 and September 20, 1957. [*Time covered by the study*] Each qualified employee was asked the same questions, which were prepared before the interviews began and which were worded so as not to bias the answers. At the beginning of the interview the employee was assured that his answers would remain confidential. [*Method of conducting the study*]

Nearly every person interviewed was co-operative and frank, less than 3% showing overt suspicion and any unwillingness to talk. [*Special information*]

DISCUSSION. In the majority of reports the discussion is the longest part; yet it requires little comment here because it raises no special problems—that is, problems that are not treated elsewhere in this book: effective writing, organization of material, viewpoint, tone, topic headings, and visual aids—the last two to be noted later.

The function of the discussion is to present and explain all the data bearing on the subject of the report. In the work report the job is explicitly described; in the examination report all the information collected during the investigation is given.

As mentioned earlier, special information is the first section of the discussion when it is fairly lengthy or it merits more emphasis than it would receive as a supplement to the introduction. When it is placed in the discussion, it should have its own topic heading if headings are used elsewhere. The heading might be "General Information,"

"Special Considerations," "Preliminary Matters," "General Matters," or some other inclusive phrase.

Often a writer finds that several minor matters belong in the report. Yet they will not be appropriate under any of the headings he is using, nor are they important enough to be given separate headings of their own. Such loose ends may be combined at the end of the discussion and given a common heading such as "Miscellaneous Matters," "Miscellaneous Information," or "Minor Considerations."

TERMINAL SECTION. The terminal section is the most important part of a report. Everything else is written to prepare for it. It brings together in one place the essential points developed in the discussion. It does this in such a way that each point is seen for its own worth and at the same time in its bearing on the thesis. In a work report this is where the high lights are summarized or the conclusions are listed. The same is true of the examination report, and if recommendations are offered, they are also presented here. A terminal section properly written is actually a synopsis of the whole report.

The phrase "terminal section" is never used as a heading. It is simply a convenient way to group under one name the various types of ending that a report may have.

TYPES AND HEADINGS: In actual practice each type of ending requires a specific topic heading of its own. The four basic ones are Summary, Results, Conclusions, and Recommendations.

1. Summary

"Summary" is the most descriptive heading when the terminal section is a brief digest of the data alone. The subject of the report calls for no judgments to be offered; therefore, the ending simply recapitulates the main points of the discussion. Typical of reports having this type of ending are those that describe the installation of equipment or the steps in a process when no evaluation is needed.

2. Results

When the data concern a test, an analysis, or an experiment and we point out their significance, "Results" is the proper heading.

3. Conclusions

If we are expected to evaluate the data and offer our judgment, "Conclusions" should be the heading. In other words, the terminal section not only will repeat the high lights of the discussion but will include our opinions on the subject.

4. Recommendations

If the report ends with our advising what should be done—that is, with our offering recommendations on the basis of the data given previously—"Recommendations" is the preferred heading.

Combinations of these basic endings are used regularly, and the heading reflects the nature of the combination:

5. Results and Conclusions

6. Results and Recommendations

7. Conclusions and Recommendations

When these headings are used, the two sets of statements are presented concurrently. Under No. 5, for example, the results and the conclusions would be given together. But if the two sets of statements deserve separate emphasis, each set can be presented under its own heading. The terminal section will then have two primary headings:

8. Results
Conclusions

9. Results
Recommendations

10. Conclusions
Recommendations

Sometimes a terminal section may include results, conclusions, and recommendations. If they are given together, the heading will read:

11. Results, Conclusions, and Recommendations

If they are presented separately, there will be three headings:

12. Results
Conclusions
Recommendations

So far we have regarded these terms as being topic headings as well as naming the types of report endings. Actually, the terminal section does not have a heading unless headings have been used in the text before it. On the other hand, if the discussion does contain headings, then the terminal section must be differentiated from it by one of the 12 foregoing terms.

Whether secondary headings should be used depends mostly on the length of the section. Unless it is fairly long, they are inadvisable from the standpoint of appearance because they give the text a cut-up effect. When secondaries are used in the terminal section, their wording is usually the same as that of the primary heads in the discussion.

TREATMENT: The terminal section may act in either of two ways:

A. It may consolidate and re-emphasize results, conclusions, and recommendations already set forth in the discussion. Since it is repeating something that has been said earlier (though the phrasing may be different), it need not be long; it can give the results, conclusions, or recommendations without summarizing the data that support them.

B. Conversely, the terminal section can present the results, conclusions, and recommendations for the first time in the report. When this is so, it is often longer than the A-type section because we may wish to support each statement by summarizing the grounds for it.

In handling conclusions we should keep in mind the following points:

1. The basic conclusion is presented first. This conclusion is the over-all opinion that we have arrived at after weighing all the data, including data that do not support our final judgment. The conclusion may be positive and may be worded quite specifically: "When the slight defect in the oil line is corrected, the engine is ready for mass production." It may be negative: "The inspection shows that further operation of the pumps at Station 2 is impractical." It may have to be worded in general terms because it embraces subsidiary conclusions of equal importance: "Several repairs must be made if the pumps at Station 2 are to continue in operation."

2. There should be at least one conclusion for each primary section of the discussion, with the possible exception of that giving general information. If a matter is important enough to receive major attention in the discussion, then it is important enough to be included in the terminal section. Frequently it may need more than one con-

clusion; each of its secondary headings, for instance, may warrant comment. The section on general information does not often require a conclusion because, as we noticed, it usually contains material that simply prepares for what is of importance.

3. These subsidiary conclusions appear in the same order as the data they bear on were presented in the discussion. If the first section of the discussion pertains to lubrication, then the first conclusion, or group of conclusions, after the basic one will pertain to lubrication. If the next section of the discussion deals with ignition, then the next conclusion, or group of conclusions, will deal with ignition.

4. No conclusion should appear in the terminal section unless it has either been given or been anticipated in the discussion. In other words, no new ideas should be introduced in the terminal section. Whatever appears must have been at least prepared for by earlier data or discussion.

5. Semitabulation is an effective way to present the supplementary conclusions, especially if they are numerous. When it is employed the basic conclusion is not in the list. It bears on the whole report and therefore should be given separate status from the ones that pertain to only the individual sections.

Semitabulation is the vertical listing of a series, usually a series of statements. It is most effective when the following details are observed.

First, the series is introduced by a statement that unifies the items in the series and shows its significance.

Second, each item is preceded by a figure or a letter.

Third, the beginning of each member of the series is indented two or three spaces more than the regular paragraph indention. This extra indention further defines the series and shows that the items are really sub-paragraphs within a larger one.

Fourth, since the members of the series have parallel values, they are made grammatically parallel. The parallelism extends only to the first period in each member. In other words, some of the listed items may be followed by discussion and others have none.

These five points, presented with special reference to conclusions, apply to results and recommendations, with the exception of No. 2. There need not be a result or a recommendation for each primary division of the discussion. For example, the data concerning lubrication may be entirely favorable; there will be a conclusion to this effect but there is nothing to recommend.

Below is a terminal section presented in semitabular form.

CONCLUSIONS

Cole's mill can be restored to complete efficiency at a cost not exceeding $23,000. The specific findings are:

1. The basement is in good repair except where seepage has slightly weakened the foundation in the southeastern corner. The outside drainage at this point needs attention.

2. The main floor, where the heavy machinery is located, requires the most work. All of the flooring on the western side should be replaced and a few of the supporting girders must be re-enforced.

3. The second floor is in good condition and needs only painting.

4. The exterior of the building requires no work.

Supplementary Parts

In addition to the body long reports may have any or all of the parts described below.

COVER BINDER. The cover binder holds the pages together, protects them against wear and crumpling, and provides an external place for data that concern the report. Ordinarily, folders made of cardboard or plastic are sufficient, but reports that are extremely long or that are going to pass through many hands should be bound in buckram. The information on the cover may be simply the title and the author's name. If the report has a government or a company classification, such as secret or proprietary, it is put on the cover. In many companies a library reference number and an abstract of the body are included.

FLYLEAVES. Blank pages inside the front and the back covers protect the first and the last pages of writing against chafing. They also provide space for comment and queries by the readers.

TITLE PAGE. The title page should contain at least five items:

a. The name of the writer's company. A common place for this is an inch or so from the top of the page. It may be written in all-capitals. If further information is added, such as the division or an identifying phrase like "Consultant Engineers," it should be placed beneath the company name.

b. The title of the report. This should be the most prominent thing on the page. Consequently, it should be written in all-capitals and underscored and should appear in the upper half of the page, midway between the center and the company name. The words "a report on" are redundant in the title, especially if the report is identified as such elsewhere on the page.

    c. The name of the person, company, or organization that the report is going to if it is not the same as item "a"—in other words, if it is not the writer's own company and his own department. For example, item "a" might be

CATAWBA POWER COMPANY
Engineering Division

and item "c" might be the same company but a different part of it:

A Report
Submitted to
CATAWBA POWER COMPANY
Purchasing Division

Item "c" should be introduced by some phrase such as the one above or simply "Submitted to" or "Prepared for." It appears just below the middle of the page.

    d. The author's name. This is best in the lower case and may be preceded by the phrase "Prepared by" or simply "By." If "a" and "c" are the same and "c" therefore does not actually appear, the writer's name can be placed midway between the center of the page and the date line at the bottom. When "c" does appear, the writer's name may come about an inch below it.

    e. The date that the report is submitted. This can be put about an inch from the bottom.

If the report is of the preliminary type, the phrase "A Preliminary Report" appears beneath the title. Progress reports are identified by such phrases as "A Progress Report," "Progress Report No. 4," or "An Interim Report." If the report has a government or a company classification, it is indicated in a conspicuous place. The page may have such additional data as the address of the writer's company, his title, and the report number.

The page is counted as the first of those preliminary to the body, but for the sake of appearance the number is better omitted.

A sample title page follows.

BORDEAUX LABORATORIES
Commercial Chemists

CATALYTIC PROPERTIES OF CARBITE 7A
Preliminary Report No. 2

CONFIDENTIAL

Prepared for
THE TERRY-LINDSTRUM COMPANY

by
Karl V. Meier
Chief Chemist

20 April 1956

LETTER OF TRANSMITTAL. The letter of transmittal usually follows the title page. Some companies put it first on the grounds that it is not really a part of the report, but the practice is not general. The contents of the letter have been explained on pages 63-64. Here, then, it is only necessary to distinguish between a letter of transmittal and a preface.

The letter is usually preferable because most reports are written for one person or a definite number of persons. Sometimes the number may be fairly large, as with a board of directors, but as long as the number is specific, the personal touch of a letter is desirable. Nevertheless, there are times when the number is great and indefinite—for example, the stockholders in a large corporation; then the more impersonal preface takes the place of the letter.

The word PREFACE heads the page, and all parts of the letter disappear except the typed name of the author at the end. The city and the state in which the author was at the time of writing the preface and the month and year when it was written often appear under his name. The preface may contain any of the items found in a letter of transmittal, but the style is more detached.

ABSTRACT. In the field of report writing, both "abstract" and "summary" are widely used to designate the digest that precedes the body of a formal report. "Abstract" is preferred here to prevent this digest from being confused with the type of terminal section called "Summary."

The abstract serves two purposes. One is to refresh the memory of persons who have read the report some time before. To act on it, they wish now to recall its main points without rereading the whole report or even the terminal section. The abstract enables them to do this.

The other purpose is to afford a bird's-eye view of the whole report to persons who are not interested in reading the report itself or who care to read only certain parts of it. As an example of the first group, a section manager may have half a dozen reports moving across his desk every day. His other responsibilities prevent him from reading any but the most important reports; yet he must know the gist of all that have been written under his general supervision. The abstract gives him this, and he can leave the details for his subsection managers and foremen to check.

Again, some readers will be interested in certain parts of the report and not in others. The legal department, the advertising department, and the treasurer's office are not likely to be concerned with all of a report that is directed to the three groups and possibly more. Yet each group is interested in the part or parts that deal with subjects in its sphere. The abstract permits each reader to get the whole framework quickly before turning to the particular sections he wishes to study.

Abstracts can be of three types. The descriptive type tells what the report covers but reproduces none of the actual contents except the thesis.

The informational type condenses the body of the report: it boils the data down to the main points they represent. To do this, we do not have to go through the report page by page culling its high lights. We may simply condense the background given in the introduction and repeat the more important conclusions and recommendations of the terminal section, for if properly written, the terminal section has all the main points developed in the discussion. The grounds for the supplementary conclusions and recommendations are usually unnecessary in the abstract.

The third type of abstract is a combination of the other two: it indicates the general coverage of the report and reproduces the vital points made in the terminal section.

The page on which the abstract begins, and often ends, is titled ABSTRACT or SUMMARY. It is the practice of many companies to include a digest of the abstract itself on the front cover or, if the abstract is short, to put all of it there and omit it inside.

TABLE OF CONTENTS. As an aid to the reader in locating sections of the report that he wishes to consult or reconsult, a table of contents is included among the preliminary elements. It may list everything that appears between the flyleaves, including what precedes it—the title page, the letter of transmittal, and the abstract—or it may list only what is in the body and the appendixes. In both cases the wording should be identical with that used to head the section which is cited, and the principles governing the capitalization of literary titles apply.

The titles used for the elements, such as "Abstract," and the first-degree headings in the body form the left margin. The introduction is listed even when the heading itself is omitted on page 1. These titles and primary heads may or may not be written in all-capitals. In either case the page looks better if the subheadings under them are not all-capitals.

Second-degree headings are indented five or six spaces, and third-degree five or six more. Unless a report is exceptionally long, so that there is considerable text under the fourth- and the fifth-degree heads, little is served by listing them here even though they appear in the discussion. Double-spacing between headings makes the table easy to consult.

The page numbers form the right margin. To keep it uniform, the figures move inward as their number increases—thus:

6
15
108

Only the initial page of each section is given. The reader can use the table more rapidly if leaders connect the entry and its page number. Leaders are periods or dashes that lead the eye across the page. The appearance is better if they are spaced four or five keys apart and successive rows are aligned under each other.

When appendixes are in the report, the table cites each one by its label (the Roman numeral or capital letter that designates it) and its title. A period or a colon may be used between the label and the title. The word "Appendix" may be repeated each time, or the primary entry may be "Appendixes" and the labels and the titles treated as secondary heads under it.

The first page of the table may be marked either TABLE OF CONTENTS or simply CONTENTS. The trend seems to be toward the latter.

LIST OF ILLUSTRATIONS.   Each figure and table used in the text is cited by label and title. Whether those in the appendixes are added is a matter of individual preference. The entries should follow the principles observed for the entries in the table of contents insofar as they can be treated alike.

The list may be put at the end of the table of contents or on a separate page. In either place it has a title. There are many possibilities, a few of which are ILLUSTRATIONS, ILLUSTRATIVE MATERIAL, LIST OF ILLUSTRATIONS, and FIGURES AND TABLES.

APPENDIXES. If an appendix or several appendixes are called for, they follow the body. A page marked APPENDIXES may be inserted to accentuate the division from the body.

An appendix may contain any of four kinds of material. Most common is material that confirms and enlarges upon statements made in the body. Such material is not necessary for an understanding of the text and, if included there, would slow down the reading. Still, it belongs somewhere in the report in case the reader wishes to verify our interpretation of it. Typical of such material are excerpts from legal documents and from pamphlets of government agencies, calculations on which text discussion is based, and the negative results of methods that were tried before the successful one was found.

A second type of appendix explains the details of a principle or a theory alluded to in the text, or it may define terms used throughout the report.

A third type contains material too bulky for the body, such as a blueprint or a fold-out map. Although often highly important to an understanding of the text, such material is best placed in a 9 by 12 envelope pasted inside the back cover. Here it does not encumber the turning of the pages, and the reader can withdraw it and spread it out before him if there are continual references to it. In the table of contents its location is shown by the phrase "back cover."

The fourth type of appendix is the list of references—books, magazine articles, pamphlets, other reports—that we consulted in preparing the report. It is entitled REFERENCES, WORKS CONSULTED, or BIBLIOGRAPHY. It should be the first or the last appendix. If material is in an envelope inside the back cover, then the bibliography is the first appendix. Details concerning its make-up are explained on pages 210-211.

Each appendix except the bibliography is cited at the appropriate place in the text. With the exception of material in the envelope, the appendixes are arranged in the order they are cited. Each should have a label, such as Appendix I or Appendix A, and a title and be on a separate page.

INDEX. Unless a report is exceptionally long, running to two or three hundred pages, the table of contents suffices as a guide for anyone looking up special parts of it. When an index is added, it is the last thing in the report unless an envelope-appendix is inside the cover. It is an alphabetical listing of topics and subtopics covered in the report, and lists every page on which the topic or subtopic is discussed to any extent.

Minor Mechanics

TOPIC HEADINGS. The use of topic headings is dictated by the particular circumstances. If the material is so homogeneous and smooth-flowing as to have no natural divisions, then nothing is gained by giving it artificial ones. Generally, however, there are natural divisions, and both the writing and the reading are made easier if they are observed and indicated by headings. In addition, headings improve the appearance of a report.

Of the many systems of headings the one illustrated below is recommended because it is uncomplicated and widely used.

This is the end of the last paragraph of a section.

FIRST-DEGREE HEADING

Centered between margins, written in all-capitals, underlined. Three blank lines above, two below. No punctuation follows.

Second-degree Heading

Flush with left margin, capitalized as a title, underlined. Two blank lines above, one below. No punctuation follows.

Third-degree Heading.   Indented as a paragraph, capitalized as a title, underlined. One blank line above and below. Period follows. Text begins on the same line.

Fourth-degree Heading: Indented two or three more spaces than than a regular paragraph, capitalized as a title, underlined. One blank line above and below. Colon follows. Text begins on same line.

A fifth-degree heading is distinguished from the beginning of any regular paragraph only by being indented as much as a fourth-degree one and by having the opening phrase underlined. This opening phrase indicates the topic to be discussed until the next heading occurs.

Other details concerning the use of topic headings depend on the material itself. For instance, primary heads may be used without secondary ones when the major sections have no natural subdivisions, or only very slight ones that paragraphing suffices to indicate.

If we do use secondary headings in one section, we are not committed to using them in every section. For example, we may employ four secondaries under the first primary, two under the next one, and none under the other primaries. Our only obligation is to avoid using single subheads; a subhead stands for a subdivision and division requires a minimum of two parts.

Whether any text separates headings of different degree depends on the particular situation. If we have something to say about the topic indicated in the primary heading before breaking it down into secondaries, then text appears between the headings. It may be a single sentence or several paragraphs. Further, we do not have to be consistent between sections; we may have text between one primary and its first secondary and in the next section have none between them.

Logic must be observed in the wording of the headings. Specifically, headings of the same degree that have a common superior heading should be parallel in structure. To illustrate, the following headings cover the first two sections of a discussion.

Workers Affected by the New Regulations
    Machinists
    Packers
    Truck Drivers
    Maintenance Crew
Aims of the New Regulations
    To Reduce Accidents
    To Reduce Waste of Materials
    To Raise Morale
        By Increasing Take-home Pay
        By Defining Duties More Clearly

Because the two primary headings have the same superior heading, the title of the report, they are grammatically parallel, both being noun phrases. The subheads under the first primary are nouns and noun phrases and therefore parallel. The subheads under the second primary are infinitive phrases parallel to each other but not to the first group of secondaries. And a third type of construction—prepositional or gerund phrase—is used for the tertiary headings under "To Raise Morale." Logic has not been impaired anywhere because headings with the same superior heading have been treated alike.

As a general thing, though, headings are most naturally worded as nouns or noun phrases; accordingly, such discrepancy as that noted above is more the exception than the rule. Probably the most common exceptions are subheads treated as adjectives, each of which directly modifies the superior heading. Below is an example.

Power Units

Gasoline

Electric

A-c

D-c

Gasoline and *electric* modify *power units* and are therefore parallel adjectives. So are *a-c* and *d-c,* each of which modifies *electric power units*.

It is because of this need for parallel structure that the words *General* and *Miscellaneous* by themselves are unsatisfactory as primary headings. Used in this way, they are adjectives; therefore, they will not be parallel with the other primary heads if those heads are substantives, as they are most likely to be. Further, as adjectives they are theoretically modifying their common superior heading—in this case, the general title of the paper. Since this is not the writer's intention, he can avoid the misreading and maintain his parallelism by adding a noun: General Information, General Remarks, General Considerations; Miscellaneous Information, Miscellaneous Remarks, Miscellaneous Data.

Another breach of logic is to use a word or phrase as a heading of one degree and then to repeat it as a subheading under itself. In effect, this is saying that a part is also the whole. Consider this example:

The Condition of the Bridge
Approaches
Abutments
Bridge
Floor

The third subhead is faulty because the whole section, not just the third subdivision, describes the condition of the bridge—the approaches, abutments, and floor also being part of it. The third subhead should be "Superstructure," "Frame," "Steel Work," or whatever the author has in mind.

The wording of the headings should be completely objective, indicating only what is to be discussed and not our reaction to it. Thus: "Drainage" or "Drainage Problems"—not "Excellent Drainage" or "Poor Drainage." Questions as headings are also undesirable. As a matter of fact, they are usually out of place anywhere in a report since a report is supposed to answer questions and settle problems, not raise them.

Also inappropriate in a report, especially a formal one, is the use of a pronoun or a demonstrative adjective to refer to a topic heading. We are tempted to do this in the sentence that immediately follows the heading. For example:

> *Drainage.* This will be one of the most difficult problems to solve. (Pronoun)
> *Drainage.* This problem will be one of the most difficult to solve. (Demonstrative adjective)

More precise is:

> *Drainage.* The problem of drainage will be one of the most difficult to solve.

Or:

> *Drainage.* One of the most difficult problems to solve will be drainage.

Sometimes a report has major divisions so long and so distinct that they are almost separate entities. Both the organization and the system of headings are simplified if these major divisions are not designated merely by primary headings. They can be made separate parts and labeled and entitled as such.

As an example let us assume that we are working on a long report that is to describe the needs of a town's sewage system. We break the body down into its major divisions and separate them by subtitle pages that read:

Part I
Introduction

Part II
Repair of Existing Facilities

Part III
Expansion of Existing Facilities

Part IV
New Construction

Part V
Conclusions and Recommendations

In this arrangement conclusions and recommendations covering all three parts of the discussion have been brought together and made the last division of the report because there was no reason to treat them separately. But if the conclusions and recommendations for each part were better considered immediately after the discussion of each part, they would be the last primary heading in each division.

Part I
Introduction

Part II
Repair of Existing Facilities

Disposal Plant
Sewers
Outfalls
Conclusions and Recommendations

Part III
Expansion of Existing Facilities

Disposal Plant
Sewers
Outfalls
Conclusions and Recommendations

Part IV
New Construction

Northside Disposal Plant
Sewers and Outfalls in Maple Heights
Sewers and Outfalls in Glendale
Conclusions and Recommendations

PAGINATION. The conventional system of page numbering uses Arabic numerals to mark the pages in the body (the introduction, the discussion, and the terminal section). The numbers may be placed in the upper right corner, in the center at the top, or in the center at the bottom. The first position is more convenient for a person looking up a topic he has noted in the table of contents. The appendixes continue the Arabic numerals used in the body. The pages that precede the body bear small Roman numerals.

The first page of the body repeats the title of the report verbatim as it appears on the title page. It should be placed two or three inches from the top and equidistant from the side margins. If it requires more than one line, it should be double-spaced. Its importance suggests that it should be underlined and written in all capitals.

GENERAL APPEARANCE OF THE TEXT. The appearance of a report has a great bearing on its effectiveness. In this connection topic headings should not be placed at the very bottom of a page. Headings of the first and the second degree should have at least two lines of print beneath them, and all others at least one. Otherwise, the heading looks much better at the top of the next page. The same applies to paragraphs. If there is room for only one line at the bottom of a page, the paragraph should begin at the top of the following one. Conversely, a single line or less ending a paragraph looks better on the page with the rest of the paragraph than at the top of a new page.

A good deal of "white space" also helps appearance. "White space" is the parts of a page that have no writing. Among them are the margins. In a bound report the left-hand margin should be at least two inches so that the binder does not absorb it. The other margins are the same as in the business letter. Other means of obtaining white space are the use of topic headings, uncrowded illustrations and tables, and semitabulation.

A formal report of medium length is reprinted on pages 128-144.

THE SHORT REPORT

Short formal reports are used as often as long ones. There is no difference in the way the essential parts are treated except that the restriction on pronouns of the first and the second persons is observed less widely. The principal difference, besides the text being shorter, is that some of the supplementary parts characteristic of the long report are omitted because they are of no real service.

The *cover binder* is used only if the report is going through many hands or is to be filed in the company library. When it is omitted the pages are stapled together.

Flyleaves are not used unless there is a cover.

The *title page* is retained.

The *letter of transmittal* appears if the report has been specifically authorized. If the report has simply grown out of the writer's work, the letter is more often omitted.

The *abstract* is useful if the conventional arrangement of the introduction, the discussion, and the terminal section is employed. If the modified order is followed, the abstract serves no purpose because the introduction and the terminal section, which it summarizes, are at the beginning of the report and are likely to be short themselves.

The *table of contents* and the *list of illustrations* are unnecessary.

An *appendix* or two may be called for, particularly a short list of references.

The *index* is omitted.

The remarks above apply to short industrial reports. For a discussion of college laboratory reports see pages 157-160.

CONSOLIDATED SMELTING CO.

Engineering Division
Ithaca, New York

BEST DESIGNS
FOR
LEAD INSTALLATIONS

A
Report
Submitted to
HARBOR CITY CONSTRUCTION CO.

Brooklyn, New York

by
H. Crandall Givens
Research Engineer

April 16, 1959

CONSOLIDATED SMELTING CO.
Engineering Division
Ithaca, New York

April 16, 1959

Harbor City Construction Co.
129 W. Trenton Avenue
Brooklyn 14, New York

Attention: Mr. Jackson H. Bell
Vice President

Gentlemen: Subject: <u>Report</u> <u>on</u> <u>Best</u> <u>Designs</u>
<u>for</u> <u>Lead</u> <u>Installations</u>

As requested in your letter of March 7, 1959 an investigation was made to determine the best designs for lead installations. Special recommendations were to be made regarding the direct applications of the various joints on stave tanks, launders, towers, and flues. A report on this investigation is now submitted.

The investigation was begun on March 15 in the laboratory of the Consolidated Smelting Co., and the tests were completed on March 25. The tests definitely established that the correct types of joints must be used on lead installations if satisfactory results are to be obtained.

The time spent on investigation was divided equally between research and actual experiments. Much important information was obtained through Dr. Alan D. Weber, Chief Research Engineer, Avil Copper Company, Ltd. Without Dr. Weber's aid, the report could not be complete.

I trust that the findings of the investigation will satisfy your requirements.

Yours truly,
H. Crandall Givens
H. Crandall Givens
Research Engineer

HCG/ml
c Dr. Alan D. Weber

ABSTRACT

An investigation of various types of lead joints was requested so that the lead installations in stave tanks, launders, and towers and flues could be properly made. Poorly designed installations can cause a complete failure of these parts.

Tests were made to determine the durability of the joints against expansion, contraction, and compression. The leakages of gas and fluid through the joints were recorded so that relative results could be seen. On the basis of the tests, recommended designs for the stave tanks, launders, and towers and flues are offered.

The body of the report is divided to include each test and the results; the recommendations deal specifically with the use of joints on the prescribed parts.

CONTENTS

ILLUSTRATIONS

BEST DESIGNS FOR LEAD INSTALLATIONS

The Harbor City Construction Company is building a plant at Rahway, New Jersey for the Bretson Chemical Corporation. The plant will require numerous and various lead installations. This report covers tests that were conducted to determine the best applications for the types of lead joints to be used, in particular, on stave tanks, launders, and towers and flues. The efficiency of these parts depends entirely on the design of the installations.

The tests indicate that the lead sheets should be joined by slip seams or welded joints, and it is recommended that the specific suggestions offered on pages 9-12 be followed.

TYPES OF SEAMS

Locking

The locking type of seam is formed by the joining and overlapping of the seam as shown in Figure 1. It can be used to join sheets

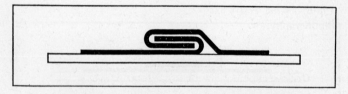

FIGURE 1   Cross-sectional View of Lock Joint

of equal or unequal thickness, but the maximum thickness of sheets that can be satisfactorily joined in this way is ¼ in. (16 psf). A thickness greater than this will not permit a tight seal.

[1]

Welded

The welded seam is the joining of two or more sheets by a simple weld as shown in Figure 2. The edges of the plates are angled at

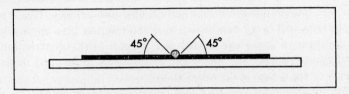

FIGURE 2   Cross-sectional View of Weld Joint

45° so that there is a larger surface area than if the edges were parallel. This assures a larger and stronger weld than would be possible otherwise. A welded seam can be used to join plates not varying in thickness by more than ⅛ in. up to ¼ in.

Lap

The lap joint is a modified combination of a lock seam and a welded joint. One of the sheets is formed over the edge of the other sheet, and the edge of the upper sheet is welded as shown in Figure 3.

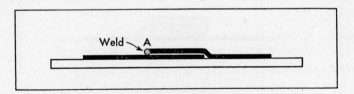

FIGURE 3   Cross-sectional View of Lap Joint

Before the weld is made, the edge of the upper plate and the top of the lower plate should be concaved as shown.

[2]

TESTS ON JOINTS

Conditions

Temperature. Each of the joints being tested was subjected to identical temperatures, both normal climatic and extreme. These tests were performed in a laboratory where the temperatures were readily controlled and where the strains and stresses in the joints could be accurately measured.

Gas. The joints of each type were checked to insure that the seals were as tight as possible. The jointed sheets were in turn placed in an air-tight case (see Figure 4) and sealed so that the case was divided

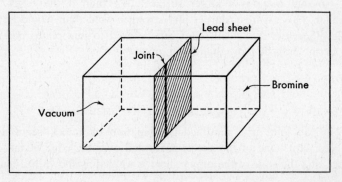

FIGURE 4   Apparatus Used to Test Gas Penetration Through Joints

into two air-tight partitions. Bromine gas was pumped into one side of the case and a partial vacuum was created in the remaining half. Sheets connected by each type of joint were tested in this manner for 48 hours, and the concentrations of the gas that leaked through were recorded.

Solution. Sheets connected by the various joints were subjected to the leaking action of a fluid. Benzene was used because of its low density and low viscosity. Here the sheets were formed into a trough with the seams at the bottom. A continuous flow of benzene passed through the trough for 96 hours, and the leakage was recorded.

[3]

Limited Area.   The working sheet combinations were designed to fit exactly in an invar frame 36 in. square. The invar frame had a thermal expansion of 0.0002 in. per 100 F, which was not pertinent to this test. The temperature was slowly raised, and the reactions at the joints were noted.

Results

Appendix A, page 11, is a graph showing the thermal expansion of soft lead and 6% antimonial lead as found in tests conducted at Consolidated Smelting Co. on July 1, 1958.

Appendix B, page 12, contains charts showing the leakages through the joints before and after the thermal and limited area tests.

Locking Joint.   When subjected to the gas and liquid tests, the locking joint proved to be fairly tight. The concentration of the gas that leaked through the joint during the 48-hour period measured 0.02%. The same joint was given the liquid test for 96 hours and a volume of 0.92 cu mm leaked through the joint.

After the temperature tests were completed, the same joint underwent the fluid and gas tests again. A substantial increase was noted in the results. The bromine concentration increased to 2.06%, and 3.42 cu mm of benzene passed through the joint during the test period.

The limited area test on this joint showed that the entire expansion was being taken up in the joint, but leakages of 1.01% gas and 1.34 cu mm liquid were recorded. However, as can be seen by comparing the leakages before and after the temperature test, the allowance for the expansion and contraction sacrifices the tightness of the joint.

Welded Joint.   The results of the gas and fluid tests on the welded joint are not surprising. Naturally, there was no leakage of bromine or benzene through the weld.

Nevertheless, the temperature test proved that just because seals are leak-proof, they are not necessarily the perfect joint. Because the expansion of the sheets could not be compensated for in the joint, the expansion was longitudinal along the sheets. When a limiting area was used to prevent the horizontal expansion of the plates, the seam buckled from the excessive stress.

[4]

The liquid and gas tests were repeated after the temperature test was completed. The joints were still sealed tightly, but the weld partially split as a result of the limited area test. A concentration of 10.48% gas and 8.68 cu mm of fluid passed through the joint.

Lap Joint.   The tests on the lap joint showed that there was no leakage of either liquid or gas during the specified initial trial.

The temperature test followed, and after its completion the joint was again subjected to the fluid and gas tests. The seams remained tight and no leakage of bromine or benzene was recorded.

The final test was that of limiting area. The process was repeated here exactly as on the other specimens, but no apparent damage was done to the joint. The overlapping seam compensated for the changes due to the temperature. As in the other cases, the liquid and gas tests were repeated, but the seals remained tight.

CONCLUSIONS

Lead sheets may be joined by slip seams or welded joints. The specific application will determine the type of joints to be used.

Locking Seams

Where drainage is the particular requirement, locking seams may be used and provision for thermal expansion may be made in the seams. When lead is joined by locking seam construction, a large number of joints should be used, each to take up a small amount of the thermal expansion. With a liberal temperature range allowance, each joint should be limited to a maximum of 1/8-in. expansion allowance and preferably less. Where lead is used as lining or covering, and where infiltration of a gas or solution may corrode the supporting structure, locking seams are generally unsatisfactory.

Welded Seams

Where welded seams are employed, separate expansion bends should be installed at frequent intervals to reduce the take-up in each joint to a practical minimum.

[5]

Lap Joints

Where corroding gasses and solution are present, locking seams are insufficient, and welded joints should be used. Provision for expansion is compensated for by the use of lap joints for sheets up to ¼-in. thickness (16 psf).

On horizontal flat surfaces, welded joints are preferable where pressure on the sheet tends to limit the deformation of the sheet under thermal expansion or contraction to a local area. Any expansion or contraction of the lead sheet will cause the bend at the lap joint to act as an expansion bend, localizing the stress and the strain. The joint will fail along line A (Figure 3, page 2) when compensation for thermal conditions is not provided.

RECOMMENDED USES

It is recommended that lead installations be used on tanks, launders, towers and flues as detailed below.

Wood Stave Tanks

Since unlined wood stave tanks depend on the swelling of the staves for tightness, it is obvious that when these tanks are lead-lined, the staves will dry and shrink. To overcome this weakness, it is suggested that a reinforcing ring be constructed around the top of the tank to maintain the original diameter and shape of the tank. This construction will reduce the volume change to a minimum.

It is recommended that the lead lining be installed in the manner shown in Figure 5, page 7. Installation of the lining as diagrammed will not permit leakage, but it will allow a 3% contraction or expansion without damage to the lining. Under normal conditions the tank should not expand or contract more than 1%.

[6]

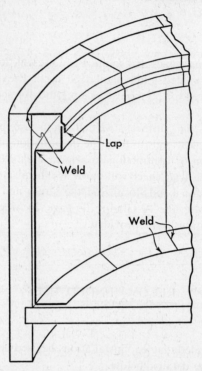

FIGURE 5   Construction of Wood Stave Tank and Recommended Joints

Launders

Wood launders have previously been used in chemical industries. Many of these installations have been provided with a lead lining to prevent solution leakage and, where the solution is corrosive, to prevent corrosion of the connectors such as bolts and nails.

These launders are now being constructed as shown in Figure 6.

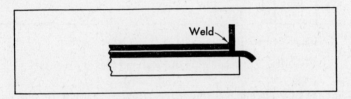

FIGURE 6   Seam Used in Construction of Launder

A minimum number of wood and steel supports are used. This type of construction improves the operation, maintenance, and inspection. Appearance is greatly enhanced.

Since the lead launder is generally self-supporting with respect to shape, the cost is not greatly increased although the serviceability is greatly improved. When the salvage value of the lead is considered, the over-all cost of this type of construction may be lower than that of the lead-lined wood.

A weld is the only joint practical for use on the launder. Expansion and contraction will not affect the launder or joint in any way. It should be noted that before the weld is made, the two pieces to be welded should be channeled slightly. Channeling creates more surface area for the weld to take hold and thus gives a stronger bond.

Towers and Flues

It is often economical to build towers and flues of laminated wood construction and line these structures with lead. Some typical details of this type of construction are shown in Figure 7.

[8]

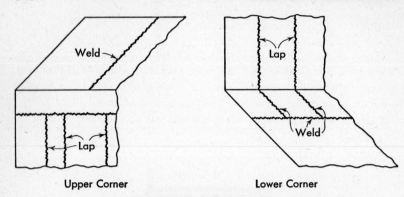

Upper Corner   Lower Corner

FIGURE 7   Installation of Lead on Flues and Towers

Leakage of a chemical through the joints of a tower or flue could cause serious damage before the leak was discovered. Therefore, welds and lap joints are the only seams used. Because of the varying temperatures, particularly on the flue, lap joints must be used to compensate for the large expansion and contraction.

APPENDIXES

APPENDIX A

Thermal Expansion Graph

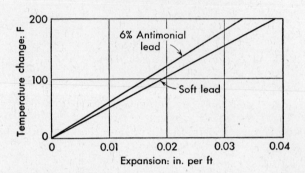

Thermal expansion of 6% antimonial lead and soft lead

APPENDIX B

Temperature Variation Test Chart

	LEAKAGE BEFORE		LEAKAGE AFTER	
Joint	Gas (%)	Liq (mm)	Gas (%)	Liq (mm)
Lock	0.02	0.92	1.01	1.34
Weld	0.00	0.00	10.48	8.68
Lap	0.00	0.00	0.00	0.00

Comparative leakage of different joints before and after the Temperature Variation Test

Limited Area Test Chart

	LEAKAGE BEFORE		LEAKAGE AFTER	
Joint	Gas (%)	Liq (mm)	Gas (%)	Liq (mm)
Lock	0.02	0.92	2.06	3.42
Weld	0.00	0.00	0.00	0.00
Lap	0.00	0.00	0.00	0.00

Comparative leakage of different joints before and after the Limited Area Test

[12]

APPENDIX C

BIBLIOGRAPHY

Allen, Homer T. Lead Structures. Boston: A. Schwartz and Company, 1954.

Bacon, A. John. "Lead in Industry." Engineering Yearbook, 23:6 (June 1957), 65-89.

Gabel, Theodore. Engineering Manual. New York: McGraw-Hill Book Co., Inc., 1956.

Gardner, G.H. Industrial Designs. Chicago: Houghton-Mifflin Co., 1943. 2nd ed.

Jackson, L.S. "Lead Design." Structural Engineering, 25:2 (February 1956), 14-23.

EXERCISES AND ASSIGNMENTS

A. Criticize the following introductions as to their completeness and the effectiveness of their organization and language.

1. This report is designed to show if it would be feasible to renovate the cabinet shop of the Amelia Construction Company. This report shows that the renovation of the shop to obtain maximum efficiency is possible. The cost of renovation will be approximately $50,000.

2. Competitors of the Valentine Mold and Machine Company have begun to underbid the company in the field of hydraulic cup molds. An investigation was conducted to determine whether the production efficiency can be improved and the company can lower its price. The study was limited to the processes from the selection of the steel to the tapping of the mold because other phases of the operation were streamlined two years ago. The study was made during the five days between April 5 and April 10, a period when production was considered average.

   The basic recommendations of this report are that the use of a different grade of steel be considered and that roughing methods be changed.

3. On March 18 the Board of Directors of Marshal Printing Company decided that a new building was needed to house their offset printing plant. The plans were drawn by Brown and Jones, Architects, and construction of the building was begun in June. At the same meeting the Board of Directors also decided that the new plant should be newly equipped in its entirety.

   The Board of Directors also decided that the Photographic Department would have to be expanded to provide the increased number of presses with plates without slowing down their output. This expansion included the necessary equipment for three-color separation.

B. The paragraph below is taken from the discussion section of a formal report written by a student. Explain the faults and eliminate them.

Main Laboratory

A minimum of 3000 cp will be needed to light this space adequately. All of the bids we have received have been ridiculously high. However, some of our finest chemists work here, so we will have to accept one of them.

C. From the standpoint of completeness and organization, criticize the following terminal sections in the light of the data preceding them.

1. Title of the report: Construction of Bracket D-8523.
Main headings in the discussion: Description, Cost Analysis, Machinery, Heat Treatment, Strength Tests, Plating, Painting.

CONCLUSIONS

From the results of the tests which have been made on the bracket, there is no reason to believe that the basic design of the part should be changed in any way. Other conclusions are:

1. The cost of producing an angle-aluminum bracket is eight times the cost of producing a cast bracket.
2. The machine time will be cut 50 percent by using a cast bracket.
3. Solution heat treatment is preferred if the angular-aluminum bracket is used.
4. Strength tests show that the cast bracket is more stable than the welded bracket.
5. The required alumilite finish is inferior to the Brytal Process for plating the part.
6. A resin lacquer is superior to an enamel paint.

2. Title of the report: The XF-III as a Fighter Plane.
Main headings in the discussion: Appearance, Speed, Armament, Flight Characteristics, Range, Safety Features, Electronic System.

RECOMMENDATIONS

It is recommended that:

1. The XF-III be placed on order.
2. The maximum elevator angle be increased from 20° to 25° in order to give the XF-III a shorter turning radius.
3. The wings be modified to include low-speed slats on the leading edges to insure greater stability at subsonic speeds.

3. Title of the report: Increasing Production at the Forrestal Radio Corporation.
   Main headings in the discussion: Overtime Work, Night Shift, Expansion of Facilities.

CONCLUSIONS

Overtime is practical only during short rush periods. The cost of labor is high and the efficiency of the assembly line is reduced. No capital investment is needed.

Expansion of the plant requires heavy capital investment but results in a permanent increase in efficiency.

Working a night shift requires no capital investment at the present, but eventually it will because it results in shortening the life of the machinery. Moreover, obtaining labor for night work may prove difficult.

D. Criticize the coverage of the following abstracts. The first one is of the descriptive type; the other two are of the informational type.

1. A complete examination was made of the surplus property located at Camp Horn, and being offered for sale by the state, to determine whether the company should buy it. Information was gathered by means of close inspection and actual operational tests. Special emphasis was placed on the electric, heat-power, and testing equipment.

2. The Detroit Payloader has an efficient engine, powerful transmissions and rear axles, excellent brakes, a sturdy frame, firm front and

rear suspensions, positive steering with a relatively small turning circle, and average visibility and control from inside the cab. The cost is also lower than that of similar trucks.

On the basis of these facts, it is recommended that a fleet of Detroit Payloaders be purchased by the Davidson Transfer Company.

3. The Sampson Fertilizer Company has authorized the construction of a new plant at Lake Charles, Louisiana, and the question has arisen whether to use the modified lead chamber process for producing the sulfuric acid.

The process consists of burning sulfur in air to get sulfur dioxide. The sulfur dioxide is then reacted with nitrogen dioxide to produce a gas, sulfur trioxide. The sulfur trioxide dissolves in steam to produce concentrated sulfuric acid.

The acid plant itself occupies little space. Its maximum dimensions are 30 by 8 by 30 ft. It consists of a sulfur burner, gas reaction tower, lead chamber, gas recovery tower, and collection tank.

This process would be advisable to install in the Lake Charles factory. The compactness of the acid plant and the economy of operation and maintenance especially recommend it. Since the product is obtained in a high yield and concentration, it is very suitable for the manufacture of fertilizer.

E. Subjects for a Formal Report

1. Replacement of streetcars by buses in a certain city (See page 107 for one possible approach to this subject.)
2. Design of a new dormitory to be erected on the campus
3. Present condition of and recommended improvements for the dormitory you live in
4. Replacement of steam locomotives by diesels on a certain railroad
5. Safety conditions in a large manufacturing plant
6. Conversion of a building to a different use
7. Causes of traffic congestion in a certain area of your home town, or proposals designed to relieve it, or both
8. Installation of an air-conditioning system in a building having classrooms and laboratories

9. Rerouting a railroad that now passes through the heart of the city
10. Proposed layout for a municipal airport
11. Design of an indoor stadium for the campus
12. Proposed layout for an experimental farm
13. Basic plan for the campus of an engineering college that is to begin with an enrollment of 2000
14. Proposals concerning the type of exhibits to be displayed by your department at the annual engineering show
15. Renovation of an abandoned mine for renewed operation

Note: Many of the topics suggested on page 176 in connection with informal reports lend themselves to expanded treatment in formal reports.

Reports:
Informal

The informal report is practical when the material can be covered in a short space, when the report is not going to a large number of people, and when its value is more or less temporary.

Its chief characteristics are: (a) it rarely has more parts than the three essential ones—introduction, discussion, and terminal section; (b) the text is single-spaced within paragraphs and double-spaced between them; (c) the style of writing is easy and personal but not colloquial or slangy; and (d) there is no curb on the use of pronouns, those of the first and the second person being used as freely as those of the third person.

The informal report has several forms. Since the most common one is probably that of the business letter, we shall begin with it.

THE LETTER-REPORT

The letter-report may have any of the mechanical parts of a business letter that were described in Chapter 4, and it must have the six basic ones: heading, inside address, salutation, body, complimentary close, and signatures. Good form calls for an identification line and, if the report exceeds one page, a continuation line. Other parts—reference line, classification line, attention line, subject line, and enclosure and carbon notices—are used when the circumstances warrant. Their position and make-up are the same as in the regular letter.

For two reasons the subject line has an added interest here. First, the practice of using it in the informal report is rather general—much more so than in the ordinary business letter. The report tends to be longer and more important than the average letter and thus merits the added dignity of having a title. Second, the words "report on" should not appear in the subject line unless the report is really about another report. Thus

Subject: Report on Stamford Apparatus for
          the Production of Methyl Alcohol

literally means that the subject of the present report is a previous one concerning the Stamford equipment—a possibility, though a rare one. But if the line reads

Subject: Stamford Apparatus for the
          Production of Methyl Alcohol

there is no question that the present report pertains to the equipment itself.

Now let us examine the body of the report.

Introduction

In its simplest and most frequent form the introduction is a single paragraph of not more than two or three sentences. These sentences cite the authorization if it has been specific, give the purpose of the report, and, if the conventional arrangement of the essential parts is used, state its thesis.

The authorization should be cited quite explicitly, telling who asked for the report, when it was asked for, and how it was asked for —that is, whether by letter, telegram, memorandum, or oral communication. If the report was not specifically requested but arose out of the routine of the writer's job, the authorization is too general to be of importance and is omitted. The introduction then opens with a statement of what the report is about—the problem that it concerns, the purpose for which it is being written, or both.

When the report elements are arranged in the conventional order and the terminal section is therefore last, the thesis should be included in the opening paragraph as a courtesy to the reader. Naturally, he wishes to learn at once what the basic finding has been if the report concerns an examination or what the basic result has been if it concerns work. If the thesis is given at the beginning, the main question on his mind is answered without his having first to read two or three pages of discussion.

When the modified order of the parts is used, the thesis is not included in the introduction because the terminal section follows immediately and, as we saw in the formal report, its opening sentence is usually the thesis itself. Consequently, there would be needless repetition.

Before proceeding, let us look at a few representative introductions. The first is from a progress report having a specific authorization and its parts arranged in the conventional order.

> As you requested in your letter of March 1, I am sending you a report on the progress of our work on highway No. 274. We have used 30 of the 245 working days allotted us and have completed about one ninth of the construction. If the weather continues to be favorable, I am sure that we can hold to schedule.

The first sentence gives the details of the authorization and the purpose of the report, the second gives the thesis, and the last points up its significance.

The next example is from a special completion report. Because the job it deals with and the writing of the report are part of the author's regular duties, there was no specific authorization. Since the author has decided to use the modified order for the essential parts, the introduction omits the thesis because it follows immediately in the terminal section. With no authorization and no thesis the paragraph tells only what the report is about.

> During the two weeks from June 10 to June 24 the air compressors in Building 600 were given their annual overhauling. The following report describes the condition that we found each to be in and the repairs that we made.

The third illustration is the opening paragraph of an analytic report. Again the authorization is omitted because the report was written by a man whose general responsibilities make it routine. Just as in the preceding case, the paragraph opens by telling what the report is about—by outlining the problem it deals with. Then comes a sentence that touches on the history of the problem. The last sentence, containing the thesis, is an example of how to word the basic conclusion when it is general rather than specific.

> During the past winter, heat losses between the steam plant and the buildings located in the southwestern part of the grounds increased steadily. Inspection at the time failed to uncover the trouble, but a more thorough investigation during the July shutdown revealed several causes. No one of them alone is serious, but together they can result in an appreciable loss and should be corrected before the onset of another heating season.

The final example is taken from an advisory report written by a consultant engineer to a client in another city. It represents a fuller type of introduction and shows how two special problems can be taken care of.

> In accordance with your request, made by long distance on February 8, I have examined the building located at the corner of 8th and Spruce Streets to determine whether it can be converted at a reasonable cost into a parking garage. As a result of my findings I recommend that you purchase the building. Except for the construction of ramps between floors no major structural changes will be needed, and the total cost should not exceed $30,000.
>
> The building is four stories high and fireproof. It has a frontage of 200 feet on 8th Street and 240 feet on Spruce Street. It was built 12 years ago by Bentley and White, local contractors, and has never suffered fire or storm damage.
>
> I hope that the report which follows answers all of your questions. If any points need clarification or you wish further study, please let me know.

Paragraph 1 performs the usual function of transmitting the report. It recalls the authorization and the purpose of the study, and it ends by giving the over-all recommendation and the grounds for it.

Paragraph 2 gives general information, facts that pertain to the whole subject rather than to any one of the particular matters to be treated in the discussion. As we have noticed before, special information can be treated in the introduction, as here, or in the opening section of the discussion.

Paragraph 3 contains the gesture of good will commonly found at the end of the straight business letter. In the letter-report it can still be put at the end provided the report does not have topic headings, as may sometimes happen. But most reports have headings, and if the gesture is at the end, it will be under a heading that is inappropriate for it—such as "Recommendations" if the conventional order of the elements is used or "Changes on the Fourth Floor" if the modified order is followed. For the sake of logic, then, it is brought forward to the introduction. Here it serves, incidentally, to begin the report on a polite note, something just as effective as ending it on one.

Discussion

The discussion section of the informal report serves in the same way as that of the formal report. It is usually the longest section, for it gives all the data and explains them.

Special information may be put at the beginning if it is too important or too detailed for the introduction, and miscellaneous matters not significant enough for individual treatment can be combined at the end.

Terminal Section

The terminal section may be any one of the types described in the preceding chapter and may have any of the 12 headings given there. It also may either repeat results, conclusions, and recommendations elaborated on in the discussion or give them for the first time when the discussion has prepared for them. Further, the basic treatment explained on pages 111-113 is the same.

Minor Mechanics

TOPIC HEADINGS. As in the formal report, the use of headings depends on the material. If it is completely homogeneous, as it is likely to be in a short report, nothing is gained by imposing headings on it. But if the data have natural divisions and subdivisions, headings aid the writer in organizing the report and facilitate the reader's understanding it.

Of the many systems of headings, the one described below is among the simplest and most common.

First-degree Heading

Flush with the left margin, capitalized as a title, underlined. Two blank lines above, one below. No punctuation follows. It is identical with the second-degree heading of the formal report.

Second-degree Heading. Indented as a paragraph, capitalized as a title, underlined. One blank line above, none below. Period follows. Text begins on same line. It is identical with the third-degree heading of the formal report but for the single-spacing below it.

Third-degree Heading: Indented two or three more spaces than a regular paragraph, capitalized as a title, underlined. One blank line above, none below. Colon follows. Text begins on same line. It is identical with the fourth-degree heading of the formal report.

Because most informal reports are fairly short, fourth-degree headings are seldom justified. Regular paragraphing suffices to mark division beyond the third degree. If fourth-degree headings are wanted, they may be treated like the fifth-degree ones of the formal report.

Informal reports often have only three primary headings and no subheads. The primaries are simply "Introduction," "Discussion," and whatever is appropriate for the terminal section—for example, "Conclusions." The heading for the introduction is frequently omitted because it might detract from the subject line, which immediately precedes. A report may then have only two headings: "Discussion" and, let us say this time, "Recommendations."

PAGINATION. The first page requires no number because the subject line and other mechanics of the business letter indicate it is the beginning of the report. Succeeding pages are designated by a continuation line.

APPEARANCE. Other than the common use of topic headings and illustrative material, the letter-report does not differ in appearance from the regular business letter.

THE MEMORANDUM-REPORT

The memorandum-report is not to be confused with the simple memorandum. A memorandum is a highly informal paper of not more than one or two pages written to remind oneself or others of something, such as a scheduled committee meeting or the chief points of a conference. A memorandum-report is not the same thing. It is a full-bodied report that can attain the length of a letter-report, can deal with the same subjects, and can have any of the parts of a letter except those noted below. It resembles the straight memorandum only in the complete informality with which the beginning and the ending are handled.

The beginning has the words *To, From, Subject,* and *Date* in some neat arrangement. A common one is

To:	From:
Subject:	Date:

Another is

Subject:	Date:
To:	
From:	

Often *Subject* and the words that follow it are written in all-capitals. *To* is followed by the addressee's name, which may be one person or a group. *From* is followed by the writer's name or sometimes just his title. *Subject* is followed by the title of the report, and *Date* by the date of its distribution.

The salutation is omitted, with the result that the text begins immediately below the heading. It has the introduction, discussion, and terminal section basic to any report and may employ topic headings. At the end of the text come the written and the typed signatures of the writer. The complimentary close is omitted.

Because of its extremely informal appearance and the omission of the two courtesy gestures, the salutation and the complimentary close, the use of the memorandum-report is generally limited to communication within the same company or organization.

THE ARTICLE-REPORT

Sometimes an informal report looks more like a magazine article than a letter or a memorandum. It has a title centered between the side margins on the first page and only the author's typed name, which may be under the title or at the end of the text. Topic headings may or may not be used.

Theoretically, an article-report may deal with any subject that other reports deal with, but actual practice seems to limit its use to subjects of general interest throughout an organization. The tone, therefore, as well as the form suggests the magazine article.

THE FORM-REPORT

Ordinarily, the report that consists of filling out a standardized form is not the kind we are interested in here. It requires little or no composition and usually lacks an introduction and a terminal section.

Sometimes, however, form-reports do fulfill the requirements of a true technical report. They are submitted on printed forms because they deal with subjects so recurrent that their treatment has become routine; but the spaces that the author fills in are large and require careful writing, not simply the entering of figures or short comments. Furthermore, there are spaces at the beginning that call for information found in a regular introduction. Sometimes it is only the purpose of the report and the time covered by the work, but often it includes a brief history of what preceded the job. At the end space is provided for conclusions and possibly recommendations.

THE COLLEGE LABORATORY REPORT

The report written in college laboratory courses is an analytic report that may be formal or informal, depending on the preference of the particular instructor. It is treated here among the informal group because it is nearly always short and because, more often than not, its topic headings correspond to those of the informal report.

Its customary elements are the cover binder, flyleaves, title page, body, and a short list of references.

The title page should display the following data: the name of the university, the college (when different), and the department; the number of the course; the number and the title of the experiment; the name of the report writer; the names of the students who composed the group he worked with; and the dates that the experiment was performed and the report is being submitted. The following page shows a practical arrangement of these data.

Duke University
College of Engineering
Department of Electrical Engineering
Course No. 103

EXPERIMENT 51

VOLTAGE REGULATION OF A SHUNT-WOUND

GENERATOR

James C. Welkins

Group 4

Performed: November 5, 1959   H.W. Brown
Submitted: November 12, 1959   L.D. Thomas
                                               J.N. Timon
                                               J.C. Welkins
                                               R.N. Williams

The body of the laboratory report has the three basic parts found in other kinds of reports, though sometimes students do not recognize them because they are broken up and given other names. The introduction is composed of the object, theory, and apparatus sections; the discussion embraces the procedure, data and results, and the discussion sections; and the terminal section is made up of the conclusions.

The names of these specific sections are the primary headings in the body. The need for subheadings is infrequent. The arrangement of the sections is generally that given below, though often *Theory* and *Apparatus* are reversed. This arrangement is not an idle and rigid convention but a description of the experiment given in the order that the experiment was conducted.

Object. The purpose of the experiment is stated in one or two sentences.

Theory. This section explains any theory, natural law, operating principle, physical property, or equation that either (a) the experiment sets out to prove or (b) the experiment is based on.

Apparatus. The equipment used in the experiment is listed here. Complete sentences are not necessary, but each piece of equipment should be identified so clearly as to its make, model, serial number, and other details that anyone wishing to rerun the experiment could get the same equipment from the supply room.

Procedure. This section is a step-by-step description of what was done in performing the experiment.

Data and Results. This section presents the material that grew directly out of the procedure—the recorded data and any computations, graphs, and drawings based on the data. Normally, no text is under the heading but simply a citation of the pages that follow and contain this material.

Discussion. The main function of this section is to interpret the data and the results, to show exactly what they mean. In addition, it may:

(a) Explain what was done and why it was done if the procedure needs amplifying. Often this amounts to showing why there were deviations from the directions given in the manual.

(b) Account for any discrepancy between the theoretical and the actual results.

(c) Note anything connected with the experiment not covered under the other headings.

Conclusions. Here the writer states whether the object of the experiment was fulfilled or not—whether the experiment showed or failed to show what it was supposed to. The wording should not be generalized but specific: "The experiment showed how to determine the voltage regulation of a shunt-wound direct-current generator."

In addition, the writer evaluates the experiment. He points out its significance in the general field and in the particular course, and explains how it has added to his knowledge of concrete techniques for future application.

SPECIMEN REPORTS

Report A is an advisory report in letter form. The report was directly authorized and covers three matters of equal importance; therefore, the thesis embraces all three. Note that the recommendations in the terminal section are prepared for but not actually given in the discussion.

REPORT A

Hadley, Inc.
1873 Northern Boulevard
Sacramento, California
November 12, 1958

Confidential

Gifford Aircraft Co.
Missile Division
15th and Oak Streets
San Diego, California

Attention: Mr. R.D. Evans

Gentlemen: Subject: Environmental Testing of
                                              the Falcon "D" Missile

In reply to your letter of August 20, 1958, my engineers and technicians began environmental tests on the Falcon "D" Missile. The

Gifford Aircraft Co.   page 2   November 12, 1958

results of our assignment show that the missile is effective only at
altitudes below 75,000 ft, temperatures above —20 C, and gravitation
forces up to 20 times the pull of gravity.

Altitude Tests

The altitude tests conducted in our laboratories proved that the
maneuverability and stability of the missile are greatly influenced by
the vertical displacement in which the missile is fired.

Maneuverability. At low altitudes maneuverability was found perfect, but at heights exceeding 50,000 ft the stabilizers of the missile
had little or no effect in guiding the missile in the rare atmosphere.
Maneuvering the missile, however, was found possible up to 75,000
ft since the forward thrust of the rocket motors helped to control
the missile to some extent.

Stability. Contrary to the results compiled on the maneuverability
tests are those of the stability tests. In this case the missile was found
to be more stable at high altitudes in the rare atmosphere and very un-
stable at altitudes below 50,000 ft. It was found in 90 per cent of
the tests held in the region between zero and 50,000 ft that the missile
had the tendency to roll and oscillate vertically and horizontally. The
stabilizers operated during this time, but they were correcting the
flight of the missile and not directing the weapon toward the target.

Temperature Tests

The missile was tested during flight in temperatures ranging from
—20 C to —100 C. At the lower temperatures the stabilizer hinges
tightened because of small droplets of condensed water crystallizing
in the joints. It was also discovered that in the higher temperatures
the automatic skin-cooling system of the missile performed excel-
lently.

Gravitational Force Tests

"Setback" and "creep" were the two major problems discovered
when the missile was influenced by gravitational forces.

"Setback Force." "Setback" is defined as the force of inertia

Gifford Aircraft Co.   page 3   November 12, 1958

which tends to move all internal moving parts to the rear as the missile is initially accelerated. In the Falcon's case the parts which move include the fuse assembly and radar scanner. In a few of the tests the primer in the fuse mechanism exploded the detonator of the missile; in addition, the radar scanner was jammed against the walls of the electric computer.

"Creep Force." "Creep" is the continuing inertial force resulting from the deceleration of the missile in flight, caused by air resistance, which tends to move forward the movable internal parts. Once again the fuse assembly and radar scanner operated incorrectly because of the existing forces.

Conclusions and Recommendations

The Falcon "D" Missile is an effective weapon below 75,000-ft altitude; it is relatively maneuverable and stable up to this height. However, I am sure that with better designed stabilizers the missile would be more efficient. Temperature has no major influence on the missile between —20 C and —100 C, but I recommend that the stabilizer hinges be redesigned to have more suitable joint clearances to prevent tightening in freezing conditions. Extremely small gravitational forces damaged the movable internal parts, but forces up to 20 times the pull of gravity did not harm the structure or fixed internal parts of the missile.

Respectfully yours,
Charles R. Yengst, Jr.
Charles R. Yengst, Jr.
Chief Engineer

CRY, Jr./lw

Report B is an instruction report. Again authorization has been direct and the thesis, ending the first paragraph, is somewhat general because it must include four procedures having the same importance.

REPORT B

Spillar & Son
Consultant Engineers
840 Louise Circle
Raleigh, N.C.

14 March 1958

Mr. M.V. Markham
Chief Engineer
State Highway Department
1313 Orange Street
Raleigh, North Carolina

Dear Mr. Markham: Subject: <u>Frost Action on Roads</u>

In compliance with your letter of 10 March 1958 requesting a résumé of current preventive measures used as protection against the damaging effects of frost action on roads, this report is submitted. The procedures described herein will minimize, if not eliminate, the detrimental effects of frost action.

I trust that this report fulfills your request. If further clarification or assistance is needed, please do not hesitate to call on me.

Definition

From an engineering viewpoint, frost action is defined as the accumulation of water in the form of ice lenses in soil under natural freezing conditions.

Conditions Necessary for Frost Action

Three conditions must occur simultaneously for ice lenses to form.

1. <u>Presence of Frost-Susceptible Soil.</u>   Silts and clays are readily susceptible, whereas cohesionless, well-drained sands, gravels, crushed rock, and granular materials having little capillarity are practically immune to frost action.

2. <u>Slightly-Below-Freezing Temperature.</u>   A sharp drop in temper-

Mr. M.V. Markham   -2-   14 March 1958

ature to well below freezing results in a rapid penetration of freezing temperatures. In such cases the water contained within the soil freezes solidly before the ice lenses have a chance to form, and the water content of the soil does not change appreciably. On the other hand, a prolonged, moderately cold spell with an average daily temperature only a few degrees below freezing gives ample time for ice crystals to form and for the underlying soil to bring up additional water by capillarity so as to develop thick, closely spaced ice lenses.

    3. Supply of Water. The sources of water for the development of ice lenses are a ground-water table immediately beneath or at the ground surface, a capillary supply from an adjoining water table, or saturated, fine-grain soils below the frost line. In addition, high moisture content may be the result of a leaky surface course or, in some cases, poor drainage.

Preventive Measures

    Preventive design begins with a soil survey. Particular attention should be given to frost-susceptible soils, water tables, capillary conditions, and the possibility of lowering or eliminating ground water by drainage measures.

    1. Removal of Frost-Susceptible Soil. Even though the site selection may be on generally ideal soil, invariably in long stretches of road there will be localized areas of frost-susceptible soil which must be recognized, removed, and replaced with select granular material. Unless this process is thoroughly carried out, differential heaving (irregular heaving as opposed to uniform heaving) or frost boils may result.

    2. Insulation. The most generally accepted method of insuring no loss in the strength of the subgrade because of frost action is to provide a thickness of paving or wearing course and a non-frost-susceptible base which will prevent freezing of the subgrade. This method is especially effective where the subgrade will be subjected to differential heave. Where subgrade soils are not subject to excessive differential heaving, less thickness of pavement and base than that required to prevent freezing of the subgrade is permissible. In the latter

Mr. M.V. Markham   -3-   14 March 1958

case the design allows for a reduction in subgrade strength during the frost-melting period.

3. Reduction of Ground Water. Because of frost action it is as important to design for the interception of ground water as it is to remove surface water. Open ditches or drain tile must be used to lower existing water tables not only to a depth below the frost line but far enough for capillary action to have no effect.

4. Prevention of Capillary Rise. Under certain conditions it is not practical to lower the ground-water table sufficiently to prevent capillary rise from reaching the subgrade. Therefore, it may be necessary to place a 6-inch interceptor layer of pervious sand, gravel, or crushed rock 2 to 3 feet beneath the surface. If the anticipated depth of frost penetration is not too great, it is more economical to increase the subgrade thickness with select granular material. Soil admixtures, such as those used for waterproofing and dust prevention, applied to a 6-inch layer of select granular material immediately below the frost line will reduce the capillary movement of water considerably. Another effective but rather costly method of preventing capillary rise is to excavate to the bottom of the frost zone, lay prefabricated bituminous surfacing, and backfill to grade with select granular material.

Summary

The conditions described above as causes of frost action can be counteracted by taking steps, singly or in combination, to select clean granular material, to control the water supply and the height of capillary rise, and to insulate against frost penetration. Such steps will minimize, if not eliminate, the detrimental effects of frost action.

                                      Sincerely yours,

                                      Robert J. Spillar

                                      Robert J. Spillar

RJS:kh

REPORT C

Henderson and Moore
14 East Lincoln St.
Des Moines, Iowa

14 September 1957

Mr. H. Byron Raley
Engineer, Quality Control
Reese Electronics Company
1414 South Broad Street
Des Moines, Iowa

Subject: Insulated Stand-Off Terminals

Dear Mr. Raley:

I have completed the investigation you requested last week by telephone. The purpose of the investigation was to determine why a large number of the insulated stand-off terminals you purchased from the Lundst Company were shorting to the chassis ground. I sincerely hope that this information will prove useful in solving your problem.

Results and Recommendations

The results of these tests prove that the insulated stand-off terminals you are now using in your electric equipment are not reliable. Continued use of the terminals will cause many electrical failures in your equipment.

I recommend that you change suppliers for this apparatus.

Continuity Test

A test for continuity was given to 500 insulated stand-off terminals. In order to do this, I placed an ohmmeter across the electrical tie point and the base which mounts the terminal to a chassis. This test would indicate if any of the terminals were shorted through the insulator body. Of the 500 terminals tested, 57 indicated a direct short and 10 gave a high resistance reading.

Breakdown Test

Dry Conditions.   A sample of 25 terminals which had passed the continuity test was mounted on a metal chassis. A potential of 500

Mr. H.B. Raley   -2-   14 September 1957

was placed across the terminals from their tie points to ground. Five hundred is the voltage at which the manufacturer rated the terminals for all conditions of operation. At the first application of voltage, three of the terminals arced through the insulation material to ground. The terminals were then subjected to a voltage cycle test to determine whether they could withstand voltage surges, and under these conditions two more underwent a voltage breakdown.

Humid Conditions. The 20 terminals which passed the breakdown test for dry conditions were placed in a humidity chamber to determine whether they would withstand high humid conditions without arcing. They were subjected to conditions which varied from 60 to 98 per cent relative humidity with the same potential applied to them that was applied under the dry conditions. No voltage breakdown occurred.

X-rays

Of the 57 insulated stand-off terminals which indicated a short circuit from the electrical tie point to the base, 25 were placed under X-ray with a sample of the 25 which had passed the continuity test. The X-ray picture revealed that 14 of the shorted terminals had no space between the electrical tie point and the base. The other 15 shorted terminals had a fine hairline extending from the tie point through the insulating material to the base. Of the 25 good terminals 11 had these hairline projections of varying lengths extending partially across the insulating material.

Destructive Test

To determine the exact nature of the hairline shown in the X-ray picture, I ground and then carefully polished two of the stand-off terminals until the defect was uncovered. A thin metal burr was revealed which passed through the insulating material and made a good electrical connection between the base and the tie point of the terminal.

Respectfully submitted,
Jerry E. Lee
Jerry E. Lee

JEL:es

REPORT D

Forsythe Electric Company
Incorporated
Greensboro Shops
413 South Warren Street
Greensboro, N.C.

February 15, 1957

Mr. John R. Cummings, Superintendent
Headquarters Engineering
Forsythe Electric Company
413 South Warren Street
Greensboro, North Carolina

Dear Mr. Cummings: Subject: Methods of Improvement
                                     for the RS-617 Project

As you requested during the conference of January 10, 1957, the
Wages Incentives Organization has made a study of the RS-617 Production Shop to determine the efficiency of present assembly methods.
The purpose of this report is to give the results of the study and to
recommend changes where we feel that such changes are justified.

We hope the information and recommendations meet with your
approval.

Cable Shop

Forming of Cable.   As on past projects the various cables have
been set up on individual boards, although most of the cables are
very small. Since there are 60 different cables to be produced each
week and only three forming positions, it is necessary that the setup
be changed 20 times each week for each position. The standard time
for changing a cable setup is 30 minutes.

Shielding of Leads.   Specifications state that all leads are to be
shielded by the wire-wrap method. This method requires that the
shielding be cut back a specified length, that a polystyrene sleeve be
used to insulate the conductor, and that the shield be wrapped with
several turns of copper wire and soldered. This work requires approx-

Mr. John R. Cummings   page 2   February 15, 1957

imately five minutes for each shield. A total of 600 shields is required
for all the cables in a single system.

Pre-forming of Pigtails

Resistors, condensers, diodes, and other such pigtail apparatus are
at present being pre-formed to a 90-degree angle on one end only. One
end of the pigtail is purposely left unformed to allow the operator to
get exact measurements during assembly, since the terminals of the
various components on some projects do not always have the same
spacing.

Assembly of Systems

The assembly area is arranged so that each operator is responsible
for the final assembly of a complete system. Since the system contains
more than 50 different sub-assemblies, several months would be required for an operator to become familiar enough with the work to
perform the complete job smoothly. The complete assembly requires
more than 12 hours, and the operator does not learn the job well
enough, with such a long work cycle, to perform efficiently.

Conclusions and Recommendations

Production efficiency on this project could be increased with some
method changes. Since most of the cables are very small, each cable
board could be wired to accommodate at least two cables. This would
eliminate the necessity for half of the setups now being made. A
Burndy Hy-Ring has been developed that gives as good quality as the
wire-wrap method and requires little more than half of the time required by the wire-wrap method. The use of this new shield would
save approximately two hundred and fifty man-hours per week. Since
all of the networks used in the RS-617 System have equal terminal
spacing, there is no reason why both ends of the pigtails should not be
pre-formed. This would eliminate the operator's having to do the work
with hand tools. A breakdown of the assembly section into several
stations would permit the operator to become more familiar with his
job, since he would be responsible for only a small part of the total.

Mr. John R. Cummings   page 3   February 15, 1957

We recommend that the new methods suggested by this report be incorporated immediately.

Respectfully submitted,
E.H. Spainhour
E.H. Spainhour

EHS:rc

REPORT E

EATON MANUFACTURING COMPANY
Engineering Division
Intercompany Communication

To: Mr. E.H. Gilgames   From: R.M. Tribble

Subject: Alternating Component   Date: July 7, 1959

During the past three months I have been investigating the alternating component of output ratio on the EA-10107 Rate Gyroscope. The purpose of my investigation was to determine the cause of alternating component and to make the necessary changes to minimize it. This report describes my findings and the changes which I have made.

Conclusions and Recommendation

I did not find any one particular factor to be predominantly responsible for alternating component. However, by controlling motor unbalance and gimbal end play, I was able to reduce it to within an acceptable limit: a motor unbalance of 225 gram-centimeters and end play of 0.0006 in. None of the other factors tested showed appreciable effect. I recommend that further studies be made on alternating component to gain background knowledge for future production of gyroscopes.

General Information

As you know, the basic definition of alternating component is the amount of electrical interference caused by movement of the contact wiper on the potentiometer. However, because of the method used for testing, other factors are included in the interference measurement and have become accepted as being part of the alternating component. The current accepted definition of alternating component is any electrical interference in the output ratio.

Contact Wiper

Materials. Paliney and neurine were the two wiper materials tested. Strength, hardness, solderability, and surface finish were examined in each case, and neither material was found to be superior to the other in these qualities. Further tests were made to determine their electrical characteristics. It was found that paliney offers the least contact resistance and is less susceptible to polymerization. Therefore, I have revised the material specification to exclude neurine as a wiper material.

Wiper Tension. Wiper tension was found to cause a decided increase in alternating component at less than 4 g and above 10 g. Our specifications call for 6 g. I do not, however, believe it is necessary to change the specifications so long as a close inspection of this requirement is maintained.

Wiring

All wiring was replaced with shielded leads to determine whether inductive pick-up was contributing to the alternating component. No significant change could be measured for this condition.

Gimbal

Bearings. The minor variations in bearings used on the rate gyroscope have no effect on alternating component.

End Play. The effect of end play on alternating component was determined to be very critical. When the end play is tight the alternating component is less. However, tight end play affects other requirements on the gyroscope, and for this reason end play below 0.0004 in. is not permissible. The specification has been revised to reflect these findings, but in order to maintain a safe limit the requirement was set at 0.0006 in.

Mr. E.H. Gilgames   -3-   July 7, 1959

Motor Balance

Balance of the gyroscope motor was found to have a substantial
effect on alternating component. The unbalance offsets the electrical
interference due to vibration and thereby reduces the alternating component. Tests showed that an unbalance of 225 gram-centimeters
would give the best results. I have requested that the motor balance
specifications be changed to require 225 gram-centimeters unbalance.
It is expected that this change will be accomplished by August 1.

R.M. Tribble
R.M.Tribble

REPORT F

VICTOR BRADLEY, INC.

Tool Design Department

THE ENGINEERING TRAINING PROGRAM

On April 2, 1958 the Tool Design Department began a study of the
possibilities of an engineering training program. The object of this report is to outline the proposed program.

Program

The program is based on the idea of letting a new engineer learn by
doing and by being exposed to many manufacturing problems. For
18 months the new engineer will work in the following organizations:
tool design, tool construction, machine shop, waveguide shop, sheet
metal shop, and engineering planning.

Tool Design.   The trainee will work six months in the Tool Design
Department and will be placed beside a regular tool designer. This
tool designer will be responsible for overseeing his work and answering his questions. Each of the trainee's drawings will be reviewed, and
constructive criticism given to him.

At first, simple design work will be assigned to him, and while doing this work, the trainee will become familiar with design techniques, our drafting system, and our specification standards. When the trainee becomes proficient, he will be asked to design complicated items. This will give him an opportunity to apply his college training in mechanics, mathematics, metallurgy, and creative thinking.

Tool Construction. The trainee will be assigned to the tool construction department for three months. While there, he will be considered as an apprentice tool maker. He will be given jobs which will require the use of all the machines. A tool maker will be responsible for showing the trainee how to set up and to use the different types of machines. The main purpose of this phase of the program is to acquaint the trainee with different machines, setup problems, tool construction problems, and machining tolerances.

Production Shops. The trainee will be assigned for two months in each of the following shops: machine shop, waveguide shop, and sheet metal shop. He will work under the direct supervision of a layout operator. He will set up different types of machines for mass-production. While in the shops, he should become proficient in operating various machines. He will also become familiar with our products.

Engineering Planning. After getting experience in the production shops, the trainee will be given the task of writing manufacturing instructions to the shop, ordering tools for the job, and solving shop problems. This part of the program will give the trainee a chance to put his experience to use.

Conclusions

The proposed training program will give the new engineer a general experience background in tool design and construction, production, and engineering planning. The trainee will also gain appreciation of good production tools, for he will actually design these tools, make these tools, and finally use these tools in production. Most new engineers have had little experience in production. They must have a good working knowledge of production, capabilities of people and machines, and tool requirements before they can do planning engineering. A total of two months in each shop will expose the engineer to the many manufacturing techniques and problems. The final stage of the program gives the trainee a chance to put his shop experience to use.

Charles A. Avera

REPORT G

LYKENS AND LUCAS MACHINE SHOPS

Report Form 8C

Date of report: June 28, 1957

Apparatus: 150-ton punch press

　Make: Bleye

　Model: 34K8

Complaint: Breakdown

History: The press was installed in July 1954. It was purchased to blank the stainless steel flanges used on round waveguide. With few exceptions this is the only job for which it has been used. The operation of the machine has been trouble-free until recently.

On the morning of June 14 of this year, the shop supervisor reported that the machine was not operating properly. The piece-part being made was the round waveguide flange. A total of 96 pieces were made without a change in setup when the operator heard a popping sound. He found that the piece on which he was working had not been blanked but, in effect, had been stamped.

Investigation: I inspected the machine and found oil leaking from the ram near the elevating nut. I also found that the bracket used for tripping the limit switches on the ram elevating nut was hanging loose. In this position it was impossible for the bracket to engage the limit switches. The purpose of these limit switches is to prevent over-travel of the nut on the screw.

All of the press controls operated properly except the ram elevating controls, which were inoperative.

To fully ascertain the nature of the damage, I authorized your maintenance men to remove the ram from the machine. This was done with some difficulty since the tools available were inadequate for a machine of this size.

When the ram was removed, I found that the cause of the entire breakdown was the loose limit switch bracket. The bracket being loose allowed the operator to raise the ram to the point where only half of the threads on the ram elevating nut were bearing on the screw. The concentrated load on these threads was sufficient to cause fatigue and failure, and thus jam the nut on the screw.

The last Preventive Maintenance Inspection Report was also checked to see whether there was any indication of the impending trouble. The check list did not specify checking the limit switches. Apparently the inspector did not notice that the bracket had worked loose because he made no mention of it in his report.

Conclusions: The cause of the breakdown was the limit switch bracket that had worked loose. Repairs were made without purchasing new equipment and without help from Bleye personnel, but maintenance equipment should be procured to expedite future repairs.

Recommendations: Since this breakdown would have been avoided if the limit switches operated properly, my primary recommendation is to revise the Preventive Maintenance Inspection Report. This revision should include checking the limit switches and bracket on the ram elevating nut every month.

A second recommendation is to purchase maintenance equipment of adequate capacity for this machine, such as 8-ton hydraulic jacks and 10-ton hoists. This equipment will allow the maintenance crew to make repairs on this machine more quickly and safely.

Engineer in charge: N.M.Lucas

EXERCISES AND ASSIGNMENTS

A. Write the terminal section for one of the letter-reports whose introductions are given on pages 152-153.

B. After examining the preceding reports C through G, identify them as to type on the basis of both function and form, and point out the features of the introductions and the terminal sections.

C. Write an informal report, 500-600 words in length, on one of the subjects listed below. Make the report of the letter, memorandum, article, or form type as directed by your instructor.

1. Solution of the parking problem in a certain area of the campus
2. Existing facilities and their arrangement in one of the engineering laboratories
3. Condition of a used automobile, radio, or television set that is for sale
4. Reducing noise in the dormitories at night
5. The need for a new dormitory on the campus
6. The best site for a new dormitory on the campus
7. Results of testing a product to determine whether it meets company or government standards
8. Comparison of automobiles or trucks in the low-price range for possible purchase by your company
9. Changes in the curriculum of your department
10. A time-study of a typical day in your college life with recommendations as to how your time can be distributed better
11. The results of a field trip you have taken recently
12. Means of improving employee morale in your company
13. Installing the console, turntable units, tape recorders, and microphones in the campus radio station
14. Instructions concerning the use of photographic equipment bought from your company
15. Operation of the power plant in the mechanical engineering laboratory

Technical
Articles

There are three general types of technical magazines: professional journals, which cover a wide field; trade magazines, which cover a particular trade; and company publications, or house organs, which are published by specific companies and whose subject matter primarily concerns company activities.

To have articles published in these periodicals can be a very satisfying experience. First, there is the sense of having done something more than the routine of our job demanded. Then there is the realization that we have not been content merely to draw on the common pool of knowledge in our field but have contributed something to it. We have also added to our own knowledge, for writing about a subject results in our learning more about it because of the research and the thorough assimilation of data that must precede accurate writing. And of course there is the reward of our work bringing credit to our company from outside and of its being recognized by our superiors.

LEVELS OF WRITING

Before beginning an article we should decide on the publication to which we are going to submit it. Different magazines are aimed at different kinds of readers, and their material is presented in the way they have found most agreeable to these readers. To stand a chance of being accepted, an article must be written at the particular level of the magazine to which it is submitted.

The levels are numerous and the distinction between them is not always clear. At one extreme are the journals that confine their offerings to highly technical subjects presented in an esoteric manner. They are intended for experts in the field, people who are familiar with the general topics and are looking for specialized information. The articles deal with theory more than application. The language is technical, definitions and examples are rare, illustrations are limited to abstract material. Elaboration of a point is infrequent. Mathematics conveys much of the information, and the equations and formulas are usually left to explain themselves.

At the other extreme are the popular magazines, such as *Scientific American* and *Popular Mechanics*. Their circulation is among the general public, and though the articles are on technical subjects, they are written in the layman's language and are copiously illustrated.

Most technical publications aim somewhere between these extremes; and though the variation in style among different magazines can be considerable, it goes under the common heading of "semitechnical." Their readers are interested in the general field and are acquainted with technical work and technical writing, but they do not have an expert's understanding of every subject treated in an issue.

As a result, writing that is intended for them must not be complicated. Technical terms are limited as far as possible to those well known in the field, and when less familiar ones have to be used, they are carefully defined. Explanations are rather detailed, and abstract points are illustrated by concrete examples. Figures and tables supplement the text; in some magazines they are so thoroughly interwoven with it as to be indispensable in understanding it. Formulas and equations are reduced to writing or, if retained, are fully explained. The subject matter may include theory, but the emphasis is on application.

Since the articles in the highly technical journals are little else than straight article-reports and since the articles in the popular magazines are done by professional writers to start with or are thoroughly reworked by the editors, we shall concentrate on the semitechnical article.

BASIC ORGANIZATION

An article can deal with a new subject or a new aspect of a subject, or it can re-examine a subject from a fresh standpoint. The general structure is the same:

I. Introduction
    A. The lead
    B. The purpose and, if necessary, the scope
II. Body proper—the presentation and discussion of the data
III. Conclusion—rhetorical device for closing

Introduction

THE LEAD. In a business letter and a report we can assume that any person they are directed to will read them because it is part of his job to read them. In a magazine article we cannot make such an assumption. We must first attract a reader's attention and then keep it; for we are competing against other articles in the magazine and even against the reader doing something besides reading. This is less true of a strictly technical article than a semitechnical one because the technical article, being addressed to the special interests of a select group, has an extrinsic appeal to begin with. Even so, there is still some necessity to capture attention.

The lead is a way of doing this. It catches the reader's notice and makes him want to continue the article. The possibilities are numerous. Some of the more common ones are listed and illustrated below. To show the variety of choice we have, each opening is for the same article, its subject being the profession of chemical engineering.

1. An arresting statement, positive or negative in its wording
Positive: In our homes, our work, and our recreation we are surrounded by the products of chemical engineering.
Negative: Chemical engineering is not a necessary profession—not if you are willing to live the life of a Cro-Magnon man.
2. A question or a series of questions
What is a chemical engineer? How does he differ from a chemist? How does he differ from other kinds of engineers?
3. A reference to a personal concern of the reader
The cost of living today is high. It would be much higher but for the economies in manufacturing effected by chemical engineers.
4. A generalization that is gradually restricted to the immediate topic
Much of today's world is the product of technology. It has been made by scientists and engineers. Some of the engineers have invented

and discovered; some have carried out the ideas of the others. Both groups are found in chemical engineering.

    5. A comparison between the thing to be discussed and something better known to the reader

A chemical engineer is like a surgeon: his training lies in two fields that are related and yet distinct.

    6. A story or anecdote—this opening is effective only if the account is brief and pertinent

    7. An apt quotation

"In the natural sciences these are and have been and are likely to continue to be heroic days. Discovery follows discovery, each both raising and answering questions, each ending a long search, and each providing the new instruments for a new search."

These words of Dr. Oppenheimer are an excellent description of where science is today, and chemical engineering—itself an early product of these "heroic days"—is making discovery after discovery and "providing the new instruments for a new search."

    8. A reference to the contemporary situation as it is related to the subject

During the past two decades the development of plastics has been amazing, and today there is scarcely an industry that does not depend heavily on them in its operation. Plastics are one of the principal contributions that chemical engineering has made to society.

    9. An example or a series of examples showing the importance of the subject

The gasoline you burn in your car, the material in the clothes you wear, the food that you eat—all are linked in one way or another to chemical engineering.

    10. The thesis of the article

The job of the chemical engineer is to put to practical use the fruits of laboratory experiment.

    11. A statement of the problem that the article concerns

One of the greatest problems facing the Air Force and chemical engineers is to find a substance light enough for space travel and at the same time strong enough to withstand the intense heat that will result on its re-entering the earth's atmosphere.

    12. A brief history of the subject

The first attempt to found a society of chemical engineers was made in London in 1880. This attempt was unsuccessful because of the small number of people interested. A series of lectures in 1887 by George E. Davis embodied the beginnings of modern chemical engineering. He stressed the importance of a chemical engineer having a broad knowledge of chemistry, physics, and mechanics. The profession experienced its first major growth between 1910 and 1920, World War I acting as a stimulus. It was during this period that the main foundation of the profession came into being: the concept of unit operations. About 1930 the unit process concept, or the study of unitary chemical aspects, attracted notice. Still in its developmental stage, this concept is being actively studied and defined today.

13. A definition of the subject or an important term connected with it

Chemical engineering is the science or profession of applying chemistry to industrial uses.

14. A description of the thing the article is about

Chemical engineering is concerned with the development and application of manufacturing processes that involve chemical or physical changes. It includes the design, construction, and operation of equipment and plants. The basic sciences that it utilizes are chemistry, physics, and mathematics.

15. A combination of any two or more of the above

What is chemical engineering? It is the science or profession of applying chemistry to industrial uses. In a wider sense, it includes the design, construction, and operation of equipment and plants. It grew out of and is related to chemistry in the same way that electrical engineering grew out of and is related to physics.

(Question, definition, description, comparison)

Although there are situations in which one of these methods might be more effective than others, usually any one of several will be good. Very broadly speaking, however, leads 1 through 9 are more suitable for semitechnical articles and 10 through 14 for more scholarly ones.

THE PURPOSE AND THE SCOPE. Early in the article the reader should be told exactly what its aim is so that he can follow it with more understanding and enjoyment. Moreover, if the scope of the discussion is not self-evident in the title, it should also be stated in the introduction so that the reader will not expect more than the article covers.

Body Proper

The body proper—that is, the body apart from its introduction and its conclusion—comprises most of the article. It fulfills the purpose given in the introduction by setting forth the data, discussing them, and showing what they mean. Theoretically, the discussion may be organized in any of the ways described in Chapter 2, but in actual practice the Order of Occurrence and the Order of Ascending Impor· tance are preferred. The data can be offered as explication, description, definition, or narration. Nearly every article of any length employs a blend of two or more of these methods. To quicken interest, any of the opening devices can also be used in the body.

The discussion should cover only four or five major points, and many excellent articles bring out only two or three. These points may be broken into sub-points for analysis, but the main points themselves should be few for the reader to absorb them thoroughly. The paragraphs that develop a major point may be introduced by a descriptive subhead. Such headings emphasize the points and add to the "eye appeal" of the article.

Eye appeal is of special importance in an article because, as mentioned earlier, the article is competing for the reader's notice. Long columns of solid print suggest "heavy reading" to most of us. For this reason the paragraphs in magazine articles, especially those at the semitechnical level, tend to be shorter than those in books and reports.

The sentences also tend to be shorter and for the same reason: to make reading look easy as well as be easy. This is not to say, of course, that the article should give a staccato effect; a telegraphic style can prove just as wearisome as a long-winded one.

Illustrations also add to the eye appeal of an article, but they must be used discriminately. Too many give a watered look to the page. In addition, they can lead a person to think that he can glean everything of importance from them and their captions without reading the text itself. The number should also be governed by the policy of the magazine. Because engravings are expensive, many publications drastically limit the number of illustrations they accept. We should examine several issues of the magazine to learn its practice.

Conclusion

Occasionally an article needs no separate conclusion because the discussion terminates itself smoothly. In general, however, this is not true, and if something is not added the reader feels that the article is unfinished, that he has been left hanging in mid-air. If this is his final impression, it can easily become his over-all one too, and the rest of the work has gone for nothing, however excellent it might be.

When we are not certain, therefore, that the end of the discussion is also a strong ending for the whole paper, we should add a paragraph that does round it off firmly. The closings most frequently used are illustrated below. Again we shall postulate that the article is on chemical engineering.

1. An indication of the future of the subject
New times will bring new needs, and new needs will mean further challenges to the chemical engineer. The boundaries of his field will not remain fixed but will expand with these challenges.
2. A summary of the major points developed in the discussion
To recapitulate, we must find a substance that is light enough to be propelled into space easily, and strong enough to resist fantastically high temperatures. Certain substances that we now possess fulfill the theoretical requirements, but so far they have not proved completely satisfactory in actual use.
3. A restatement of the purpose or the thesis
The purpose of this article has been to broaden the definition of chemical engineering. Whether the one given here is entirely adequate may be debatable, but at least it reveals that the old one is not comprehensive enough for the present status of the profession.
4. A quotation that drives home the thesis
The chemical engineer has truly proved that "today's experiments are tomorrow's products."
5. An effort to stimulate the reader to action on the subject.
Any high-school student who is considering engineering for his lifework should investigate chemical engineering. It is a profession that rewards its members in many ways.

6. A rhetorical question that suggests the future of the subject, recalls the thesis, or inspires action

With these accomplishments as evidence and with the techniques now being perfected, is there any question about the rich productivity of chemical engineering in the future?

The two articles that follow show the wide spectrum of treatment found in semitechnical journals. The style of the first one is formal and terse, and there is only one visual aid. Although topic headings do not mark the divisions in the text, the divisions are nevertheless present and sharp, as a breakdown of the material shows:

    I. Introduction (paragraph 1)
   II. Body proper
      A. Advantages and disadvantages of tape (paragraphs 2-5)
      B. Non-superiority of tape over other media (paragraphs 6-11)
      C. Actual and potential superiority of tape over other media (paragraphs 12-19)
  III. Conclusion (paragraph 20)

The two major sections of the discussion, B and C, are carefully introduced by transitional paragraphs (6 and 12).

This article illustrates a technique that is fairly common: namely, the two-level approach. Paragraphs 2 through 5 list the advantages and disadvantages with little or no comment, as the abstract of a formal report would, so that a reader who wants only the pith of the article need go no further. The use of semitabulation further expedites his getting the facts. The remaining paragraphs elaborate on these points for the benefit of the reader interested in details. The repetition does not offend the second reader because it reveals and emphasizes the high lights of the article for him.

Is Tape the Ideal Medium for Audio? [1]

Ross H. Snyder

Thesis [1] The question which is the title of this discussion is answerable, if at all, only in a partial way. There is no *ideal* audio recording medium today, if by "ideal" we mean a recording medium which combines all the operational and convenience features of each of the present-day methods, none of the disadvantages of any of them, and which will preserve faithfully the entire dynamic and frequency range which sensitive ears can perceive, adding no perceivable extraneous sound.

Advantages [2] The family of operating advantages which has made tape the preferred medium for record mastering, radio broadcasting, and stereophonic sound recording and reproduction, includes the following:

1. Re-usability
2. Spliceability
3. Freedom from the effects of wear
4. Immediate replay, without processing danger of deterioration
5. Permanence of original recording
6. Comparatively low per-minute cost of recording medium

Comparison [3] Other audio recording media share some of these advantages, of course. Photographic sound recordings are, for example, spliceable; but photographic film is not reusable, is highly susceptible to deterioration from normal wear, requires processing before replay; original photographic recordings are permanent only if preserved in almost never-played condition; and, of course, photographic film is costly in per-minute terms, compared with tape.

[4] Lacquer disc masters share only the advantage of comparatively low medium cost, and then only where reusability is not desirable.

Disadvantages [5] But the tape medium also has disadvantages in its operational and convenience characteristics:

[1] *Journal of the Audio Engineering Society*, 6:2 (April 1958), 99. Reprinted by permission of the Audio Engineering Society.

1. It is not easy to find a given point inside a reel of tape, simply and quickly.
2. Tape is somewhat subject to breakage and stretching.
3. Tape threading is, in some applications, inconvenient.
4. All other things remaining approximately equal, tape reproducing apparatus is more costly.

Transitional paragraph

[6] If we continue to set aside the question of ultimate reproduced sound quality, and assume, for the moment, that all the sound recording media are equal in this respect, the reasons for the preference for one or another of these in a given kind of service are quite plain.

Comparison expanded

[7] Magnetic tape is clearly the most satisfactory medium for the original recording of masters which are later to be copied and released in large numbers to the public, by reason of its spliceability, freedom from the effects of wear, immediate replayability, permanence of original recording, and comparatively low medium cost. In mastering service, these advantages are compelling.

[8] Magnetic recording on oxide-coated sprocketed film, for ease of synchronizing with picture, is the preferred medium in motion-picture film recording, by reason of reusability, freedom from the effects of wear, immediate replayability, permanence of original recording, and comparatively low medium cost, in comparison with processed, non-replayable photographic film. These reasons for preferring the magnetic medium are all, of course, separate entirely from the sound-quality advantages which are attributed to magnetic recording, in comparison with photographic.

[9] On the other hand, photographic sound recording is, except for multi-track stereophonic releases, the medium of preference for motion-picture release prints, because in this service it is much less costly to copy, and, in the practical situation, much less costly to reproduce in the theatre or other commercial release situation.

[10] While still ignoring any differences which may exist in the ultimate quality of sound reproduction, the single-channel disc (release) has certain unquestionable advantages over duplicated tape. One of the greatest of disc's advantages is the sheer familiarity with the process. And, of course, quality for quality, the disc reproducer is somewhat cheaper to build and buy. The re-usability of tape is

of importance to a small, but growing proportion of consumers; the same is true of its spliceability, and of its ability to be played back immediately after recording. In comparison with disc pressings, the basic tape, aside from the common cost of music, is more costly. So, in the home, tape as it is now used is of interest mainly because of its freedom from deterioration due to wear; and because of its gift of the recording possibility to the consumer, so long as we set aside the question of its superior reproducing quality.

[11] Until very recently, tape has been the only suitable medium for the reproduction of stereophonic sound in the home. The successful demonstration of single-groove stereophonic disc pressings has been accomplished, however. So. still leaving out considerations of relative sound quality, we can begin to inquire concerning the relative merits of tape and disc for home stereo sound. Once more, the main advantage of tape is its freedom from deterioration due to normal use, and its gift of the facility to record, as well as reproduce, in the home. It is quite clear that the stereophonic disc pressing, if satisfactory in sound quality, has the same advantages over present-day stereo tape that the single-channel disc has over single-channel tape.

Transitional paragraph

[12] In sober analysis, however, we cannot assume that the reproduced quality of these two media is identical, and we cannot assume that tape mechanisms cannot be improved in the direction of easier threading, greater security against tape-breakage, and lower cost.

Advantages expanded

[13] Tape has several great advantages to offer the consumer, even in its present form. The ability to replay hundreds or thousands of times without audible deterioration, yet to be erased and re-recorded at will, is prime among these. Looking to the future, there is every reason to expect that threading and tape-handling will be greatly simplified, perhaps through development of some automatic threading device, or fully-enclosed cartridge. If present technology is any indicator, tape speeds may come down, permitting a reduction in per-minute medium cost. The "Videotape" recorder has clearly proved that recorded signals of half the former minimum wavelength are commercially usable, and that higher values of bandpass times s/n ratio are obtainable.

[14] Tape has always had the advantage of requiring no mechanical parts which must vibrate in precise unison with the transmitted signal, eliminating, thus, the complex mass-compliance problems which are inherent in a system using such moving parts. Tape's constant linear velocity removes the problems which surround the recordist in handling inner-groove distortion and dynamic limitations.

[15] Perhaps the most appealing of the advantages of tape to the designer is the definability of its performance. From beginning to end, a recording on tape is constant in several respects:

1. The uppermost undistorted recording level, at any given frequency
2. The noise spectrum
3. The gentle overload characteristic
4. The frequency response characteristic

Explication of figure (advantages continued)

[16] It is possible to express all this in a single graph, and thus to define the working area for the recordist. Figure 1 demonstrates this. The uppermost line shows the curve of maximum recordable intensities. This curve was determined from the following considerations: It could not be simply a curve of the output level at constant percentage distortion due to the approach of tape overload, because single-tone distortion analysis at medium and high audio frequencies would not include, inside the bandpass of standard measurement, the significant distortion partials. The tape, which is one selected so as to be median among commercial tapes in its sensitivity to short-wavelength recording, was first recorded to that level at which distortion was 3% due to the approach of saturation, at 1000 cps. It was then recorded fully to saturation at that frequency. The level of fundamental tone, excluding all distortion products, in the saturated recording, was then measured, and compared with the level of fundamental in the 3%-distorted recording. The level-difference between these two was determined. Then tones of all frequencies, from 30 to 15,000 cps, were recorded, beyond saturation on the tape and the level of maximum recoverable fundamental on each determined. This figure was reduced in each case, by the difference between maximum recoverable fundamental at saturation, and maximum recoverable fundamental at the 3% level,

in the 1000-cycle recording, the resulting figure thus being expressed on the graph. This method assumes, therefore, the very worst condition, relating a level of every frequency which is reduced from the total output, to the total of noise. Note that this still gives us, in an original 7½-ips half-track recording, an attainable s/n ratio of 60 db.

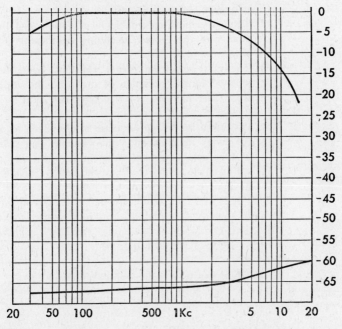

FIGURE 1   Relation between maximum useful output (upper curve) and cumulative noise (lower curve) for an average commercial tape. The curves were taken at 7½ ips, half-track, and NAB equalization.

[17] The lowest line on the graph displays the accumulating total of noise, measured in half-octaves from the lowest to the highest frequencies. Thus at any frequency of the graph, the noise figure is the total of the noise in that half-octave, plus the noise in all lower half-octaves. The noise in the whole spectrum is, of course, at the level shown at the highest frequency.

Problem

[18] No such simple chart can be prepared for the disc recording for several reasons:

1. The uppermost reproducible level, at any given frequency, from a disc pressing is not determined by the angular velocity of the groove, but by the characteristic of the whole reproducing stylus-cartridge-arm-turntable complex, and may not be the same in any two reproducing situations.

2. The uppermost recordable level varies with the diameter of the groove, declining significantly toward the center of the disc.

3. The noise spectrum is not constant, being heavily affected by the presence of dust and the effects of wear, and, likewise, is not equal from outer to inner groove.

4. Distortion in the reproduction at any given level and frequency depends upon the variable characteristics of the replay mechanism, including the state of its maintenance at the time and the relative diameter of the groove.

[19] It is, thus, impossible to make direct comparisons in sound-quality between disc and tape, since s/n ratio, distortion, character of noise and frequency-response of the disc all vary within rather wide limits, depending on the history of the particular pressing, the condition and type of reproducer, and the diameter of the groove.

Summary and restatement of thesis

[20] It may, then, be said in summary that there is no entirely ideal audio recording medium, whether for professional or consumer purposes, except that tape has outstanding advantages in re-usability, spliceability, freedom from deterioration with use, permanence of recording, and clearly definable sound-reproducing characteristics. It has disadvantages, such as inconvenience of threading, the possibility of breakages, the difficulty of spotting inside the recording, and somewhat higher medium and equipment costs, at least in consumer service. It is clear that tape has

Indication of future

advantages which cannot readily be matched by technological progress in the other media, and that its disadvantages appear susceptible to great improvement through new tape-packing devices and improved tape-handling mechanisms.

The higher cost of the tape and its reproducing equipment may also reasonably be expected to come down gradually, as wider usage encourages mass production, which, in turn, justifies the application of more research toward lower cost production methods.

The second article is intended for a wider, more diversified group of readers. The tone is informal, and the author gives the impression that he and the reader share the same point of view. For instance, the last sentence of paragraph 1: "First, let's review the laws." Colloquialisms are frequent; in paragraph 2, for example, "Russia's sputniks jumped the gun." There are eight visual aids, counting the table near the end, and they are integral to the text. The discussion flows smoothly from one point to the next, and we would hardly be aware of the transitions if there were no topic headings.

Power for Space[2]

B. G. A. Skrotzki

Arresting statement

Thesis

[1] Today we are just beginning to move the frontiers of civilization to the far reaches of outer space. This advance will not be won easily. Though we know what we must do to meet the basic laws governing space travel, we face a staggering energy-supply problem. First, let's review the laws.

Reference to laws on which article is based

[2] Newton's genius and painstaking study uncovered the laws of motion and gravity that explain the behavior of our planets and their satellites (see panel). Russia's sputniks jumped the gun in the Geophysical Year to dramatically demonstrate the soundness of these laws and to start the exploration of "outer" space.

2 *Power*, 102:4 (April 1958), 84. A McGraw-Hill Publication. Reprinted by permission of *Power* magazine.

BASIC LAWS FOR ROCKETS AND SATELLITES

Newton's three laws of motion:

1. Law of inertia. A moving body travels in a straight line (and a stationary body stays at rest) unless acted on by an unbalanced force.
2. Law of momentum. Acceleration of a body varies directly with the unbalanced force acting on the body and inversely with the mass of the body.
3. Law of reaction. For every force acting on a body (action) there is an equal and opposite force acting on another body (reaction); or action equals reaction.

Newton's law of gravity:

The force of attraction between two bodies varies directly with the mass of each body, and inversely as the square of the distance between their centers.

Definition

[3] *Space travel.* We have two versions of space travel: (1) Satellite orbiting about the earth, in which a body travels in space around the earth but is tied to it by the force of gravity. (2) Complete escape from the earth, in which a body speeds away until the force of gravity becomes negligible or at least balanced by the forces from other planets, satellites, and the sun.

Rhetorical question Comparison

[4] What are the mechanics of satellite motion? For a quick answer, swing a stone on the end of a string (Figure 1). Because of its motion the stone has kinetic energy and it obeys the first law (inertia) by trying to travel in a straight line. But the string tugs at the stone with a centripetal force that makes it travel in an orbit. You generate the centripetal force which balances the centrifugal force you feel through the string generated by the orbiting stone; here we have the third law—action equals reaction.

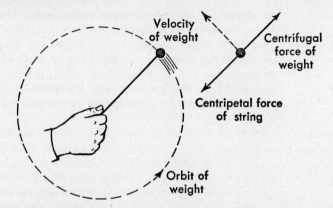

1. Satellites move like weight whirling on end of string; weight wants to go in straight line but string pulls it into orbit

Specific case [5] This closely parallels what happens to our natural satellite the moon. Instead of a string the invisible force of gravity tethers the moon to the earth (see law of gravity, panel). The moon's massive kinetic energy coupled with its diversion from a straight-line course creates a centrifugal force that balances the centripetal force of gravity tending to pull the earth and moon together. Figure 2 shows that

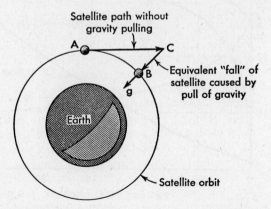

2. Force of gravity keeps satellite tied to earth, making it "fall" toward earth in an orbit that has constant altitude

the moon in a paradoxical sense continuously "falls" to the earth—without ever reaching it.

Explication of Figure 2

[6] If the pull of gravity could be cut off at *A*, the moon would go off in a straight line towards *C*. But the force of gravity *g* keeps tugging at the moon to make it travel in its orbit to *B*. In a real sense we can say that the moon falls from *C* to *B* in traveling through the part of its orbit from *A* to *B*.

Arresting supposition

[7] If the moon slowed up it would create a smaller centrifugal force. This would be overbalanced by the force of gravity and the moon would spiral towards the earth for a tremendous collision. On the other hand, if the moon went faster, its centrifugal force would overbalance the centripetal force of gravity, and it would spiral away from the earth and escape to outer space.

Explication of Figure 5

[8] *Satellite speeds.* We can place a satellite in an orbit at any altitude above the earth if we give it the right speed. Figure 5 shows what the orbit velocity should be for altitudes from 0 to 25,000 miles. At zero altitude this is about 26,000 fps or 17,700 mph, assuming that air friction is zero.

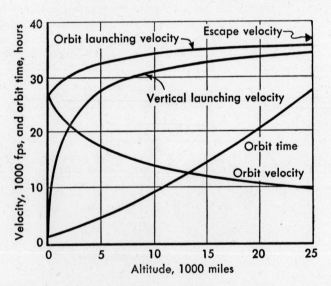

5. Orbit launching velocity includes effect of vertical launching velocity and orbit velocity needed to stay aloft in orbit

3. High-altitude satellites move slower, turn less in their orbits in given time, must move in plane through earth's center

4. Multistage rocket must exert steady force on payload to get it up to speed needed; stages fire in succession without pause

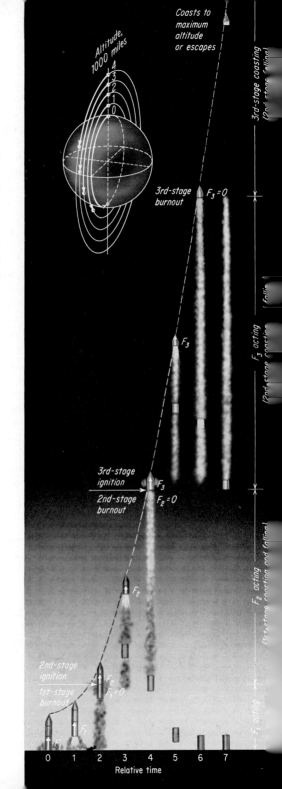

Altitude, 1000 miles

Coasts to maximum altitude or escapes

3rd-stage burnout $F_3 = 0$

3rd-stage coasting (2nd stage falling)

F_3

F_3 acting (2nd-stage coasting)

3rd-stage ignition F_3
2nd-stage burnout $F_2 = 0$

F_2 acting (1st-stage coasting and falling)

F_2

2nd-stage ignition F_2
1st-stage burnout $F_1 = 0$

F_1

F_1 acting

F_1

0   1   2   3   4   5   6   7
Relative time

The satellite would make one complete circuit around the earth in about 85 minutes.

[9] At 1000 miles altitude (5000 miles from the earth's center) the satellite speed must be 23,300 fps or 15,900 mph for the centrifugal force to balance the force of gravity. At this altitude the force of gravity is only (4000/5000)^2 or 64% of its pull at the surface of the earth; the satellite circles the earth in just under two hours.

[10] A satellite about 22,500 miles above the earth has an orbit velocity of 10,000 fps or 6800 mph and circles the earth in just 24 hours. Gravitation force shrinks here to 2.3% of its surface pull. If this satellite is above the equator headed in the same direction that the earth turns on its axis, it would always be in the same place in our sky, day and night.

Restressing a point

[11] At 240,000 miles altitude a satellite circles the earth in 28 days—you'll recognize this as the moon. Remember, for all orbits in Figure 5 the centrifugal force of the satellite just balances the centripetal pull of the earth.

Explication of Figure 3

[12] Figure 3 compares satellite speeds for altitudes of 0 to 4000 miles. While the surface satellite makes a half revolution around the earth (180 deg) the higher ones successively make less of a turn; the one at 4000 miles makes only 0.177 turn (63.7 deg) in the same time.

Explication of Figure 5

[13] *Vertical speeds.* Figure 5 also shows the vertical launching speeds we would have to give a body to reach the altitudes shown. These speeds rise very rapidly up to an altitude of 5000 miles and then increase more gradually for higher altitudes. To completely escape the earth a body must be launched at the terrific speed of 36,900 fps or 25,100 mph.

Explication of natural law

[14] These velocities represent the kinetic energy we first give the body. As the body rises it slows down—the kinetic energy converting to potential energy. When the body stops at its peak altitude all the kinetic energy has converted to potential energy. It then falls back to earth and the potential energy reconverts to kinetic as the body speeds up. Without air friction, the landing kinetic energy would equal the initial launching kinetic energy. Actually air friction absorbs some of the kinetic energy and might be so great as to burn up the body if it travels at high enough speed, going up or down.

[15] *Satellite launching.* To get a satellite up in the sky from the earth's surface, we have to give it enough speed to (1) suit the orbit it will take and (2) hoist it up to the orbit altitude. Total launching velocity is less than the sum of the orbit and vertical launching needs, because we can aim the rocket at an angle for best performance.

[16] The kinetic energy needed by a satellite to stay in its orbit fixes the orbit velocity. On the other hand, the vertical velocity component depends on the potential energy the satellite must have when it reaches its orbit altitude. During its launching the satellite must be given the sum of these two energies.

[17] Figure 6 shows the two components and their total for altitudes up to 25,000 miles. Zero altitude satellites must have 13,600 Btu per lb of mass when launched. At the other extreme, for complete escape we have to give satellites, or rather space travelers, just double this energy, or 27,200 Btu per lb mass.

[18] As orbit altitude increases, the orbit kinetic energy drops, but potential energy rises. Growth of potential en-

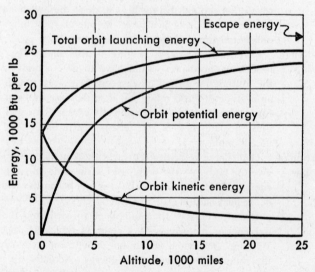

6. Orbit launching energy equals sum of potential and kinetic energies for any given altitude; gravity fades with altitude

ergy is faster than kinetic energy shrinkage, so the total energy grows with rising altitude to a maximum of 27,200 Btu per lb at complete escape.

Explication
of principle
shown in
Figure 7

[19] *Rockets.* Rockets launch our artificial satellites into their lofty orbits. A rocket's operating principle uses the third law of motion—reaction equals action. Motive power develops in a combustion chamber with an exit hole or nozzle in one end.

[20] The chamber burns either a mixture of solid fuel and oxygen or liquid fuel and oxygen (propellants). The solid propellant is placed as a complete charge in the chamber, while liquid propellants are sprayed in by pumps. Their combustion products develop pressures ranging from 300 to 2000 psig and temperatures of about 4000 F. These measure the tremendous kinetic energy of the gas molecules that scream out through the nozzle at the rocket rear. The momentum of the escaping gases represent the direct *action.*

[21] The *reaction* is an unbalanced force acting on the chamber wall exactly opposite the nozzle through which the gases escape (see Figure 7b). The reaction force propels the rocket. Let's study this a bit. A uniform gas pres-

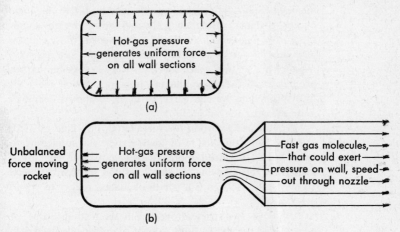

7. Rocket works on Newton's third law of motion: action equals reaction. Unbalanced reaction force propels rocket, gets bigger with chamber pressure, temperature

sure acts at right angles on every bit of interior area of the combustion chamber. For any unit area on one wall having a given total pressure there will be an equal area on the opposite wall with an equal pressure acting in the opposite direction.

[22] If the chamber were completely closed, Figure 7a, equal and opposing internal forces would act in all directions and exactly balance each other. But making an opening in one wall to let gases escape, removes pressure on that wall at the opening. This removes a force that balanced an opposing force on the facing wall. The remaining *unbalanced force* or reaction propels the entire rocket.

Explication of problem

[23] *Energy demands.* Let's look at the energy needs again. A rocket must use 13,600 Btu for every pound mass thrown into a low-altitude orbit. But good coal (mostly carbon) just about develops this amount of energy per lb of fuel. But in addition, a rocket must carry along *its own oxygen* as well as fuel. So for each pound of carbon in the fuel it must also carry 2.66 lb of O_2, neglecting H_2 in the fuel for the moment. On an overall basis the coal and oxygen can only produce $13,600/3.66 = 3710$ Btu *per lb of propellants.*

[24] As if this isn't discouraging enough we must remember that the rocket itself—combustion chamber, pumps, turbines, casing, controls, fuel tanks—weighs something; this is a dead-load. Finally, this rocket must carry a payload, in our case, a satellite. Deadload and payload must be hurled into space together. Rocket engineering has progressed to the point that in large rockets for every 90 lb of propellant we can carry 10 lb of combined deadload and payload.

[25] But using carbon for fuel would only give us 3710 $\times 0.9 = 3340$ Btu per lb of loaded rocket at launching to work with. We need more than 13,600 Btu per lb of loaded rocket; allowing for deadload and payload we need $13,600/0.9 = 15,120$ Btu per lb of loaded rocket to get to orbit speed.

[26] Let's look at hydrogen with its heating value of 62,000 Btu per lb. To burn 1 lb of hydrogen we need 8 lb of O_2. So each pound of propellant develops $62,000/9 = 6890$ Btu—far short of the 15,120 Btu we are looking for. Hence, the push for exotic fuels we hear so much about today—but practically all of which is classified information.

Solution:
explication
of process

[27] *Multistaging.* The solution to overcoming our weak fuels was proposed over 50 years ago—multistage rockets (see Figure 4). Suppose that for stage of a 3-stage rocket, 90% was propellant weight, 5% was deadload and 5% payload. Relative weights, and energies given the payloads, are:

Stage	1	2	3
Total lb	1000	50	2.5
Propellant lb	900	45	2.25
Deadload lb	50	2.5	0.125
Payload lb	50	2.5	0.125
Btu per lb	6200	12,400	18,600

[28] The first-stage rocket accelerates its payload consisting of the second and third stages and the satellite until all its propellants are consumed (burn out). For hydrogen propellant this gives a speed corresponding to a kinetic energy of $6890 \times 0.9 = 6200$ Btu per lb of payload and deadload.

[29] At the instant of first-stage burnout the second-stage rocket fires and continues accelerating itself and payload (third stage) until it has added another 6200 Btu per lb energy for a total of 12,400 Btu per lb payload.

[30] At the instant the second stage burns out the third-stage rocket fires. At burnout the third stage has added another 6200 Btu per lb energy as increased speed for a total of 18,600 Btu per lb payload. The payload then has an energy well above the 13,600 Btu per lb needed for a zero-altitude satellite. Figure 6 shows that for 18,600 Btu per lb we could loft the satellite into an orbit at 2500-miles altitude.

Statement
of related
problem

[31] The weight proportions to achieve this are staggering—we need a 1000-lb rocket of which 947 lb is propellant to launch a 0.125-lb load, a weight ratio of 8000:1.

Analogy

[32] Let's compare this to what we need to travel 2500 miles on our globe in a 4000-lb automobile. At 15 miles to the gallon of gasoline we need 1170 lb of fuel, but the car carries only a maximum of about 140 lb with it any one time—refueling along the way. During the trip, the car engine gobbles up about 17,900 lb of air to get the 4100 lb

of O_2 it needs to burn the gas and immediately spews it out as exhaust.

[33] If the car carried all its fuel with it at one time it would have a weight ratio of 0.29:1. If it carried all its propellants, gasoline and O_2, the ratio would be 1.32:1; compare with the 8000:1 for the rocket. At the end of 2500 miles the car would stop dead; but the rocket payload travels forever at 14,000 mph.

Restatement of thesis
[34] The energy problems of space travel, as well as the environment, need a viewpoint entirely different from anything we use in our earth-bound activities.

OUTSIDE SOURCES

Although most technical articles and reports are the outgrowth of work that the writer has been engaged in personally, he still needs to know something about library research. Even in an article or a report drawing on his own experience, he may wish to compare his findings with those of other men or he may want to buttress some of his statements by citing other sources. In addition, he may be called on for an article or a report that must be based primarily on research. And, of course, with both the professional man and the student there is always the pleasure of reading simply for one's own enlightenment. Regardless of motive, a person can save many hours if he knows where to find the material he wants and how to use it.

Research

LOCATING MATERIAL.   All the books and bound periodicals in a reference library are listed in the card catalogue. They are classified according to the Dewey Decimal System or the Library of Congress System. Most technical libraries use the Dewey System, which divides publications into 10 main categories numbered as follows:

000-099	General reference works
100-199	Philosophy and Psychology
200-299	Religion and Mythology
300-399	Sociology, Education, Economics
400-499	Philology
500-599	Natural science
600-699	Useful arts
700-799	Fine arts

800-899	Literature
900-999	History

These main categories, in turn, are further divided and subdivided. For example, the 600's—Useful arts—are divided thus:

600-609	General works
610-619	Medicine
620-629	Engineering
630-639	Agriculture
640-649	Home economics
650-659	Communication, Business
660-669	Chemical technology
670-679	Manufactures
680-689	Mechanic trades, Amateur manuals
690-699	Building

In the card catalogue of most libraries a book can be found under at least three headings: the name of the author, the title of the book, and the subject it deals with. In large libraries it is listed under several subjects. The author and the title listings are the most direct ways to find a specific book we already know about. The subject listings are of great help when we have no particular book in mind or when we are selecting a reading bibliography preparatory to doing a paper. The card below is an example of an author listing and an explanation of the data.

---

2) **Seeley, Walter James,** 1894-

1) 517.7
    S452   3) An introduction to the operational calculus by Walter J. Seeley . . . 1st ed. Scranton, Pa., International textbook company, 1941.

4) xi p., 1 1., 167 p. diagrs. 21½ ^{cm}. (Half-title: International texts in electrical engineering; E.E. Dreese . . . consulting editor)

5) 1. Calculus. Operational. i.Title. ii.Title: The operational calculus.

6)
41-24830

7) Library of Congress   QA432.SL

8) 517.7

---

1) The call number, showing exactly where the book can be found in the stacks.

2) The author's name and the date of his birth. Since no date follows the hyphen, he is still living.

3) The title of the book, author's name in its normal order, edition, place of publication, publisher, year of publication.

4) Description of the book: 11 prefatory pages, one leaf, 167 pages of discussion, diagrams included, height of book in centimeters. It is one in a series of books published under the common heading "International texts in electrical engineering" and under the general editorship of Mr. Dreese.

5) Subjects under which the book is also listed.

6) The card number in the Library of Congress.

7) The call number in the Library of Congress System.

8) The call number in the Dewey System given by the Library of Congress cataloguers.

Three other cards for this book are in the same catalogue. It is entered under its title: "An introduction to the operational calculus." The title is typed above the author's name and the card is alphabetized among the *i*'s. It is entered under its subject: Calculus, Operational. This is typed in red above the author's name and the card is alphabetized under *c*. Under *o* is a cross-reference: Operational calculus— see Calculus, Operational.

The location of magazine files is also given in the card catalogue, but first we must know which magazines have articles on the subject we are exploring. This task is simplified by the periodical indexes— volumes that list under subject headings what has been published in different magazines. The entries are abbreviated to conserve space, but directions for using the index are given in the front of each volume. The indexes described here are the ones most helpful in locating articles on technical, scientific, and general topics.

Engineering Index   1884-present
Lists articles by subject and author from journals in every field of engineering. Includes some foreign publications. Of particular help is an abstract of each article.

Industrial Arts Index   1913-present
In addition to articles on engineering subjects, lists those from maga-

zines devoted to science, business, and some fields of government.

International Index to Periodicals 1907-present
Primarily a guide to articles on science and the humanities but includes some engineering subjects. Lists articles in foreign publications.

Reader's Guide to Periodical Literature 1900-present
Lists articles by subject, author, and title from magazines with circulation among general public.

Poole's Index to Periodical Literature 1802-1906
Lists articles of general interest published in American and English magazines before *Reader's Guide* was founded.

New York Times Index 1913-present
Indexes articles from the *New York Times*. Issued every two months and, in bound form, annually.

Engineering Abstracts 1900-present
Summarizes and gives source of articles on engineering subjects.

Science Abstracts 1903-present
Lists articles on electrical engineering and physics.

Chemical Abstracts 1907-present
Indexes all types of publications dealing with chemistry, chemical engineering, and allied sciences.

The more useful general reference works are:

Encyclopaedia Britannica
Encyclopedia Americana
Hutchinson's Technical and Scientific Encyclopedia
Van Nostrand's Scientific Encyclopedia

The most highly regarded technical dictionary is *Chambers' Technical Dictionary*.

Biographical sketches can be found in:

Dictionary of American Biography
Dictionary of National Biography
Who's Who
Who's Who in America
Who's Who in Engineering
Who's Who in Science
American Men of Science

TAKING NOTES. The first step in writing an article or a report drawing on outside material is to make out a reading list from the card catalogue and the other sources given above. This list should be arranged to minimize duplication and yet ensure complete coverage of the subject. A good idea is to begin with an article in a reference work that gives a broad picture of the subject, follow with a book that treats the whole subject in more detail, and then proceed to books and articles that amplify various aspects. We can judge the value of a book quickly by reading the table of contents and the value of an article by reading an abstract of it or, if no abstract is at hand, by skimming the article itself.

In culling data we should not mark a book or a magazine unless it belongs to us, but should take notes on cards. Cards, measuring 3 by 5 in. or 4 by 6 in., are more manageable and less likely to get lost than slips of paper. Two sets of cards are advisable, one for bibliographical data and the other for the actual notes.

On the first set we record the information that will go in the list of sources that we are indebted to and that will appear at the end of our article or report. For a book this information consists of the author's name, the title of the book, the city in which it was published, the publisher, the date, and any special information, such as the edition, if other than the first, and the volume number if it belongs to a set. For our own convenience we might add the call number to save time if we have to reconsult the book.

For a magazine article we record the author's name, the title of the article, the name of the magazine, the volume and issue number, the month and year, and the inclusive pagination of the article. For an article in a reference work we give the author if the article is signed, the title of the article, the name of the work, the edition, the volume number, and the inclusive pagination of the article.

Examples of these types of entries plus others are given on page 211.

The second set of cards is for our notes. At the top of each card we write the specific topic that the note concerns, using the wording of our preliminary outline. Identifying the information by the actual topic is better than identifying by the outline label (say, III.C.2) because the final working outline will probably have the topics in a different order from the preliminary one and the label alone on the card could be confusing. It is also better to use a separate card for each note, and for the same reason: in our final arrangement of the material, points that we originally thought would come together may be treated in separate places. At the end of each reading period or upon completing all the research we sort the cards according to their topic headings.

The notes themselves, as a general rule, should be careful paraphrases of the source; that is, we should record the information with

Dimensional analysis

"Dimensional analysis makes possible the 'theory of models,' whereby scale test models can be used in experiments to predict the performance & improve the design of large, expensive equipment."

Ref & Air Cond, p. 158

Note Card with Direct Quotation.

Dimensional analysis

Permits use of models for predicting performance & improving design of equipment.

Ref & Air Cond, p. 158

Note Card with Paraphrasing

scrupulous accuracy but mostly in our words. Articles and reports stuffed with quotations make tiresome reading and strongly suggest laziness on the writer's part. Direct quotation should be reserved for extremely important points, for controversial ones, and for passages that would lose their effectiveness if paraphrased.

At the bottom of every card we note the source from which the information was taken and the page number. To save time, we can abridge the source by using only the author's name or an abbreviation of the title.

On the preceding page are sample cards showing direct quotation and paraphrasing. The bibliographical entry would read:

Jordan, Richard C. and Gayle B. Priester. *Refrigeration and Air Conditioning.* New York: Prentice-Hall, Inc., 1948.

Quotations

In the article or the report itself indirect quotations and paraphrases are treated no differently from our own thoughts, except that we acknowledge our indebtedness. An indirect quotation gives someone else's thought in his own words, but for changing the tense of the verbs and the person of the pronouns to fit our point of view. A paraphrase gives someone else's thought in words that are largely or entirely our own. Neither requires quotation marks or special punctuation and capitalization.

Direct quotations, on the other hand, call for special treatment, and its exact nature depends on the length of the quoted material. A quotation of average length (fewer than 50 words) is worked into the regular text. It continues the line that our own words begin, and the transition from our words to it and, at the end, from it back to our own words is marked by double quotation marks. If the excerpt makes a sentence in itself, the first word is capitalized and a comma (or a colon if a formal note is desired) separates our words from it. An example follows:

As pointed out in Mr. J.L. Asher's report, "The cost per unit does not decrease appreciably until the total number of units produced reaches 40,000." There are several explanations for this lag.

If the excerpt completes a construction of our own, the capital and the punctuation are omitted.

> As noted in Mr. J.L. Asher's report, the cost of the individual lock "does not decrease appreciably until the total number of units produced reaches 40,000. At this point the decrease is about four cents." There are several explanations for this lag.

Notice that quotation marks are not used before and after each quoted sentence but only at the beginning and the end of the full quotation.

If we wish to omit part of the excerpt, suspension points—also called ellipsis points—mark the omission. These are three consecutive periods, and they suffice to indicate the gap whether it is a single word or several sentences. Quotation marks are not used before and after them.

> In his report Mr. J.L. Asher says, "The cost per unit does not decrease appreciably until the total . . . reaches 40,000."

If the omission comes at the end of a sentence, the suspension points immediately follow the period ending the sentence. Suspension points are not needed when the omission comes at the beginning or the end of the excerpt; the reader assumes that something precedes and follows it.

Quotations more than 50 words long are set apart from the regular text. If the text is single-spaced, as in a letter and an informal report, one or two blank lines precede and follow the excerpt. If the text is double-spaced, as in a magazine article and a formal report, two or three blank lines separate the quotation from the text above and below it. The excerpt itself is single-spaced and is not enclosed in quotation marks. It may be indented from the side margins or be flush with them. It is introduced by a colon and begins with a capital letter.

> One of the problems of stray capacitances is discussed by Mr. R.W. Clark, Jr., on page 6 of his report. He says:
>
> In radio-frequency work stray capacitances often affect the measurements. In general, stray capacitances are uncertain in magnitude and

often vary with the adjustment of the bridge and the position of the operator's body. If these capacitances are not properly controlled, serious errors may result in measurements. Shielding will eliminate some stray capacitances and localize many others. Since stray capacitance cannot be eliminated entirely, the substitution method should be used in making measurements.

Other problems caused by stray capacitances will be explained later. For the present let us examine Mr. Clark's statement more fully.

Acknowledgment

Material borrowed from others, whether paraphrased or given in their words, should be acknowledged as a matter of courtesy and plain honesty. The acknowledgment is made in the body and, in articles and formal reports, in an appended bibliography as well.

FOOTNOTES. In a business letter and an informal report the acknowledgment is worked into the text. It may be a parenthetical remark:

> As explained by C.A. Brandon in *The Isothermal Characteristics and Strength of Sandite,* p. 131, "The formations of the ferrite and dissolved carbide are determining factors of flexural strength."

Or:

> According to C.A. Brandon (*The Isothermal Characteristics and Strength of Sandite,* p. 131), "The formations of the ferrite and dissolved carbide are determining factors of flexural strength."

Or it may be a direct statement:

> In his book, *The Isothermal Characteristics and Strength of Sandite,* p. 131, C.A. Brandon says, "The formations of the ferrite and dissolved carbide are determining factors of flexural strength."

Textual acknowledgments may be used also in magazine articles and formal reports, or the citations may be in footnotes. Both methods should not appear in the same article or report.

When footnotes are used, an Arabic numeral is placed in the text at the end of the material being acknowledged and a corresponding numeral is placed at the bottom of the page against the left margin. Symbols can be used instead of numerals if the footnotes are very few. A line extending an inch or so from the margin separates the text and the footnotes. The numerals may begin with No. 1 on each page or be consecutive throughout the paper.

The exact form of footnotes varies somewhat among publications. The system described here is sufficient when the paper has a bibliography. The first citation of a work consists of the author's name in its regular order, the name of the work, and the page reference. This is an example of a book:

1. Myril B. Reed, *Alternating-Current Theory,* p. 209.

Reports and pamphlets are treated in the same way.

The following is an example of a magazine article that was co-authored:

1. R.P. Bobco and A.L. Gosman, "Volumetric Efficiency," *Engineering Education,* March 1956, p. 566.

Articles in general reference works are cited thus when the author is given:

1. Alfred A. Cowles, "Copper and Brass Industry," *Encyclopedia Americana* (1941 ed.), 7:662.

The edition may be identified by number instead of year. Note that no abbreviations are used when both volume and page appear. If the author is not given, the entry begins with the title of the article. When the editing of a reference work has been the responsibility of one man, it is customary to cite the work after his name and to distinguish him from an author by the abbreviation *ed.*:

1. Otto de Lorenzi, ed., *Combustion Engineering,* chap. 13, p. 4.

The chapter has to be identified because, to simplify revision, the pages in this book are numbered by chapter, and the abbreviation keeps the reference from being mistaken for a volume number.

After the first citation of a work the forms can be shortened. To indicate that the reference is exactly the same as in the preceding footnote, *Ibid.* is used. If everything is the same except the page number, the new page is designated.

1. John D. Ryder, *Networks, Lines and Fields*, p. 80.
2. *Ibid.*
3. *Ibid.*, p. 81.

Ibid. is followed by a period and underlined because it is an abbreviation of the Latin word *ibidem*, meaning "in the same place." It does not have to appear on the same page as the footnote it refers to; several pages can intervene provided no other work is cited.

If a work is cited a second time and one or more other references come between the two citations, the surname of the author of the work being re-cited and the page number are given. When there is no author's name, which can be true of articles, the title of the article and the page number are used. Examples are:

1. W. S. Ireson and E.L. Grant, *Handbook of Industrial Engineering and Management*, p. 831.
2. *Ibid.*, p. 848.
3. "Chemical Engineering," *Hutchinson's Technical and Scientific Encyclopedia*, I:307.
4. Ireson and Grant, p. 848.
5. "Chemical Engineering," p. 308.
6. *Ibid.*

BIBLIOGRAPHY.   The bibliography lists all works used in preparing the paper. The entries are alphabetized. They need not be divided into categories (books, articles, pamphlets, reports) unless the list is long. In this alphabetized arrangement, numbering the entries has no purpose.

Some technical periodicals use a different system. The entries are not alphabetized but are numbered in the sequence in which they are cited in the text. Numerals in the text refer to these entries in the bibliography and not to footnotes. Thus the first citation in the text is marked 1 and refers to the first work in the bibliography; each succeeding reference to this same work, no matter where it comes in the paper, is also marked 1. The second work cited in the text is marked 2, the 2 refers to the second entry in the bibliography, and all later citations of this work are also marked 2. And so on with all the references.

The advantage of this system is that it saves the space that footnotes would require. The disadvantage is that the reference is not precise enough to be of much help to a reader who wishes to follow it up; he knows the author and the work but not the page number.

Whether the entries are alphabetized or numbered, the following forms are common for the various types of material. The phrases enclosed in brackets do not appear but are appended here to indicate the type of entry.

American Standards Association. *Abbreviations for Scientific and Engineering Terms* (Z10.1-1941). New York, 1941. [Bulletin published under auspices of an organization; no author or editor given.]

Bobco, R.P. and A.L. Gosman. "Volumetric Efficiency." *Engineering Education,* March 1956, pp. 565-568. [Magazine article by two authors; inclusive pagination.]

"Chemical Engineering." *Hutchinson's Technical and Scientific Encyclopedia.* I:305-308. [Unsigned article in reference work; inclusive pagination.]

Cowles, Alfred A. "Copper and Brass Industry." *Encyclopedia Americana* (1941 ed.), 7:660-665. [Signed article in general reference work; inclusive pagination.]

De Lorenzi, Otto, ed. *Combustion Engineering.* New York: Combustion Engineering, Inc., 1955. Chapter 13. [Limited reference work edited by one man; only a certain part used.]

Faires, Virgil Moring. *Thermodynamics.* New York: The Macmillan Company, 1957. [First edition of book by one author.]

Givens, H. Crandall. *Best Designs for Lead Installations.* A report submitted to Harbor City Construction Co., Brooklyn, N.Y. April 1957. [Technical report.]

Penkan, James C. and others. *Magnetic Fields.* 3rd ed. 2 vols. New York: Benson-Smith, 1953. [Work co-authored by more than three men; edition other than first; two volumes, both consulted. If only one were used, the reading after *ed.* would be *Vol. I* or *Vol. II.*]

EXERCISES AND ASSIGNMENTS

A. Name the types of lead suitable for

   1. An article in your college magazine
   2. An article in a company publication whose circulation includes everybody from stenographers to specialists in aerodynamics
   3. An article in a magazine whose circulation is primarily among persons of scientific and technical backgrounds

B. Using five different leads and addressing a different group in each case, write the first two or three sentences for an article about your college.

C. For the same article write three different conclusions illustrating three of the methods listed on pages 183-184.

D. The following information pertains to a book: title—*Power Plants;* authors—Alexander H. Zerban and Edwin P. Nye; edition—second; publisher—International Textbook Company in Scranton, Pennsylvania; date—1956; price—$6.50.

   1. Cite page 193 in a footnote.
   2. Cite the same page in the next footnote.
   3. Cite the same page three footnotes later when the intervening footnotes refer to other works.
   4. Show how the book would be entered in a bibliography.

E. Using the facilities of the school library, write a semitechnical article on some development that took place in your field several years ago.

Oral Communication

The engineer is called on daily to express himself in person. It may be to deliver an oral report to his superior or his colleagues or to take part in a conference where some problem is to be threshed out. Or it may be a much more formal and trying occasion, such as giving a talk before a meeting of all the company's executive officers or reading a paper before a group of several hundred people. In all these situations and the many others where he is called on to speak, it is important that he acquit himself well.

THE SPEAKER

The following remarks about effective speaking do not apply uniformly to the various occasions described in the latter part of the chapter. Since most of the differences, however, are in degree rather than in substance, it seems best to begin by examining the common problems as a unit.

Observing the General Rules

Good speaking is the ability to hold someone's attention on what is being said. The last words are important: on what is being said. They mean that effective speaking is not an exhibition. Rather, it is simple, straightforward and, to all appearances, unstudied. This is not to say that good speaking requires no thought, that it comes naturally. Certain qualities enter into it, and most of us have to cul-

213

tivate them consciously. There are rules to follow and we have to learn them. But the end result should be a smooth, natural-looking performance. In other words, we observe the rules but make no show of it. Let us consider these rules.

1. Enunciate clearly. This is the most important one. Clear enunciation—the sounding of words and syllables distinctly—is the surest way to hold attention and be understood. Mumbling, swallowing syllables, slurring phrases, letting the end of sentences fade away—these faults annoy listeners and cause them to lose interest in what is being said.

Clear enunciation is also a guide to proper speed. This speed will vary from person to person, depending on individual vocal characteristics, such as the size and shape of the mouth and the flexibility of the vocal chords; and it will vary with the complexity of the material being discussed and the vocabulary being used. For most of us, however, it is between 125 and 160 words a minute. In enunciating distinctly we automatically avoid speaking too fast, which is a much greater temptation than speaking too slow.

2. Maintain eye contact with the listeners. Nothing detracts more from a talk, whether it is in a conference room or an auditorium, than the speaker seeming to be preoccupied with the table, the ceiling, or something outside the window. The contact should be inclusive and specific. We should look at people in different parts of the room, not just those directly in front of us; and we should let our eyes come to rest on them, not merely sweep over them. Good eye contact is a means of holding attention, and except when we glance at our notes or turn to trace the discussion of a visual aid, it should be continuous.

3. *Talk;* do not shout. The tendency to speak too loud is greater before a large gathering than a small one, but even in an auditorium there is no need to shout. A well-modulated voice actually carries more clearly than a loud one. We can tell whether our words are reaching the people in the rear by watching their expression. If our voice reaches them at a conversational level, it is likely to be at a pleasant pitch. Since our impulse in speaking to a large group is to strike too high a pitch, we should make it a practice to begin in a voice slightly lower than that which we feel is right.

Most auditoriums are equipped with microphones, which further reduce the need for speaking loudly. When we are to use a microphone, we should try to learn its peculiarities and the best pitch for our voice by practicing with it beforehand. When this is impossible, we can gauge whether our mouth is too close or too far from it by listening to our opening remarks and, again, by noting the expressions of the people in the rear. Generally, a person's normal pitch and volume are satisfactory. Coughing or clearing the throat is especially strident over a microphone. If we have to do either, we should turn aside.

4. Observe good posture. Whether standing or sitting while we speak, we should be comfortably erect—not stiff-backed but straight. If there is a lectern and we are not using it, which is usually true in giving a talk, we should stand beside it rather than behind it. The most comfortable position for the feet is 8 to 10 inches apart and one foot advanced about halfway of the other, with the body's weight on the rear one. The best position for the hands is wherever they feel most natural, except that they should not be in our pockets.

5. Let gestures be spontaneous. Forced ones nearly always look forced and suggest insincerity. If using our hands and moving our head is natural in conversation, then we may move them when we have the impulse during a speech; but if such movements are not instinctive, we should not try to adopt them. Successful speakers are found in both groups, those who use gestures and those who do not.

6. Avoid irritating mannerisms. Nearly all of us have habits that pass unnoticed in ordinary conversation but that can be annoying in a talk. Smacking the lips, batting the eyes, pulling at an ear, frowning, laughing and talking at the same time—these and other mannerisms can distract and alienate listeners. Since they are habits we are likely to be unaware of, pointing them out to us is one of the jobs of a trial audience—that is, two or three friends before whom we rehearse the talk.

Controlling Nervous Tension

One of the hardest obstacles to overcome in speaking well is nervousness, or stage fright. It will differ among people and, in the same person, with the occasion. Some people manifest little or none when addressing a large assemblage; others tighten up in answering a question in the classroom.

This nervousness is a perfectly natural and honorable reaction—honorable because it stems from the desire to do well. There is no sure way to eliminate it, and even if there were, its total absence is probably undesirable because a certain amount is stimulating and conducive to a better effort. Rather than eliminate it, we should try to control it and prevent its detracting from what we are saying. Remembering the following points is helpful.

1. We are in a very large and good company, for nearly all speakers, including some of the best and most experienced ones, feel some tension, particularly at the beginning of a talk.

2. In all likelihood the tension will subside after the first moment or so, as soon as we get used to the sound of our voice alone in the room.

3. It is probable that nobody else realizes we are nervous. We tend to be self-conscious and feel that the symptoms are more visible than they are. A pounding heart, shortness of breath, even a flushed face and trembling hands and knees are things that we can be acutely aware of without others noticing. Because this self-consciousness can aggravate the tension, we should force our thoughts off how we are feeling and fix them on something else—the audience, the surroundings, what we plan to say, what another speaker is saying if the occasion is a conference, a panel discussion, or a program of speeches.

4. We should speak, especially at the beginning, a bit more slowly than we normally do and adopt a tone somewhat lower than our impulse tells us is appropriate. Under nervous compulsion some speakers add to their trouble by starting out fast and high, with the result that they panic themselves. But by deliberately "playing it down" we can calm ourselves rather effectively.

5. Thorough preparation can prevent anxiety and thereby lessen tension. If we decide on exactly the points we want to cover and gather ample data to support these points, we can enter the situation with a self-confidence not possible when we know we are ill prepared.

Part of this preparation should be a good outline to consult as we proceed with the talk. An outline relieves us of the fear that we may omit something we planned to say or say it in the wrong place. The outline should not have so many details that it is hard to follow. It will be easiest to handle if it is on 3- by 5-in. cards, which fit conveniently into the palm, and easiest to follow if only two or three phrases are on each card.

6. Much of our nervousness is due to finding ourselves in an unfamiliar situation, and it decreases as we become oriented. Notice how at the beginning of a term the students in a class, not knowing each other or the instructor, are hesitant to ask questions or volunteer answers but how as the months pass this shyness diminishes.

The same thing happens in other situations. As we get used to them, we are more at ease and more ready to voice our opinions, whether at a small conference or a large convention. Our control over nervousness increases as our experience in group and public speaking increases. Consequently, the student should accept every chance to speak before a group in college so that later he will be trained for the talks he may want to give and even may have to give.

Using Visual Aids

Visual aids can add a great deal to oral communication of any kind: conference, panel discussion, interview, report, speech, and society paper. They must, however, be carefully adapted to the occasion as to type, content, and size; and they must tie in directly with the subject matter. Although part of their purpose is to heighten interest, they should not be introduced solely for the sake of novelty. Their main object is to contribute to the listener's understanding, to make vivid to him what we have just said or are saying. An apt illustration focuses the listener's attention; an inapt one deflects it.

Visual aids are of three types: projective material, such as films and slides; non-projective material, such as maps or charts held by the speaker, supported on a stand, or drawn on a blackboard; and physical exhibits, such as a fuel pump or a Geiger counter brought into the room. Each type has its merits and its drawbacks.

Projective material is best when the subject concerns movement. We can show how a machine operates or a process is carried out, tour a mine or a plant, follow the course of a stream or a highway. Film is the usual medium for such subjects, though a series of photographs or slides can serve the purpose. Projective material, especially slides, can also be used to display data tables and the various kinds of figures.[1]

The disadvantages of projective material are the cost of preparing it, which with film can be rather high; the bulkiness of the projector and screen; the need for smooth timing between the speaker and the operator; and the fact that the personal contact between speaker and listeners is weakened by the darkness of the room. For these reasons this type of visual aid is most satisfactory when cost is no issue, the meeting is held in a room where the equipment is permanently set up, the operator is familiar with it and he and the speaker have had the chance to synchronize their parts, and the speaker prepares an introduction and a conclusion to precede and follow the period when the room is darkened. If the material requires comment while it is being shown, as it frequently does, the comments should be made without turning on the lights; continually having to adjust the eyes to light and dark irks an audience.

For general purposes, non-projective material is the most practical of the three types. The expense of preparing it need not be great, it is portable and usually requires no assistance, it is easily adapted to the particular situation, and it does not necessitate the speaker breaking direct contact with the audience.

The illustration is better presented on cardboard or a movable blackboard than on paper or a stationary blackboard. Tables and figures drawn on paper can be hard to discern because of the translucence of the paper. A stationary blackboard offers the problem of the speaker either interrupting his talk to draw the figure or table, talking with his back to the audience as he draws, or drawing it beforehand and having it present to divert attention all through his talk. Of course a mobile board is quite practical; the figure can be drawn ahead of time and displayed only when it is pertinent.

The only disadvantage of material shown on cardboard or a movable blackboard is that it cannot be seen in every part of a very large room, even though it is presented from a platform.

Physical exhibits can be samples, scale models, or the object itself. They are most feasible when the group is small. The exhibit can be

---

[1] The function and the preparation of the different types of tables and figures are explained in Chapter 10. For the present we shall note only their use as an aid in speaking.

placed in the center of the table around which the listeners are gathered, or placed on a stand before them. Its actual features can be pointed out. To show interior parts, we can make the outer ones removable.

The principal drawbacks to physical exhibits are that they can be cumbersome, they may not work when we come to the point of demonstrating them, and they are ineffectual if the group is so large that everybody cannot be near them during the demonstration. Some speakers try to offset this last objection by passing the exhibits among the audience, but the attempt often results in distraction rather than enlightenment.

Sometimes we may find a visual aid already prepared and suitable to our purpose—for example, the map of a city issued by its chamber of commerce, the drawing of a machine made for an advertisement, or a chart published in a magazine—but for the most part, such material has to be ruled out because it is too small or includes details extraneous to our purpose. This means we must prepare the aid ourselves or have somebody prepare it especially for us.

A successful one has to meet certain requirements. First of all, it must be large enough for every detail to be seen throughout the room. By experimenting before we draw it, we can avoid the risk of making it too small. We can place blank pieces of cardboard or objects similar to the aid in the front of the room, or one like it, and study them from different spots, mentally imposing our illustration on the dummy. Lighting and angles as well as distance should be taken into account.

The thickness of lines and the size of print are governed by the size of the aid, large drawings and tables requiring heavier lines and print than small ones. When colors are used they should be the more distinct ones—for example, red and orange in preference to yellow, green in preference to blue. When placed side by side, they should offer sharp contrasts.

The numbers, letters, or words that designate the parts—and any other explanatory matter, such as arrows to show direction and human figures to suggest relative size—should also be clear. Such aids to understanding are really obstacles to it if they are just discernible enough to puzzle the observer.

Even when an illustration is large enough and the markings are legible, its purpose can be defeated by overloading. A good illustration covers no more than one or two points. Three slides each illustrating a single point and exposed for 20 seconds will be grasped more quickly than one slide covering three points and shown for 60 seconds. Likewise, in explaining an involved subject we should not try to picture all the details in one diagram. Instead, we should first show a drawing of the whole unit with the main parts labeled and then show drawings in which these parts are enlarged, or "blown up."

To summarize, we should remember that a visual aid is meant to save words and answer questions. It can do this only if (1) its size is ample, (2) the lines, explanatory matter, and colors are distinct, (3) it is simple and uncrowded, and (4) it has been done neatly, without ink splotches and signs of erasure.

In displaying the aid we should stand to one side of it so that the view of all observers is unobstructed. In commenting on something in the left-hand part of the figure, we should stand on the left so as not to block the view of those people on the right side of the room. The position is opposite when we are commenting on something in the right-hand part. If the room has no platform, we should hold the display high enough for those in the rear to see it without rising, or if possible, we should have a stand for it.

A pointer of some sort—a reed or even a yardstick—is advisable. It allows us to stand farther aside while discussing the illustration, and it enables us to trace the discussion with precision instead of pointing a finger at vague areas. Insofar as we can, we should face listeners while explaining the aid. A pointer makes this easier because it can be held on a spot while we turn to the audience.

The question now arises: when do we use the visual aid? Where is the best place for it? At the beginning of the talk? at the end? or somewhere in between? The answer depends on the circumstances. Sometimes illustrative material makes a good introduction because it is dramatic and because the audience gets a working knowledge of the subject before hearing about it in detail. Another advantage of beginning with a visual aid is that it focuses attention away from us at the time when nervous tension is greatest, though this should not be our primary consideration in choosing the place for it.

At the end of a talk the explanation of a graphic aid can serve as an excellent summary of the main points that were brought out. It leaves the audience with a clear-cut visual impression of the subject. A physical exhibit is especially well placed at the end because some listeners may want to inspect it more closely or operate it personally while the explanation is still fresh in their minds.

A visual aid that does not pertain to the whole subject is best placed somewhere between the opening and the ending, at the point to which it applies. Often, of course, we may have two or more aids that pertain to different parts of the talk. We may begin with one, use one or two during the discussion, and end with a summarizing one; or all of them may be presented in the body proper.

The best place for an aid, then, is not a fixed matter but is determined by where it will be of the most service.

THE OCCASION

The ability to speak well can be of value in different kinds of situations. In some of them we share with other people the task of developing an idea or dealing with a problem. At other times we carry all or most of the burden alone.

Participation with Others

THE CONFERENCE.   Much of the work done in the business world is transacted in conferences. In fact, it is not unusual for an engineer to spend as much time conferring with other people as working by himself.

A conference differs from ordinary conversation in that the meeting is generally prearranged, its object is to discuss certain business, and remarks on other subjects are kept to a minimum. A conference may be between only two people or it may be among several. When only two or three persons are involved, the meeting may be unplanned and may take on some of the air of a social conversation, but the talk is still directed at a problem of mutual interest and digressions should be few and brief. Here we are primarily interested in the more formal conference—that is, one that is scheduled ahead of time and attended by several people.

The chairman has a great responsibility. It is mainly he who decides that a conference is desirable and what its subject and scope will be. He sets the time and place and makes any other arrangements called for. He chooses the participants, or at least invites the affected departments to send representatives, taking care to limit the group to a practical number. Large conferences are unwieldy and seldom produce worth-while results.

He works out the agenda and sends copies to the other conferees well in advance of the meeting date so that they will have time to prepare themselves. The number of items on the agenda should be restricted so that each can be discussed fully in the time allotted for the meeting. In addition, no item should be included that does not concern all the members unless it is scheduled for the end of the meeting, when uninterested persons can excuse themselves.

During the conference the chairman keeps the discussion from straying to irrelevant topics and summarizes the points as the meeting progresses. This summary is most constructive if it is given visually as well as orally—for example, by tabulating the points on a blackboard as each is developed and agreed on. A good conference leader is clever at eliciting and balancing comments from his different colleagues. He can do this by addressing specific questions to the reticent members—questions that require full answers—and letting the more talkative persons have their say apropos of questions addressed to the group.

At no time should the chairman forget that even though he represents special interests himself, his main function is to bring about an agreement in thought that will result in unified action.

The meeting is by no means the responsibility of the chairman alone. The preparation, the attitude, and the conduct of the other members directly affect the outcome. Upon receiving the agenda each participant should study it carefully. He should note what is expected of him and what he must do to prepare himself. He should list the questions he wants to raise and those he thinks he will be asked.

To be fully productive, the meeting must result in a free flow of ideas. For this to happen the participants must feel they have the same status during the conference, whether they have it outside or not. There can be no real exchange of opinion if the meeting is dominated by one or two persons whose consciousness of rank intimidates the others. Each member should look on the meeting as a forum where his views will have equal weight with those of others, but no greater.

During the meeting itself he should state his points forcefully but tactfully, making certain that the interests he speaks for are understood and get favorable consideration. He should avoid giving the impression he is trying to make a speech. He should listen attentively to what his colleagues have to say and wait until they have finished to ask questions or to comment.

A genuine spirit of co-operation should pervade the meeting. After all, the purpose of a conference is to solve a problem of mutual concern to the participants. Therefore, each should be willing to give as well as to take. If one or two members stubbornly insist on their position, the meeting can end in deadlock, without even these members gaining anything. But if everyone regards the conference as an opportunity to clear away misunderstanding and to benefit from the experience and the outlook of the other participants, an advantageous compromise will be effected—and compromise means a conference has been successful.

THE PANEL DISCUSSION. We may think of a panel discussion as a more formalized conference, for like the conference it is a group discussion of a predetermined topic. There are only three real differences.

First, there is an audience and it usually joins in the latter part of the discussion. It may ask questions of the panel or add to what the panel has said.

Second, the chairman of a panel is not representing the interests of any special group, whereas the conference leader is. The leader of a panel acts more as a moderator. He takes part in the discussion, but his remarks serve mainly to introduce the subject and to point up and tie together what the other members have to say. Finally, before opening the floor to the audience, he summarizes and evaluates what has been covered.

Third, each member of the panel is assigned a certain aspect of the topic beforehand. His chief responsibility is to familiarize himself with this aspect and to present it during the discussion. He outlines it on his first turn to speak. His subsequent remarks and exchanges with the other members are aimed primarily at developing it and showing how it fits into the general subject.

THE INTERVIEW. An interview is different from an informal conversation in that the talk is concentrated on special business and consists mostly of questions and answers. It differs from the two-man conference in that the status of the persons is not the same and the fact affects the conduct of both people.

There are two kinds of interviews, and the inequality of status shifts between them. In one kind the interviewer asks questions to learn whether he wants what the other person is offering: a product, an idea, a service (in job application, the offerer's own service). The interviewer is in the position of accepting or rejecting. In the other kind of interview he is seeking information for an article, a report, or a job he is planning. He is in the position of asking a favor.

In the two types of interviews, then, the roles of the participants are reversed. Let us examine them separately.

The man who has granted an interview so that he can appraise what the other person has to offer fixes the time. He should arrange the appointment so that there is ample time for this appraisal to be fair and complete. Before the interview he should learn something of the other man and the product or service being offered so that he will have a better perspective during the meeting. He should list the points he wishes to inquire about so that none will be forgotten and so that the talk will not become diffusive. During the interview he should maintain a comfortable atmosphere and invite comment, not just yes-or-no answers. It is his part to terminate the meeting gracefully.

The man hoping to interest the interviewer in his product, idea, or service can make his job easier by giving it some forethought. He should define his precise reason for requesting the appointment. Does he want the other person to buy his product outright or on a trial basis? Or does he want him simply to endorse it? Does he want his idea accepted unreservedly or subject to modification? He is applying for a job. Exactly what kind of job or jobs does he prefer? Is he willing to accept a position in some other department until there is an opening in the one he prefers?

He should also find out all he can about the company the interviewer represents. Just what he needs to know will depend on what he is trying to do. If it is to get a product or an idea accepted, he ought to learn such things as the company's buying policies, purchasing system, credit rating, and reputation for being progressive or not. If he is applying for a job, he should get the facts about such things as its general organization, fields of interest, training program, insurance and retirement plans, and policy of promotion. These matters may not come up during the interview, but because they can color the interviewer's attitude, the other man ought to be aware of them.

He should be punctual in arriving for the interview. Most businessmen dress neatly and conservatively and tend to form a good impression of men who do the same. Though the interviewer's position is easier, the other person should bear himself with confidence. If he knows his product, his idea, or his qualifications are good, he has nothing to fear from the questioning. On the contrary, he should welcome it as a chance to reveal more that is in his favor. Although it is the interviewer's prerogative to direct the conversation, the other participant may occasionally introduce points he believes are to his additional credit. He should not, of course, so assert himself that his confidence is mistaken for egotism.

In the second kind of interview it is the questioner whose role demands the greater thought. He is under an obligation because he is being accommodated. He has sought the interview to further his own knowledge or work by drawing on the knowledge and experience of the other person. Not to waste this person's time is the core of the interviewer's obligation. In asking for the meeting he should state what information he wants and how he intends to use it so that the other man can determine whether he can give the information and, if so, whether it is worth his time to do it.

Before the meeting the interviewer should list his questions. He should include none that are superfluous or that might be awkward for the other man on personal or professional grounds. The questions should be worded so that the answers can be brief, many of them requiring only a "yes" or "no." The respondent can always elaborate if he cares to. If the information is for an article, a book, or a report, the answers should be taken down verbatim to ensure that the informant is not misquoted. And of course his assistance is acknowledged in a suitable place.

Individual Performance

In the situations described so far there is a continual exchange of remarks between two or more people. The remaining types of oral communication—the report, the speech, and the society paper—call for one person to do most of the talking. When others speak, it is either to introduce the principal speaker or to ask him questions.

THE ORAL REPORT. In a measure, all three types of communication discussed on the next few pages are oral reports. They comprise data gathered for a special audience. Beyond this common object, however, each has a separate object and the material is treated in the way that will best serve it. We shall begin with the oral report because in the technical field it is far more common than the speech and the society paper.

A minority of oral reports have no written counterpart. That is, they are the only report ever made on the subject or a certain aspect of it. Some of them are authorized as a preliminary examination report, and because the basic finding is negative, the project is dropped. Others are progress reports made to let a superior know how a job is proceeding. They can be quite informal, sometimes amounting to nothing more than a business conversation. When the job is completed, it is written up as a special work report, probably making no reference to the oral reports.

But most oral reports have a written form too. It may precede the oral. When it does, the oral report is likely to be an expanded abstract of it, delivered before officials who are not concerned with the full details but who wish to know more than the original abstract would tell them and want the writer present for questioning. The tone of such reports is formal.

On the other hand, the oral report may come first. It can rise out of the following circumstances:

a. At the start the oral report was intended as the only one, but because of the unexpected importance of the findings a written form is made for the records.

b. A detailed written report will be submitted, but meanwhile an oral one is given so that the project can be started without delay.

c. The oral report is an early, condensed draft of a report going outside the company, or perhaps just the department, and the writer's superiors want to pass judgment on it before he puts it in final form.

An oral report can be entirely read or it can be made extemporaneously from notes. The importance and complexity of the subject are the determining factors. Usually it turns out to be a combination of reading and speaking—in other words, a speech based on full notes in which the more important points are recorded as sentences and read verbatim. The basic parts can be in the conventional order— introduction, discussion, terminal section—or in the modified order: introduction, terminal section, discussion.

The coverage should be complete, but supporting data should be confined to what is essential. Large masses of statistics cannot be absorbed by ear. Unless they are needed to fortify conclusions and recommendations, they should be reduced to general terms. If they are needed, they can be put in writing and distributed among the listeners at the point they are to be discussed. Other kinds of visual aid are also helpful. They can be single copies that the speaker displays before the group, or they can be duplicates passed out to the listeners.

The following report is the "oral" version of the formal report on pages 128-144. It represents an early draft; it covers the important points but most of the details remain to be filled in.

The Harbor City Construction Company is building a plant at Rahway, New Jersey, for the Bretson Chemical Corporation. On March 7 the company asked us to determine the best designs for the lead installations at the plant. We were to give special attention to the types of lead joints to be used on stave tanks, launders, and towers and flues.

A series of tests have shown that the lead sheets should be joined by slip seams or welded joints. More specific suggestions will follow.

Locking, welded, and lap seams were tested.

The locking type is formed by joining and overlapping the seam, as shown here.

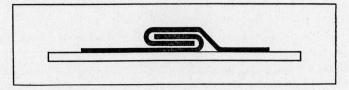

FIGURE 1   Cross-sectional View of Lock Joint

The welded seam is the joining of two or more sheets by a simple weld. This is a drawing of it.

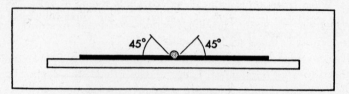

FIGURE 2   Cross-sectional View of Weld Joint

A larger and stronger weld is made possible by giving the plates a 45° angle. This gives a larger surface area than if the edges were parallel.

The lap joint is a modified combination of a lock seam and a welded joint. Here is a sketch of it, showing how one of the sheets is formed over the other one and the edge of the upper sheet is welded.

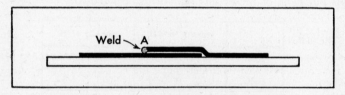

FIGURE 3   Cross-sectional View of Lap Joint

Each joint was tested for its durability against expansion, contraction, and compression. The leakages of gas and fluid through the joints were recorded and compared. Tables 1 and 2 summarize the results of the tests.

It is clear that lead sheets may be joined by slip seams or welded joints. The specific application will determine the type to be used.

Where drainage is the particular requirement, locking seams may be used and provision for thermal expansion may be made in the seams. A large number of joints should be used, each to take up some of the expansion. When lead is used for lining or covering and when gas or a solution may corrode the supporting structure, locking seams are generally unsatisfactory.

When welded seams are employed, separate expansion bends should be installed at frequent intervals to reduce the take-up in each joint to a practical minimum.

When corrosion is a threat, welded joints should be used. Provision for expansion is compensated for by using lap joints for sheets up to ¼-in. thickness (16 psf).

Joint	LEAKAGE BEFORE		LEAKAGE AFTER	
	Gas (%)	Liq (mm)	Gas (%)	Liq (mm)
Lock	0.02	0.92	2.06	3.42
Weld	0.00	0.00	0.00	0.00
Lap	0.00	0.00	0.00	0.00

TABLE 1 Temperature Variation Test Chart

Joint	LEAKAGE BEFORE		LEAKAGE AFTER	
	Gas (%)	Liq (mm)	Gas (%)	Liq (mm)
Lock	0.02	0.92	1.01	1.34
Weld	0.00	0.00	10.48	8.68
Lap	0.00	0.00	0.00	0.00

TABLE 2 Limited Area Test Chart

Welded joints are also preferable on horizontal flat surfaces, where the bend at the lap joint can act as an expansion bend.

We are recommending that lead installations be used on tanks, launders, and towers and flues as follows.

On wood stave tanks that are lead-lined, a reinforcing ring should be constructed around the top to offset drying and shrinking. If the lining is installed as shown here, it will not permit leakage but will allow a 3% contraction or expansion without damage to itself.

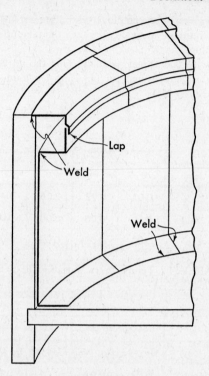

FIGURE 4   Construction of Wood Stave Tank and Recommended Joints

Until now wood launders lined with lead have been used in chemical industries. Lead launders, however, will give better service, and when the salvage value of the lead is considered, the over-all cost may be lower than that of the lead-lined wood.

A weld is the only practical joint for the launder. Expansion and contraction will not affect it or the launder in any way.

Towers and flues can be built of laminated wood and lined with lead. Details of this type of construction are shown in Figure 5.

Leakage of a chemical through the joints could cause serious damage before the leak was discovered. Therefore, welds and lap joints are the only seams used. Because of the varying temperatures, particularly on the flue, lap joints must be used to compensate for the large expansion and contraction.

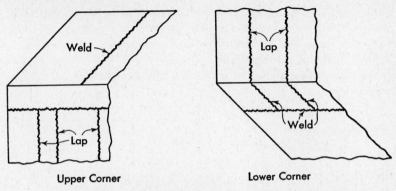

Upper Corner   **Lower Corner**

FIGURE 5   Installation of Lead on Flues and Towers

THE SPEECH.   A speech can be based wholly on personal experience or on reading, or it can be the product of both. When reading is part of the preparation, the same sources are available and the data can be collected in the same way as explained in the discussion of technical articles (pages 200-206).

The talk should be prepared for the specific audience. A speech on the manufacture of silk can be made interesting to men and women, adults and children, silk manufacturers and laymen; but it must be adapted to the special group. The speech describing a new process would be of much interest to the manufacturers but would bore children. The aspects of silk manufacturing that would fascinate a group of women would hardly be the same as those that would engross men.

Of course, many audiences are mixed; they are made up of people in different age groups and with different backgrounds. All they have in common is an interest in the subject, and this will vary from one person to another. A talk given before such an audience should have a broader range than one made to a homogeneous group. When talking to any group, but especially a composite one, the experienced speaker keeps his material flexible, adjusting it according to the reaction he sees—rephrasing points that seem not to have been grasped; expanding here, cutting there as he notes the rise and fall in interest.

If the speaker is gifted and the subject is piquant, a talk can be long and still enjoyable, but instances are scarce. Most good talks are fairly short, ranging from 15 to 45 minutes. Like the semitechnical article, a talk should cover only four or five major points; and unless the audience is well versed in the subject, it should concern general features and omit involved data.

The basic organization of a speech is the same as that of a magazine article:

   I. Introduction
      A. The lead
      B. The purpose and, if necessary, the scope
  II. Body proper—the presentation and discussion of the data
 III. Conclusion—rhetorical device for closing

The lead is a means of capturing the listeners' attention at once. Any of those listed and illustrated on pages 179-181 are also effective in opening a talk, and any of the conclusions listed on pages 183-184 are cogent ways to end it. In addition, the humorous opening or closing can be used successfully—much more so than in a published paper.

In the body proper (see pages 182-183 for more details) short sentences are to be preferred to long ones. They lessen the chance of the speaker getting his thoughts entangled and they are easier for the audience to follow. The listeners' understanding is also aided by the speaker's indicating the transitions between his major points. He can do this by pausing longer than he does between sentences and by making some perceptible movement—adjusting his notes, moving from one side of the lectern to the other, or using a visual aid to summarize the point.

There is no objection to such summarizing on the ground it is repetitious. Since the attention of a listener is more likely to wander than that of a reader, repetition is more common and more serviceable in a speech than in a magazine article. It should not be overdone, of course, for too much repetition will be monotonous; but to repeat an important point, in the same or different language, is the surest way to have it grasped.

A few remarks on delivery may be added to what was said at the beginning of the chapter. First is the question: should the speech be memorized? The answer is no. A professional speaker sometimes gives a memorized speech, but it is usually an incidental result of giving the same talk many times rather than a deliberate effort. Most of us do better if we make no attempt to memorize but instead speak from notes, putting the sentences together as we go. At the places we wish to be sure of accuracy we can read. A talk given in this way —it is called "extemporaneous speaking"—has a freshness and a sincerity often lacking in memorized efforts.

The related question of whether to rehearse the talk depends on the person. Some people speak well when they have not actually rehearsed but have simply thought through the talk as they worked with their notes. Others benefit from rehearsal. This is especially true for an inexperienced speaker. He will profit most from going through the talk aloud and on his feet. A miniature audience, composed of two or three friends, can simulate the real situation so that when he faces it he will be more composed. Further, his friends can spot faults in his enunciation, speed, eye contact, and posture and in the way he uses his visual aids and develops his talk in general.

Many speakers make the mistake of "dressing up" for the occasion. This can add to their self-consciousness and nervous strain. Instead, they should wear clothes they are used to so that while speaking they are comfortable and no part of their mind is on their appearance.

Last, the effect of a good talk can be spoiled at the end. Our natural impulse, especially if we are under tension, is to hurry when the end is in sight. But the close of a talk should be the most important part and should be delivered, if anything, with extra care and clarity. Thanking the audience also weakens the final impression; the concluding words should not be an adjunct of the speech but part of its climax.

If a discussion period follows, there should be a marked break between the end of the talk and the invitation to the audience. When the gathering is large and someone in the front of the room asks a question, we should repeat it for the benefit of those in the rear. In answering we should address the questioner first and then include the other listeners if our reply is of any length. We should admit when we do not know the answer and should make it clear when we are giving a qualified one. An audience is quick to detect when a speaker is pretending to know more than he really does.

THE PROFESSIONAL SOCIETY PAPER.   Ordinarily, a speech should not be read because it can lack the spontaneity it would have if delivered from notes. Nevertheless, there are times when reading a speech is advisable either because accuracy of statement must be ensured or because a fairly rigid time limit must be observed. Sometimes both conditions exist; a common instance is the paper read before a meeting of a professional society.

The paper is a combination of the magazine article and the speech. In contents and composition it resembles the article. The only difference is that since it is absorbed through the ear instead of the eye, the structure is less compact. A reader can back up to understand a point but a listener cannot—at least, he cannot and keep listening too.

The paper is delivered as a speech. Accordingly, the same points that make a speech effective are observed in presenting the paper, with two slight modifications. One is that if a lectern is present we should lay the paper on it and stand behind the lectern rather than beside it. The other is that since we are reading, eye contact has to be interrupted. Still, it can be frequent if we know the contents of the paper thoroughly and we triple-space the text so that we have no trouble finding our place again after glancing up.

If visual aids are used, any remarks about them should be extemporaneous. Tracing the discussion of an aid while trying to read is difficult and looks awkward.

In Chapter 8 we analyzed two semitechnical articles that reveal the wide difference in treatment that is possible. The first one (pages 185-190) was originally presented before the Sixth Annual West Coast Convention of the Audio Engineering Society, a somewhat specialized group. To be grasped aurally by a lay audience, however, it would have to be rewritten in a less compact style and some of the terms would have to be defined. On the other hand, the second article (pages 191-200) is written in such an easy, full style and is so amply illustrated that it could be read, without change, to practically any audience.

EXERCISES AND ASSIGNMENTS

A. Prepare the agenda for a six-man conference on some campus problem, such as
   1. The menu offered by the dining halls
   2. Ways to raise funds for hiring a "name" band for a dance
   3. Noise in the dormitories
   4. A code of ethics for political campaigning

B. Prepare your part in a panel discussion of the opportunities and responsibilities in your profession, or a discussion of one of the topics suggested above in A.

C. Prepare an oral report on some aspect of campus life, such as
   1. The intramural sports program
   2. The library facilities
   3. The dining facilities
   4. The jobs open to students

D. Prepare a five-minute speech on your favorite hobby.

E. Write a professional society paper to be delivered before your class. It is not to be less than six minutes nor more than eight in length. Use visual aids and invite questions at the end. Choose a subject of which you have first-hand knowledge or on which you have done extensive reading.

Illustrative Material

Because of the masses of statistics and the complexity of many things with which the technical man works, he continually needs to express himself through tables and figures. On occasion they are as much a part of his vocabulary as words are. They serve four important purposes:

1. They show what words cannot show quickly and accurately.
2. They confirm and reinforce words that are used.
3. They make description and comparisons vivid.
4. They help the writer to organize and define his knowledge.

TABLES

A table is two or more columns of written data. The data are usually in numerical form, but phrase tables—tables in which the columns consist of words—are not infrequent and are rather striking when used with discrimination.

Function and Types

Although tables add to the appearance of a paper, their main function is to present data in an accurate, concise, and easily readable form—to save space and time with no loss of accuracy. For example, the principal features of a steam generating unit can be described in the text and, to conserve space, the dimensions of its various parts can be listed in a table. Tables are also an excellent means of juxtaposing data about two or more subjects to permit quick comparison. For instance, the results of time-and-motion studies made in several departments can be tabulated so that the eye picks up the comparisons instantly.

Tables make it unnecessary for us to stuff paragraphs full of statistics, so that their significance is lost and the reader ends up more mystified than informed. They enable us to draw comparisons without tediously repeating words and sentence patterns.

Tables can be classified as dependent and independent. The former are also called "informal" and "text tables"; the latter, "formal."

A dependent table is not set off from the text but is a continuation of it. The table has no number, title, or legend but depends wholly on the text for identification. It has only three or four columns and eight or ten lines at most. It frequently completes a sentence and is introduced by a colon. The example given below shows the percentage of time that the engineers in a certain company devote to company projects either assigned to them or elected by them:

	Assigned	*Elected*
Company time	62	38
Own time	7	14

An independent table is separated noticeably from the text and is intelligible without extrinsic comment, though the text may point up its significance and explain some of its details more fully. The table has a number, a title and, if helpful, an explanatory legend. An example of an independent table and the text and citation preceding it follows.

The records show that absences were again more numerous during this period than during any of the other three quarters. As in past years, the increase can be attributed to the bad weather, which caused sickness and interfered with traffic.

Table 1

ABSENCES DURING LAST QUARTER 1957
MANUFACTURING DEPARTMENT

(Figures represent man-days lost)

| | PRODUCTION | | | |
Cause	*Component Development*	*Assembly*	*Shipping*	*Quality Control*
Accidents †	0	1	1	0
Family affairs *	3	4	2	0
Illness	18	26	22	11
Personal business	0	0	2	1
Weather	9	17	18	4
Unexplained	0	0	2	0
Totals	30	48	47	16
Grand total	141			

† On company property.
* Includes illness other than of employee himself.

The example shows the parts of an independent table seen most often. Below, the table is reproduced in skeletal form with the names of these parts given.

Label
Title

Subtitle
(Legend)

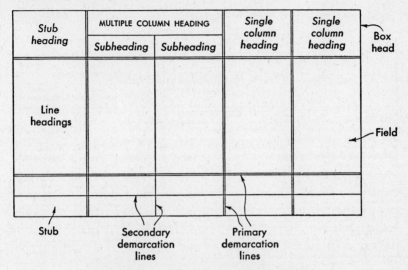

FIGURE 6   Parts of an Independent Table

These tables exemplify the closed type, in which the body is framed by vertical and horizontal lines. In the semi-closed form the vertical lines are omitted. In an open table no lines appear, although it is still distinguished from a dependent table by being set off from the text and having a label and title.

Preparation

Both the appearance and the effect of a table are improved if we observe a few simple principles. To some extent these principles apply to dependent tables as well as independent, but it is the latter type they concern primarily.

1. Plan ahead for the table.

As noted earlier, a table is either an actual part of the text or an important complement of it. Accordingly, we should prepare for each table, and not merely insert it as an afterthought when the text is complete. We should word the text to anticipate it and, before continuing with the writing, we should sketch in the table. If we postpone all work on it until the text is finished, we have a much harder job of smoothly integrating it with the discussion. Moreover, we have

CHARACTERISTICS OF CONTACT AND CLEARANCE TYPE
OF SEALED BEARINGS

SEAL TYPE	RELATIVE FRICTION CHARACTERISTICS	RELATIVE SEAL EFFICIENCY		
		GREASE RETENTION	WET CONTAMINANT EXCLUSION	DRY CONTAMINANT EXCLUSION
Felt Rubbing-Type Seal (Fig. 1a)	Moderate	Very Good	Fair	Fair
Felt Rubbing Labyrinth Seal (Fig. 1b)	High	Excellent	Fair	Good
Double Felt Rubbing Seal (Fig. 1c)	High	Excellent	Fair	Excellent
Removable Notch Rubbing-Type Seal (Fig. 1d)	Moderate	Excellent	Very Good	Excellent
Fixed Notch Rubbing-Type Seal (Fig. 1e)	Moderate	Good	Fair	Good
Spring Loaded Lip-Type Seal (Fig. 1f)	High	Excellent	Excellent	Excellent
Simple Plate Shield (Fig. 2a)	Nil	Fair	Poor	Poor
Metal Slinger Labyrinth-Type Seal (Fig. 2b)	Nil	Good	Fair	Fair

FIGURE 7   Independent Phrase Table

Michael T. Monich and Carter T. Bragdon (New Department Division, General Motors Corporation), "Properties of Integral Seal Ball Bearings and Their Use by the Engineer," *General Motors Engineering Journal,* 4:3 (July-August-September 1957), 11.

passed up the chief service that a table renders the author himself— the sharpening of his thoughts on a subject before he writes about it.

2. Choose the most suitable place for the table.

The ideal place is in the midst of the discussion to which it pertains and slightly above the center of the page. It is convenient to refer to and looks best there. But of course the ideal is not always practicable, and we often have to put it lower on the page. If there is not room for the entire table on the same page with the discussion or if it is a full-page display, it belongs on the page immediately following the pertinent text. When a table is referred to throughout several pages, it is best placed on or after the last one because reference is easier for the reader when he turns pages forward rather than backward.

The rule, then, is to put tables in the text itself. In magazine articles there are no exceptions, but in reports there are two. A table to be consulted throughout a report is better in an appendix than at the beginning because, again, the reader will be turning pages forward instead of backward. A long table, covering several pages, is also better in an appendix, where it does not create a lengthy break in the discussion. A shorter one, summarizing the main points of the long one, can be put at the appropriate place in the text.

3. Select the data with care.

Choosing between what should go into a table and what should not is far from an easy job. On the one hand, we must remember that the principal object of a table is to offer statistics in a form that can be easily read. We defeat that object at the outset if the table is complicated by too many items and too many details about them. Rather than overload a single table, we should divide the material and present it as two or three simplified ones.

On the other hand, an independent table should be literally independent. True, its import is nearly always stressed in the text, and quite often the textual discussion is woven around it; but the relationship should never be reversed: the text should not be essential to an understanding of the table.

4. Identify the table and its parts.

Because an independent table should be understandable without reference to the discussion, we should clearly identify it and all its data. It should have a label and a title. The label is the word *Table* plus a number that distinguishes the table from any others in the paper.

The title tells what the table shows. It should be worded concisely and either capitalized as a literary title or written in all capitals.

The label and the title may be placed above or below the table, but their position should be consistent throughout a given paper. If a subtitle or a legend is used, it goes underneath the title. Footnotes, of course, go below the table. When they are necessary, the other identification material looks better above the table. Footnotes should be cited by symbols rather than by figures or letters that can be misread as part of the data.

Whether or not to employ a subtitle, legend, headnotes, and footnotes is a question that rests solely on necessity. Every factor needed for an accurate and thorough interpretation of the data should be stated: the time and place to which the data pertain, the units in which they are given, any special circumstances that affect them, and reference to the text or any other source that might add to their use-fulness. When such explanatory devices are employed, they should be kept as brief as clarity permits.

5. Make the table large enough to prevent crowding.

We can select the data wisely and identify them clearly and still have a table that is difficult to read because it is so small that the lines and the columns run together. There should be enough white space between the lines and between the columns for the eye to follow any one of them without being sidetracked to an adjacent one. In more detailed tables demarcation lines are helpful—double lines to separate the different bodies of data, single lines for interior rows and columns. In a long table having no distinct groupings, primary demarcation lines after every fifth row facilitate the reading.

By using abbreviations freely we can also increase the white space. Standard abbreviations are safest but others are permissible if they are self-explanatory.

6. Arrange the data in a logical pattern.

A table should be constructed so that the statistics presented verti-cally are read from top to bottom and those presented horizontally are read from left to right. It is customary for the first column on the left, called the stub, to give the independent variable—such as time, equip-ment, or the objects being compared—and for the other columns to give the dependent variables, such as temperature and gauge readings, costs, or performance data. If a table is wider than it is long and must be put at a right angle to the page, the top should be on the inside margin; in other words, before the reader adjusts the page so that the stub is in its proper position on his left, the stub forms the bottom margin.

The entries in the stub should follow some logical arrangement; for example, they can read from the most important item to the least important, from the most expensive object to the least expensive, or from the largest group to the smallest. When there is no other basis for a systematic arrangement, the entries can appear in their alpha-betical order.

Each line and column should be designated by a word or a phrase that indicates the nature of the data comprising it. To save space and avoid repetition, we can include additional information, such as the unit of measurement or the temperature scale, in the heading instead of in the row or column. By putting this information in the headings, we also ensure that comparisons are made on the same basis, a requisite if the comparisons are to be valid.

The totality of impression, which is one of the features of a table, is weakened when the table is interrupted and part of it is carried to another page. If possible, therefore, we should not divide a table. When we are forced to do so, we should use the same scale on the second page we used on the first and should repeat every column heading, even those under which the data are not resumed. At the bottom of the first page and the top of the second, we indicate the continuation of the table.

7. Cite each table.

Unless we specifically cite a table, there is always the risk that a reader will be unaware of its existence at the time he needs to consult it. The form of the citation is variable. It may be simply "See Table 3 below" enclosed in parentheses. It may be a phrase woven into the sentence: "as may be seen in the following table" or "as shown in Table 3 on page 16." It may be a separate sentence in the paragraph: "See Appendix A for details."

If the table does not appear on the page with the citation, we should give the page number, at least on the first reference. Even when they are on the same page, we reduce the chance of the table being overlooked by giving its location.

FIGURES

A figure presents data in a form that is primarily nonverbal. Words may be included to assist in its interpretation, but fundamentally it is a graphic representation.

Function and Types

Sometimes illustrations are used to "dress up" a piece of writing; they add little or nothing to the text but are inserted to attract notice. Their use in this way is common in magazine articles written for popular appeal and in reports going to lay stockholders. Even in these, illustrations should never be used simply to pad an otherwise thin paper or to cover up lazy writing.

In more specialized articles and reports, figures should be strictly functional. This means that they should be informative and supplement the text, making a recognizable contribution to it. They can serve this purpose in either of two ways: they can act as a visual summary of what has been detailed in the text, or they can show particulars that are passed over in the discussion. An example of the first function would be a photograph showing the general features of a cyclotron described at length in the text; an example of the second function would be a drawing of the cyclotron showing its parts and their dimensions.

Figures can be divided into two basic categories: charts and pictures.

CHARTS. A chart is a table in pictorial form. As a matter of fact, a careful writer sets his data down first as a table and then translates it into a chart. Their purpose is identical: to present statistics in such a way that they can be grasped quickly.

The only real difference is that tables are more exact and are therefore preferable when extreme accuracy is desired. Charts are more effective for showing round totals, trends, direction, and distribution and for dramatizing comparisons. Often the two are employed in combination—a table, let us say, giving an item-by-item breakdown of the operating costs of five departments and a chart comparing the total costs of the same departments.

The most common type of chart is the *line chart,* or graph. It is made by plotting points on a framework of parallel lines, called a grid, and then connecting these points by an index line to show continuity of the data. It has two scales: a horizontal one, called the abscissa, and a vertical one, called the ordinate. The ordinate rises from the left end of the abscissa, although it can be repeated on the right side to expedite reference. Generally, an independent variable is plotted on the horizontal scale and a dependent one on the vertical.

Theoretically, each scale should begin at zero, the zero being placed where the two scales intersect. Sometimes this is impossible. For example, one of the scales, usually the abscissa, may represent a variable where zero value is meaningless. An instance would be years during which censuses were taken. Or one of the scales, usually the ordinate, may assume meaning only at values far above zero and yet the difference in these values is not great. An instance would be costs that begin at a million or more dollars.

To solve these problems, we must do one of two things: either we can put some value higher than zero at the point where the scales intersect, or we can break the scale. That is, we can start the scale at zero and then depict a fracture that represents all the values between zero and the first one drawn after it on the scale.

The values of each scale should be chosen carefully because the calibration directly affects the rise and fall of the line drawn between the points. And the movement of this line, in turn, affects the reader's impression. A sharp rise or fall suggests an important change; a gradual rise or fall suggests an unimportant one.

ACTIVITY OF EMPLOYMENT OFFICE
FIRST HALF OF 1959

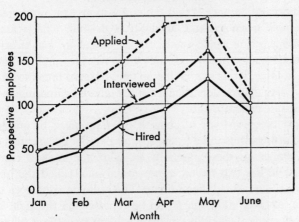

FIGURE 8   Multiple Line Chart

The line may go from point to point and be more or less jagged, it may go through the middle of the space between the points and be straight, or it may move through or near the points in such a way as to form a smooth curve. The last two patterns are less accurate than the first one, but they are useful for indicating a general trend or for extrapolating—that is, showing a possible future trend on the basis of a past and present one.

A multiple line chart, depicting data about related units, has more than one index line. The lines should be carefully identified and should be distinguished from each other by being differently colored or designed. A single chart should not have more than three or four index lines if the reading is to be kept easy.

The *surface chart* is a variation of the line chart. It is used to show the cumulative total of two or more components. Attention is drawn to the area between the index lines instead of to the lines themselves.

A surface chart is made by shading or crosshatching the areas between index lines so that the areas are markedly differentiated. The shading is darkest in the bottom area and becomes progressively lighter in the zones above. Surface charts are impractical when the index lines cross each other or when their patterns are extremely divergent.

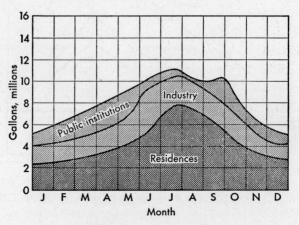

WATER CONSUMPTION 1959

FIGURE 9   Surface Chart

The *bar chart* emphasizes comparisons. Units are represented by bars of the same width but of varying length. The chart has three forms: the bars can extend horizontally from the left-hand scale, vertically from the bottom scale, or to both sides of the ordinate. To compare different parts of the units as well as the whole units, we shade different portions of the bars accordingly.

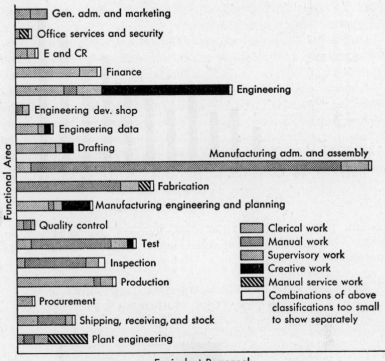

DISTRIBUTION OF PERSONNEL

FIGURE 10   Horizontal Bar Chart

Arthur F. Maynard, "Automation for Small-lot Producers." Reprinted from *Automation* (March 1958), a Penton publication.

In magazine articles a popular variant of the bar chart is the *pictorial chart*. Instead of bars to represent the units, drawings of the units themselves are shown, each picture standing for a specified amount. For instance, one man represents 200 man-hours and one freight car represents 500 tons transported. Partial amounts are shown

PERCENT OF SHIP STRUCTURE COMMITTEE RESEARCH FUNDS SPENT ON FUNDAMENTAL RESEARCH EACH YEAR SINCE 1946

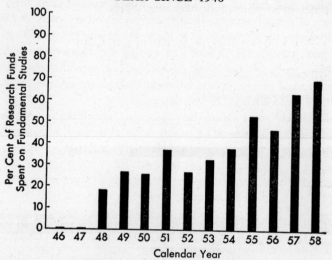

FIGURE 11   Vertical Bar Chart

David K. Felbeck, "Today's Trend in Ship Research." Reprinted from the *Welding Journal Research Supplement* (June 1958), published by the American Welding Society.

RELATIONSHIP BETWEEN MANUAL DEXTERITY TEST AND OPERATORS' PERFORMANCE

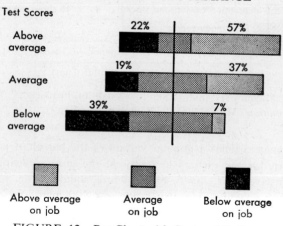

FIGURE 12   Bar Chart with Centered Ordinate

by partial pictures; one fourth of a man's image would mean 50 man-hours, and half of a freight car would indicate 250 tons. For purposes of comparison the images are presented in rows. Occasionally, however, the comparison is made by having the images of different size, though the difficulty of getting the proportions accurate makes this form unreliable except for rough approximations. In fact, neither form of pictorial chart is precise enough for reports or articles other than those intended for popular appeal.

A *directional chart* shows the course that something follows during a process—for instance, the route of material through a factory, from its entering as raw goods until its leaving as a finished product. The movement is indicated by arrows, and the various stages may be represented by labeled boxes or by drawings. More explicitly, this type of chart is called a *flowsheet*.

CONTINUOUS METHOD OF TREATING SPENT SOLUBLE OIL
EMULSIONS WITH ALUMINUM SULFATE, CAUSTIC
AND SULFURIC ACID

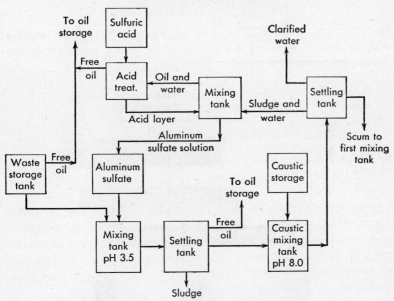

FIGURE 13   Directional Chart: Flowsheet

Reprinted from the Texas Company's *Lubrication*, 43:4 (April 1957), 47.

The *organizational chart*, another form of the directional chart, shows the line of authority in an organization. The titles of the men or the names of the departments are printed in boxes. The general reading is from top to bottom, with equal functions drawn to the left and right. Direct relationships are indicated by solid lines connecting the boxes, indirect relationships by broken lines.

THE INSPECTION ORGANIZATION

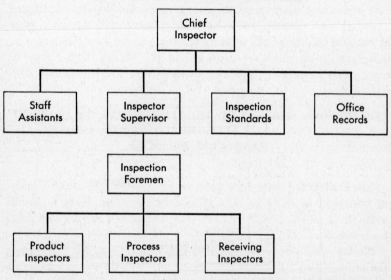

FIGURE 14   Directional Chart: Organizational Type

R. C. Davis, *Industrial Organization and Management.* Copyright, 1928, 1940 by Harper & Brothers.

The *circle chart,* known also as the pie chart, is excellent for showing relative percentages. The circle is marked off in more or less wedge-like slices. These are labeled and proportioned to suggest how much of the whole the unit named by the label represents. Because its shape is the same as that of a silver dollar, the circle chart is frequently used to show the distribution of money.

PICTURES.   The other category of figures comprises photographs, drawings, diagrams, and maps. Their common merit is that they simplify passages of explication and description.

MAJOR COLLEGE EXPENSES
OF A STUDENT

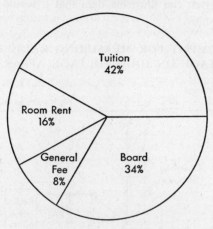

FIGURE 15   Circle Chart

The *photograph* is superior when we want to give the actual likeness of an object or show an actual place or condition. It is especially valuable as proof of what we have said. The reader can see and judge for himself.

Photographs, however, have their limitations. One is that they show the unimportant as well as the important. This objection can sometimes be eliminated by blanking out background material or by retouching the film to bring out the high lights. Another limitation is that photographs have to be taken here and now; they cannot be created from our notes, as other figures can. The picture of a working model has to be taken before the model is torn down, that of one stage of a job before the next stage supersedes it. A third limitation is that a photograph can show only the exterior of its subject. It cannot reveal what lies beneath the surface. To overcome this disadvantage, we can use the photograph in conjunction with a drawing that discloses what the photograph does not.

This is the special virtue of the *drawing* and the *diagram*: they can reveal the interior. The two words are used interchangeably. If there is any difference in their connotation, it is that a drawing gives a visual likeness of its subject and a diagram shows its operation. Not only can they show the inside of a thing as well as the outside, but they can reveal them simultaneously when we wish. Thus a single drawing or diagram can illustrate data that it would require several photographs to show.

TEST EQUIPMENT FOR MEASURING RADIO-INFLUENCE VOLTAGE ON HIGH-VOLTAGE APPARATUS

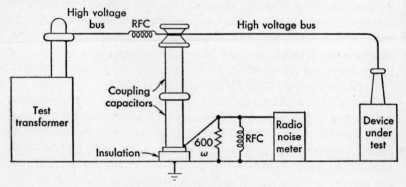

FIGURE 16   Drawing or Diagram

Reprinted from the Westinghouse *Engineer*, 18:3 (May 1958), 73.

There are three general kinds of *maps*. The most common is a location map, showing the location of a place or several places under discussion. Such maps should be drawn to scale, especially if distances between points are germane to the discussion.

A physical map shows the natural features of an area, such as hills, valleys, and water. It can include soil strata and stream soundings.

A distribution map reveals the distribution of the units being discussed, such as a product, dealer outlets, or mineral deposits. Dots or drawings of the units can indicate the distribution. Such things as population density and temperature range can be shown by shading or crosshatching the different areas.

Preparation

Besides what has already been said about the make-up of the specific types of figures, we might note a few general rules to follow in preparing them. Illustrations in articles and reports that are to be printed or reproduced in some other way require special treatment and are usually turned over to professionals. Our only concern at present, therefore, is the typed report.

1. Integrate the figure and the text.

We observed earlier that a figure should not be merely ornamental. It should be functional, either summarizing what has been explained in the text or expanding on details only alluded to in the discussion. To perform either function smoothly, the figure should be prepared before the text is written. Then we shall have a clear image of it in mind as we write, and the discussion and illustration will mesh automatically. Further, we shall know exactly how much we can show in the figure and therefore how much we need to explain in the text.

2. Choose the best place for the figure and cite it.

What is true of tables is also true of figures: as a rule, the best place for them is in the part of the discussion to which they pertain and, when feasible, a little above the middle of the page. A half inch or more of white space should set them off from the text that precedes and follows them. Preferably the illustration should extend from the left margin to the right. When this is impractical it should be centered between the margins. In books and magazines we often see a figure, particularly an elongated one, placed against one margin and the text continued alongside it, but on a typed page this arrangement is difficult and usually unattractive. If an illustration must be put sideways on a page, the bottom should be to the right before the page is turned from its normal position.

When a figure is referred to on several pages, it should be put on or after the last one. Likewise, an illustration referred to throughout the text is best placed in an appendix.

There are other times when it is better to put illustrative material in an appendix than in the body. Figures that are tangential to the main subject should be relegated to an appendix. An example is photographs of two or three models of a machine that were tested and found unsatisfactory before the successful model, which the report concerns, was built. Illustrations that fill several consecutive pages should be made an appendix to avoid spreading out the text—for instance, diagrams showing various stages in a process or graphs giving readings taken at successive intervals.

Last, folded material belongs in an appendix. If we attach it to one of the text pages, it gives the report an ungainly look and hampers the turning of the pages. We eliminate both objections if we put it in a large envelope glued to the inside of the back cover. Even there the appearance and the handling of the report will be awkward if the material is too bulky. Rather than have one large, cumbersome drawing or photograph we should reduce the size of the master illustration and show the details in drawings or photographs of the separate parts.

Every figure, whether in the text or an appendix, should be cited. If it appears on a different page from the citation, its location should be given.

3. Do not clutter the figure.

Besides spoiling the appearance of an illustration, too much detail can impede its being understood. Only what is important should be shown. Any details that add nothing to the discussion should be omitted. Point-by-point plotting of a graph, for instance, is unnecessary if our intention is to give a general impression; curves are just as reliable and look much better. Minute readings usually serve no purpose on physical maps, and places that have no bearing on the subject do not belong on a location map. Irrelevant background should be excluded from photographs.

Sometimes the cluttered effect is not the result of too many details but of the figure being too small. Since economy of space means nothing in a typed manuscript, we should not hesitate to give half a page or a full page to a figure in order that it be clear.

4. Identify the figure and its parts.

Above or below the illustration, or inside if space permits, there should be a label and a title. The label is the word *Figure* and a number. Figures are numbered independently of tables; thus the illustrative material in a paper might read: Figure 1, Figure 2, Table 1, Figure 3, Table 2.

The title should be brief but descriptive. Even though the figure and the text are tied closely together, the figure should still be comprehensible by itself. The title should make clear what it represents, and any other necessary information should be supplied in a subtitle, legends, and keys.

A key is a word or phrase that names a part or indicates its function. The keys may be inside the figure, placed in or adjacent to the parts and, whenever practical, in a horizontal position. Or they may be in a group to themselves. In this arrangement the word or phrase is placed opposite a number, a letter, or a color that corresponds to one marking a part of the figure. The group may be put beneath the illustration or, if it will cause no crowding, inside the border.

5. Use black as the basic color.

Nearly all technical journals require that black ink, preferably India ink, be employed for the basic parts of charts, drawings, and diagrams; it is also the practice in report writing. Other colors can show different motifs in the figure, but black should be used for the border, the main lines, and the captions.

6. Enclose each figure by a border unless it is self-defined.

On typing paper a figure loses some of its perspective if its outline is not distinct. To keep it from flowing off into white space, we can put a border around it. A border is unnecessary if the figure outlines itself, as it does in photographs, circle charts, line charts on printed graph paper, and figures taken from a published source.

EXERCISES AND ASSIGNMENTS

A. The following sentences give data obtained from tests conducted by a large paper producer. The data concern the moisture content (expressed in percentages) and the unit weight (expressed in pounds per cubic foot) of waste wood as it was received at the mill. Make a table of the data.

1. Drum Barker (pressed) had a moisture content of 63.4 and weight of 19.3.
2. Hemlock had a weight of 19.4 and moisture content of 53.7.
3. Douglas fir had a weight of 17.4 and moisture content of 44.4.
4. Regular paper mill waste wood had a moisture content of 56.9 and weight of 21.5.

B. Present the data concerning moisture content as a bar chart.
C. Assume that the total enrollment in a certain engineering school is 5414 and that it is distributed among the departments as follows:

Aeronautical 446
Chemical 518
Civil 803
Electrical 1780
Mechanical 1867

Present these statistics as a circle chart.
D. Present the performance data in the following table as a multiple line chart.

Speed (in rpm)	Brake horsepower	Fuel (lb per hr)	Friction torque (lb-ft)
400	17	9	24
800	39	21	26
1200	60	33	30
1600	82	45	34
2000	104	57	40
2400	125	67	48
2800	139	75	56
3200	148	83	64
3600	152	88	72
4000	148	90	80

MANUAL OF GENERAL COMPOSITION

The following discussion reviews the problems that come up most frequently in writing. For more detailed study the student should consult a handbook devoted entirely to general composition.

The grammatical terms used in the discussion are explained on pages 313-318.

GRAMMAR

Nouns

NUMBER

1. The majority of nouns pluralize by adding *s*.

cylinder	cylinders
employee	employees
fuse	fuses
motor	motors
Brown	Browns
Stone	Stones

Note: Special care should be taken not to omit the *s* for the plural of a word ending with a sibilant.

blast	blasts
desk	desks
flask	flasks
scientist	scientists
specialist	specialists
test	tests

2. If the addition of the *s* creates a glide sound between the stem and the *s*, the plural is formed with *es*.

box	boxes
bunch	bunches
gas	gases
latch	latches
Williams	Williamses

3.a. Words ending in *y* pluralize in the normal way by adding *s* if the *y* follows a vowel or if the word is a person's name.

alloy	alloys
clay	clays
pulley	pulleys
Kelly	Kellys
McKinley	McKinleys

b. Words ending in *y* pluralize by changing the *y* to *i* and adding *es* if the *y* follows a consonant and the word is not a person's name.

accessory	accessories
property	properties
supply	supplies
January	Januaries

4. A few nouns have the same form for the plural as for the singular.

apparatus (or apparatuses), chassis, forceps, gross, means, series, species

5. Many nouns have an irregular plural, and some have both an irregular and a regular form. In the latter instance one form is often preferable to the other in certain senses. The safest practice is to consult a dictionary for the specific usage.

analysis	analyses	
antenna	antennae	antennas
appendix	appendices	appendixes
axis	axes	
criterion	criteria	criterions
curriculum	curricula	curriculums
datum	data	
draftsman	draftsmen	
formula	formulae	formulas
half	halves	
life	lives	
medium	media	mediums
phenomenon	phenomena	phenomenons
radius	radii	radiuses
stratum	strata	stratums
wharf	wharves	wharfs

6.a. Most compound nouns pluralize by changing the final element.

circuit breaker	circuit breakers
cylinder head	cylinder heads

drill press	drill presses
instrument panel	instrument panels
journal box	journal boxes
pound-foot	pound-feet
right of way	right of ways

b. The first element of a compound noun is pluralized when that element designates a person.

attorney at law	attorneys at law
director of information	directors of information
engineer-in-charge	engineers-in-charge
notary public	notaries public
son-in-law	sons-in-law

CASE

In connection with nouns, the subjective (nominative) and the objective (accusative) cases offer no problems because the form is the same for both and it is the form in which the word is entered in dictionaries. Accordingly, our present interest is in the possessive case only.

1.a. The possessive case of a singular noun is usually formed by adding an apostrophe and an *s* to the stem.

Benson's plan, the supervisor's duty, Jones's office

b. If the additional *s* would cause unpleasant sibilance either in the word itself or between it and the word that follows, only the apostrophe is added.

Sessoms' job, Archimedes' principle, Jones' suggestion

2.a. Plural nouns ending in *s* form the possessive by adding only the apostrophe.

the Bensons' plan, both supervisors' duty, the Joneses' office

b. Irregular plurals add the apostrophe and *s*.
the alumni's part, the children's room, the workmen's task

3. Joint ownership is shown by the ending of the last word; separate ownership by the ending of each word.

Drexel and Cobb's new buildings (one firm)
Drexel's and Cobb's new buildings (two firms)

the managers and assistant managers' duties
(duties common to both groups)
the managers' and the assistant managers' duties
(separate duties for the two groups; repetition of *the* emphasizes the distinction)

4.a. As a general rule, nouns designating objects without animal life
should show possession by an *of* or *in* phrase rather than by the
apostrophe.

the strength of the chemical—not: the chemical's strength
the valves in the engine—not: the engine's valves
the accuracy of the data—not: the data's accuracy
the leaves of the oak—not: the oak's leaves

b. Certain exceptions are common.

Time expressions: three months' work
Monetary expressions: a thousand dollars' worth
Distance phrases: a three blocks' drive
Things made up of people:
  the company's payroll
  New York's tax rate
  General Motors' expansion
The proper name of manufactured objects:
  the Ford's ignition system
  the Crosley's cabinet
  the B52's performance

Pronouns

CASE

The case forms of the personal pronouns are given in the table below.
They are arranged according to person.

Singular

	SUBJECTIVE	POSSESSIVE	OBJECTIVE
1st	I	my, mine	me
2nd	you	your, yours	you
3rd	he	his	him
	she	her, hers	her
	it	its	it

Plural

	SUBJECTIVE	POSSESSIVE	OBJECTIVE
1st	we	our, ours	us
2nd	you	your, yours	you
3rd	they	their, theirs	them

For the relative pronoun *who,* the subjective is *who,* the possessive *whose,* and the objective *whom.* The form of other pronouns is not affected by case except that all of the indefinite pronouns add an apostrophe and *s* to show possession.

1. The subjective case is used for
   a. The subject of a verb
      You and *I* have been assigned the job.
      He is the chemist that *we* hired recently.
   b. A subjective complement
      It is *they* who are delaying the work, not *we.*
2. The possessive case is used
   a. To show ownership
      It is *her* notebook.
      Their guarantee is more comprehensive than *ours.*
   b. To indicate the subject of a gerund
      The manager forbade *their* leaving early.
   Note 1: The possessive is not used if another pronoun or a noun comes between the gerund and its subject.
      The manager forbade *anybody* in the office leaving early.
   Note 2. The possessive is not used when the emphasis is on the agent rather than the act.
      The manager saw *them* leaving early.
3. The objective case is used
   a. For the object of a verb or a verbal
      The blow struck *him* in the chest. (direct object of verb)
      We are going to award *them* the contract.
         (indirect object of verbal)
   b. For the object of a preposition
      The letter is addressed to *us.*
   c. For the subject, the object, and the objective complement of an infinitive.
      We asked *them* to work overtime.
      I want to see *him* at once.
      I assumed *it* to be *him.*

4. An apostrophe is not used to form the possessive case of any personal pronoun. This rule should be especially remembered in connection with *its*, which is often confused with *it's* (*it is*).

The notebook is *hers*.

The company has *its* own insurance department.

5. The object of a preposition that follows the subject is not attracted into the subjective case.

Several of *us* new men needed fuller instructions.

6. The case of a relative pronoun is determined by its use in its own clause.

You are the one *who* I believe can do the job best.

(*Who* is the subject of *can do*. The parenthetical *I believe*, which could be set off in commas, has no effect on it.)

Give the copy to *whoever* calls for it.

(*Whoever* is the subject of *calls*. The object of *to* is the whole clause.)

Whomever you name will be satisfactory with us.

(*Whomever* is the object of *name*. The subject of *will be* is the clause.)

7. The *-self* and *-selves* forms of a pronoun are used to intensify the antecedent or to show reflexive action. It is a questionable practice to use them as substitutes for the regular subjective and objective forms.

Correct (intensively): Smith *himself* is at fault.

Correct (reflexively): Smith blames *himself*.

Questionable: You and *myself* are to be in charge.

The responsibility has been given to *ourselves*.

AGREEMENT

1. A pronoun agrees with its antecedent in person, number, and gender but not necessarily in case.

Mrs. Nixon was praised for *her* work.

The city has not submitted *its* estimate.

The clerks have said that *they* want a five-day week.

Every man has punched *his* time card.

2. A pronoun is plural when it has two or more antecedents joined by *and*.

Maxton and Lounes say that the new arrangement suits *them*.

3. A pronoun is singular when it has singular antecedents joined by *or* or *nor*.

The chief engineer or an assistant must give *his* approval.

4. When a pronoun has antecedents differing in number and joined by *or* or *nor*, it agrees with the nearer one.

Either the motor or the pumps must have *their* annual overhauling this month.

Neither the pumps nor the motor is performing as *it* should.

5. A pronoun is singular when its antecedent is an indefinite pronoun, even though the meaning may be plural.

No one is expected to do more than is asked of *him*.

Somebody has lost *his* pen.

Does everybody understand when *he* is to return?

6. A singular pronoun is used to refer to a collective noun when the group is considered as a unit.

The company plans to expand *its* holdings.

The Green team has already passed *its* quota.

The Green team were assigned *their* individual quotas.

Better: The members of the Green team were assigned *their* individual quotas.

REFERENCE

The antecedent of a pronoun should be clear at once. In specific, we should guard against the faults listed below.

1. Ambiguous reference. A pronoun should not be used in such a way that either of two words can be read as its antecedent.

Vague: The platform will extend along the rear of the building, *which* is only 100 feet from the railroad.

Clear: The platform will extend along the rear of the building. The rear (or The building) is only 100 feet from the railroad.

2. General reference. A pronoun should not refer to a whole idea if a single word can be misread as its antecedent.

Vague: If the tank is patched, *it* will reduce the losses.

Clear: If the tank is patched, the losses will be reduced.

Clear: Patching the tank will reduce the losses.

Clear: The wires are soldered together before they are inserted; *this* saves considerable time.

(*This* refers to the preceding statement, but it is clear because the statement contains no singular noun that could be mistaken for the antecedent.)

3. Implied reference. The antecedent of a pronoun should not be a word merely suggested by another.

Vague: Because my father is a combustion engineer, I have always been interested in *it*.

Clear: Because my father specializes in combustion engineering, I have always been interested in *it*.

4. Indefinite reference. *You* and *they* should not be used unless they have specific antecedents.

Doubtful: Delayed ignition occurs when *you* have a short circuit in *your* transformer.

Acceptable: Delayed ignition occurs when there is a short circuit in the transformer.

Doubtful unless the preceding remarks identify *they:*

A new era began when *they* finally split the atom.

Acceptable: A new era began when scientists finally split the atom.

5. Superfluous distinction. *His or her* should not be used to refer to an antecedent of common gender unless it is important to distinguish between the sexes. The masculine pronoun alone is usually sufficient.

Correct: Anybody can resign if *he* gives a month's notice.

Correct: Every person in the company will be asked to give *his* opinion after *he* has studied the new forms.

Correct: Each student was asked for *his or her* address.

Verbs

AGREEMENT

1. A verb agrees with its subject in person and number. Below is the declension of a regular verb in the most troublesome tense, the present.

	SINGULAR	PLURAL
1st person:	I work	we work
2nd person:	you work	you work
3rd person:	he, she, it works	they work

Errors occur most often in the singular of the 3rd person when the final *s* is omitted. It is especially easy to commit this error when the stem ends in a sibilant.

Model 103 *costs* more than 102.

A grille *masks* the front.

The timer *consists* of chains connected to a gear-reducer.

2. A verb is usually plural when it has compound subjects joined by *and*.

The transmission and the main driveshaft *need* repair.

Oaks and Dunn *are* business partners.

   a. A verb is singular if the compound subjects represent a single object.

      The first vice-president and chairman of the board *is* Mr. Parks.

      Oaks and Dunn *has* been given the work. (Name of firm)

   b. A verb is singular if the compound subjects are modified by *each* or *every*.

      Each stenographer, file clerk, and messenger *was* given a raise.

      Every coil and shield *has* been accounted for.

3. When compound subjects are joined by *or* or *nor,* the verb agrees with the subject nearer to it. For practical purposes this rule holds true whether the subjects are both singular, both plural, or different in number.

      Either the operator or the machine *is* at fault.

      Either the operators or the machines *are* at fault.

      Either the operator or the machines *are* at fault.

      Either the machines or the operator *is* at fault.

4. Words that separate the subject and the verb usually have no effect on the verb.

      The main factor, weather conditions, *is* in our favor.

      Weather conditions, the main factor, *are* in our favor.

      One of the causes of these frequent shutdowns *is* the age of the equipment.

Note: Words intervening between the subject and the verb affect the verb when they show whether the subject is singular or plural.

      Half of the men *have* reported.

      Half of the force *has* reported.

5. A subjective complement has no effect on the verb.

      The chief thing to discuss *is* ways to increase production.

6. When *there* is the subject of the verb, the number of the verb is determined by the first noun or pronoun that follows it and that is not in the possessive case.

      There *is* considerable rain in the summer.

      There *are* numerous storms in the summer.

      There *is* the men's attitude to consider.

7. When a relative pronoun is the subject of the verb, the number of the verb agrees with the number of the antecedent of the pronoun.

      They are the lubricants that *have* proved best.

      It is a practice of the employees that *has* existed for years.

8. When a collective noun is the subject, the verb is singular if the noun designates a unit, plural if the noun designates members of the unit.

   The group *was* larger than we expected.

   The group *were* told how to read their manuals.

9. A verb should not be omitted in the second part of a sentence unless it is identical in form to the verb in the first part.

   Questionable: The bumper *was* replaced and the fenders straightened.

   Acceptable: The bumper *was* replaced and the fenders *were* straightened.

   Acceptable: The bumper *was* replaced and the fender straightened.

Note: In more formal expression this principle is carried even further —the two verbs must be identical in function as well as form. That is, both must be main verbs or both must be auxiliaries.

   Questionable: The dynamo *will be* here tomorrow and *rewound* next week.

   Acceptable: The dynamo *will be* here tomorrow and *will be* rewound next week.

   Acceptable: The dynamo *will arrive* tomorrow and *be rewound* next week.

   Acceptable: Bradley *is* in Chicago and Donelli in New York.

10. When the word *number* is the subject of a verb, the verb is singular if *the* modifies *number* and plural if *a* modifies it.

    The number of absentees *is* small.

    A number of men *are* out today.

TENSE

Tense is the time relationship expressed by a verb.

1. The present tense is used (a) to describe an action occurring at the present moment (b) to describe a state existing at the present moment (c) to describe an action that recurs regularly although it may not be taking place at the present moment, and (d) to indicate a permanent truth.

   a. The stream *moves* swiftly through the gorge.

   b. The flywheel *needs* grease.

   c. The furnace *uses* coal.

   d. The earth *revolves* around the sun.

2. The past tense shows that an action was completed or a state existed before the time of speaking.

   We *submitted* our bid yesterday.

The flywheel *needed* grease.
3. The future tense indicates an action that has not yet occurred or a state that has not yet existed.
   We *shall submit* our bid later.
   The flywheel *will need* grease regularly.
4. The present perfect tense describes an action or a state that began before the time of speaking and continues up to it.
   We *have submitted* our bid.
   The flywheel *has needed* grease a long time.
5. The past perfect tense indicates an action that was completed or a state that existed before some other past action or state.
   We *had submitted* our bid before learning of the change.
   The flywheel *had needed* grease a long time.
(In the second example, what occurred afterward is left to implication: namely, the wheel has been greased by the time of speaking.)
6. The future perfect tense describes an action that will be completed or a state that will have existed by some specified time in the future.
   We *shall have submitted* our bid by the deadline.
   The flywheel *will have needed* grease before then.
7. The present infinitive is used with the past tense.
   We intended *to submit* our bid before now.
Not: We intended *to have submitted* our bid before now.

VOICE

1. The active voice is superior to the passive as long as the agent performing the action is as important as the one receiving it.
   The intense heat *melts* the tin quickly.
2. The passive voice is better when the agent receiving the action is of more interest in the particular context than the one performing it.
   The tin *is melted* quickly by the intense heat.
The passive voice is quite common in reports, especially formal ones, because pronouns of the first and second persons are generally frowned on and because the writer (the performing agent) is of less interest than what he is describing or recommending.

Adjectives and Adverbs

AGREEMENT

The adjectives *this-these, that-those* agree in number with the first noun that follows them.

this man's files   that kind of liquids
these men's files   those types of soils

DEGREE

Adjectives and adverbs have three grades of comparison: the positive, the comparative, and the superlative.

	POSITIVE	COMPARATIVE	SUPERLATIVE
	fast	faster	fastest
ADJECTIVES:	economical	more economical	most economical
		less economical	least economical
	good	better	best
	fast	faster	fastest
ADVERBS:	quickly	more quickly	most quickly
		less quickly	least quickly
	well	better	best

1. The positive degree is used when only a single unit or a single group is concerned.
   It is a *fast* automobile.
   The operators do their job *quickly*.
2. The comparative degree is used when one unit or group is compared with another unit or group, or several units or groups taken as a whole.
   This is a *faster* car than that one.
   This car is *faster* than the others.
   The operators work *more quickly* at the beginning of a shift (than at other times).
3. The superlative degree is used when one unit or group is compared with other units or groups taken separately.
   This is the *fastest* car on the market.
   The operators work *least quickly* near the end of a shift.
4. Certain adjectives and their adverbial forms can be used logically only in the positive degree. Some of them are *dead, perfect, round, square*, and *unique*.
   Colloquial: a more perfect job, a squarer box
   More logical: a more nearly perfect job, a more nearly square box

USAGE

1. An adjective modifies a noun or pronoun either directly or predicatively. In the latter position it is called a predicate adjective and

the adjective modifies the subject of the clause in which it appears.
The *tall brick* chimney has become *dangerous.*

2. An adverb can modify a verb, an adjective, another adverb, a clause or phrase used adverbially, or a whole sentence.

Verb: The chimney rocks *dangerously* in a strong wind.
Adjective: The support is *dangerously* weak.
Adverb: The engine is running *quite* smoothly.
Clause: It should be oiled *only* when it is idle.
Phrase: The primer is needed *only* in cold weather.
Sentence: *Naturally,* we are pleased by the news.

3. The adjectives *real, good, bad,* and *considerable* should not be used for the adverbs *really, well, badly,* and *considerably.*

Wrong: It is a *real* sound investment.
The feeder works *good* since it was overhauled.
The wood has warped *bad* in some places.
Our sales have been *considerable* better this month.

4. The use of *most* for *almost* is unacceptable except in highly informal writing.

Unacceptable: We inspect the boiler *most* every week.
He found *most* everybody satisfied.

5. Even though it follows the verb, an adjective is used to describe a condition pertaining to the subject of the verb.

We feel *bad* about this mistake.
The mixture smells *good.*
The second row is laid *horizontal* with the first one.
The plan has proved *satisfactory.*

Sentence Fragment

A sentence fragment is a part of a sentence that has been cut off from the rest of the sentence and treated as if it were an independent construction.

If placed judiciously an occasional sentence fragment is effective in a magazine article and oral communications, particularly as the answer to a question; but it should not be used in business letters and reports.

Objectionable: The circuit breakers should be replaced every 10 years. And at shorter intervals if they are housed in a damp place.

Acceptable in informal situations: Why was this danger not detected sooner? Because our method of inspection is antiquated.

PUNCTUATION AND OTHER MECHANICS

The purpose of punctuation marks and the other mechanical signals used in writing is to expedite the reader's grasping what we have to say. They are to writing what vocal inflection is to speaking: they show how we wish our ideas to be grouped and, to a less extent, what the relative emphasis on them should be.

Today's trend is toward using as little punctuation as is practical, toward constructing sentences so clearly that they do not require much punctuation to be readily understood. Still, it is well for the writer to be familiar with the basic rules listed below and to be able to recognize the situations in which they apply.

Comma

With the possible exception of the period the comma is the most common mark of punctuation. It is also the weakest mark and accordingly is used to show where the shortest pauses are to be made. For the most part, the places for these pauses are now standardized; a writer should observe them—*and no others*. It is a mistake to put a comma wherever an automatic pause occurs. The reader will sense the pause for himself, and the superfluous comma only retards the reading.

1. A comma is generally used to separate independent clauses joined by a co-ordinating conjunction. The established co-ordinating conjunctions are *and, but, for, or,* and *nor;* but there is a growing tendency to include *so, yet,* and *whereas* in the group.

    Trains pass the school throughout the day, and the classes are interrupted continually.

    a. No comma follows the conjunction unless nonrestrictive material happens to follow it. The temptation to insert this unnecessary comma is especially strong when the conjunction is *but* or *yet.*

        Wrong: We have tried several plans, but, none of them has yielded good results.

        Correct: We have tried several plans, but, in my opinion, none of them has yielded good results.

    b. No comma is needed before the conjunction when it joins the two parts of a compound predicate.

        Trains pass the school throughout the day and interrupt the classes continually.

    c. No comma is needed when the conjunction joins dependent clauses.

This is the machine that we paid the most for and that has given us the most trouble.

d. The comma may be omitted when the clauses are short and closely connected in thought. Before *for* and *yet*, however, it should always appear.

It is raining but we shall go anyway.

We waited an hour, for the train was late.

2. A comma usually follows a phrase or dependent clause that precedes an independent clause.

To give optimum performance, the machine should be oiled every morning.

If our mechanics cannot locate the trouble, we must send the motor back to the factory.

The delay is costing us heavily, and unless the shipment arrives within the next week, we shall have to cancel the contract.

a. The comma is regularly omitted after prepositional phrases that are neither very long nor parenthetical (compare Rule 4), and it may be omitted after short clauses if the reading is still clear.

Throughout the summer we work only five days a week.

By the end of the week they should be back on schedule.

When the sluice is opened the pressure drops immediately.

b. The comma is omitted when the phrase or dependent clause follows the independent clause (unless Rule 4 applies).

The machine should be oiled every morning to give optimum performance.

We must send the motor back to the factory if our mechanics cannot locate the trouble.

The delay is costing us heavily, and we shall have to cancel the contract unless the shipment arrives within the next week.

3. A comma separates the items in a series.

We have inspected the main wheel, the drive shaft, and the differential.

a. Usage is divided with regard to the comma before the conjunction. The safest practice is to include it, for there are times when its omission can be confusing, as in these sentences:

He consulted two board directors, the business manager and the vice president. (Two men or four?)

Lines will connect New York and Boston, Philadelphia and

Washington and Richmond, Cincinnati and Cleveland and Chicago and Detroit. (Three lines or four?)

  b. The comma is omitted when a conjunction is used between all the members of the series.

One line will connect Philadelphia and Washington and Richmond.

4. Nonrestrictive material is set off by a comma if other punctuation precedes or follows it, and by two commas if no other punctuation precedes or follows it.

Nonrestrictive material is a clause, a phrase, or a word that does not limit (restrict) the meaning of the sentence. It contributes to the thought or the tone of the sentence, but the contribution is not essential to understanding the main idea. A simple test is to read the sentence without the material in question. If the main thought is unimpaired, the material is nonrestrictive and commas are called for.

Clause: The main office is at Twelfth and Tryon Streets, which are in the heart of the business district.

Clause: He is, I believe, one of their best salesmen.

Phrase: The temperatures may be varied, depending on the degree of viscosity desired.

Phrase: He is, in fact, one of their best salesmen.

Phrase: Hendricks, the head cashier, is handling the loan.

Word: Sales always decline during January and February; consequently, we have to lay off part of the help during those months.

Note: Sometimes it is quite difficult to determine whether material is or is not essential to understanding the thought, and the writer must take extreme care to ascertain and reflect the exact situation. Consider these sentences:

He took his seat by the door *which was open.*

The suggestion is in the report *which I just read.*

He questioned the watchman *who was on duty at the time.*

Whether a comma should set off the italicized clauses depends, respectively, on whether only one door, one report, or one watchman is involved. If only one is, the clause is nonrestrictive and requires a comma before it. But if the italicized material points out which door or report or watchman out of two or more possibilities is meant, the material is necessary and a comma would be misleading.

5. Restrictive material is not set off by commas.

This rule complements No. 4 and requires no further comment except to point out that as part of the general tendency to simplify punctuation, the comma is frequently not used with mildly parenthetical elements. Typical of such elements are the adverbs *also* and *too,* the conjunctive adverbs (except *however*) when they are closely related to the verb, and *I believe* or *I think* when inserted in a relative clause.

> The filter also needed cleaning.
>
> We expect him tonight; his supervisor is coming too.
>
> We do not have all the figures yet and must therefore postpone a decision.
>
> This is the brand that I believe will serve you best.

6. A comma separates two parallel adjectives or adverbs when they are not joined by a conjunction.

> He is an intelligent, conscientious worker.
>
> He is an intelligent and conscientious worker.
>
> It will be a bold, costly operation.
>
> It will be a bold but costly operation.
>
> The gears mesh smoothly, silently.
>
> The gears mesh smoothly and silently.

a. The comma is omitted if the adjectives or adverbs are not parallel.

A quick way to determine whether they are parallel is to insert *and* between them mentally. If the reading is smooth, they are parallel; if it is awkward they are not parallel. The comma is omitted in the following examples because *and* would give an unidiomatic reading.

> We entered a large brick building.
>
> At the side will be a long concrete platform.
>
> The job has been too carefully planned to fail.

b. No comma is used between an adverb and the adjective it modifies.

> The outlook is exceptionally good.
>
> It is a conveniently designed building.

7. Miscellaneous uses of the comma are:

a. To separate the day from the year when a date is given in the American form.

> Construction was begun on June 1, 1948 and was completed on November 8, 1951.

Note: A comma after the year is optional. It is also optional between the month and the year when no day is given. Commas are omitted when the date is given in the European style.

> in June 1948   in June, 1948   15 June 1948

b. To separate the different items in an address when they appear on the same line.

You can reach him at the Terrace Plaza Hotel, Cincinnati, Ohio.

He is from Sao Paulo, Brazil.

c. To facilitate the reading of sums comprised of more than four digits. A comma is placed before each third numeral, counting from the right. In numbers comprised of only four digits the comma may be omitted unless the number appears in a column having numbers that do require commas.

51,809   1,407,261,841   1841 or 1,841

d. To separate titles, degrees, and other abbreviations that follow a person's name.

Henry R. Boone, M.P., is to speak.

J. L. Ritter, Ph.D., has been hired.

Holmes J. Reid, Jr., is in charge.

Arnold Dunster, AIEE, is club secretary.

8. A comma may be used to prevent temporary misreading even though no specific rule calls for it.

In the future, models will be submitted six months in advance. (To prevent *future* being read as a modifier of *models*.)

The pipeline will pass under the inner basin, or the harbor proper. (To show that *inner basin* is being redesignated. Without the comma it would seem that alternate routes are being named.)

When he left, the company was still solvent. (To prevent *company* being read as the object of *left*.)

Semicolon

The semicolon indicates a fuller pause than the comma but a lesser one than a full stop (period, question mark, exclamation point).

1. The principal use of the semicolon is to separate independent clauses that are not joined by a conjunction.

We have tried several plans; none of them has yielded good results.

a. The semicolon is necessary even though the second clause is introduced by a conjunctive adverb or some other transitional term. These connectives serve *part* of the function of full-fledged conjunctions and are therefore deceptive; but since they do not connect the clauses as completely as conjunctions do, the semicolon —and not a comma—should be used.

We have tried several plans; however, none of them has yielded good results.

All of the materials have now arrived; therefore, we shall begin at once.

We can effect savings in several ways; for example, we can combine the shipping and the receiving departments.

We have two choices; namely, we can expand our present facilities or we can build a new laboratory.

At the moment the situation is static; in other words, there is no immediate danger.

Note: The semicolon marks the end of the first clause. It does not move if we move the transitional term.

We have tried several plans; none of them, however, has yielded good results.

b. A comma may be substituted for the semicolon provided the clauses are short and the second one is not introduced by a transitional term.

We tried two plans, neither worked.

We have one choice, we must expand.

But: We tried two plans; however, neither worked.

We have one choice; namely, we must expand.

2. The semicolon may be used between independent clauses even though they are connected by a conjunction (a) if we wish to emphasize the separation, (b) if either clause has several commas within it, or (c) if one clause in a series is to be given the same weight as the others combined.

a. The union leaders have agreed to negotiate; but I doubt that they will make any real concessions.

b. The company has assembly plants in Newark, Louisville, Atlanta, Denver, and San Francisco; and I understand it is planning to build one in Dallas.

c. The union has yielded on several points, and the management has yielded on others; but the basic issues are still unsettled.

3. Semicolons may separate the members of a series when any member has a comma within it.

He has written the Whitney Tool Company, our most important supplier; the Blackstone Die Makers; and Ronson and Stevens.

Note: If the semicolon replaces the comma between any two members, it should be used between all of them, including the last two even though they are joined by a conjunction.

Colon

1. The colon may introduce a formal series that comes at the end of a clause.

   The company has assembly plants in five cities: Newark, Louisville, Atlanta, Denver, and San Francisco.

2. The colon may introduce a phrase or a clause that restates more specifically what precedes it.

   There is only one drawback: lack of funds.
   There is only one drawback: we lack funds.

3. The colon is the conventional punctuation after the salutation of a business letter.

4. The colon is the usual punctuation before a long quotation. For an example see page 207.

Dash

1. The dash is used to set off nonrestrictive material that has commas within it.

   Some of your objections—the initial cost, the difficulty of replacing parts, and the long period required to train operators—are quite sound.

   Four of the men have recovered and will report tomorrow—namely: Jennings, Kistler, Capello, and Stransky.

Note: If *namely* were omitted, the dash could introduce the series, though when a series comes at the end of a clause, as here, the colon is probably better.

2. The dash may set off nonrestrictive material that does not contain commas but is inserted abruptly in a sentence for emphasis.

   The personnel office and the treasurer's office—these are the two that were explicitly named—should be reorganized first.

   Many of the men—possibly a majority of them—do not use all of their sick leave.

3. A dash precedes an expression that summarizes a series named at the beginning of a clause.

   The thermostat, the motor, the dehumidifier, and the filter—all have been replaced.

   The thermostat, the motor, the dehumidifier, and the filter—each of the defective parts has been replaced.

Parentheses

1. Parentheses are commonly used to set off cross references.

   The principle has been explained earlier (see page 148); now let us examine some of its more recent applications.
2. Parentheses may be used to set off a definition that is inserted abruptly in a sentence.

   He warned us that the engines were not to be warmed up by "revving" (rapid acceleration) except in an emergency.
3. Parentheses are the common mark for setting off letters or numbers designating members in a series when the series is listed horizontally, and they may be used when it is listed vertically.

   My objections are (a) that the initial cost is too high, (b) that it will be difficult to replace parts, and (c) that training operators will require a long time.

   I have three objections:
   >   (1) The initial cost is too high.
   >   (2) It will be difficult to replace parts.
   >   (3) It will take a long time to train the operators.

Brackets

The chief use of brackets is to enclose a remark of our own interpolated in material quoted from someone else.

> "During the first winter of operation [1938] breakdowns occurred frequently."

> "Every effort was made to raze [sic] morale."

Hyphen

1. A hyphen marks the break when a word is divided between two lines. The break should be made only between syllables as marked in a dictionary.

   Note: A word should not be broken unless at least three letters will be on each line. If the word is already hyphened, as in the case of the adjective or verb *air-conditioned,* it should be broken only where the hyphen already occurs.
2. A hyphen joins the components of a compound adjective.

   A compound adjective is two or more words acting temporarily as a unit to modify a noun that follows them.

   | a high-frequency wave | an up-to-date appearance |
   | their seventy-fifth anniversary | an A-type joint |

a. It is not necessary to repeat the second component when it is common to two or more compound adjectives.

a two- or three-week delay

in 25-, 50-, and 100-lb lots

b. Care should be taken not to confuse a compound adjective with two separate adjectives, the first of which modifies the second plus the noun.

a reinforced-concrete floor (a floor made of reinforced concrete)

a reinforced concrete floor (a concrete floor that has been reinforced)

a brick-loading platform (a platform for loading bricks)

a brick loading platform (a loading platform made of brick)

3. A hyphen joins the components of a compound noun or verb.

20 man-hours   an I-beam   the secretary-treasurer

to short-circuit   (but a short circuit)   to air-cool

4. A hyphen follows the prefix *self*, the prefix *ex* when it means "former," the prefix *re* when the hyphen will expedite understanding, and the prefixes *non* and *anti* when the main component is capitalized.

self-starting   self-confidence   ex-marine

to re-sort vs. to resort   to re-lay vs. to relay

re-argue   re-engage   non-Diesel   anti-American

Apostrophe

The principal use of the apostrophe (to show the possessive case of nouns and pronouns) is explained on pages 259-262. Two other uses are frequent.

1. The apostrophe shows where the omission occurs in a contraction.

it's = it is   isn't = is not   I'll = I shall (or will)

2. The apostrophe may be used to show the plural of numbers, letters, and words used apart from their meaning and of years when written as figures.

Both *8's* should be *5's*.

The *e's* and *w's* are smeared.

He uses too many *and's*.

It was first explored in the 1840's.

Note: Except in the second case, the plural of letters, present usage omits the apostrophe as often as not.

Italics

In typing and longhand, italics are indicated by underlining.

1. Italics are used for the title of any work that is normally published as a separate unit, such as a book, a magazine, a newspaper, a pamphlet, or a long report.

    On the table lay a copy of *The Adventures of Huckleberry Finn* and the *Christian Science Monitor.*

Note: *A, an, the* are italicized when they are the first word in the title of any publication except a magazine or newspaper.

2. Italics may be used sparingly for emphasis.

    We must consider *all* the issues before acting.

3. Italics may be used for numbers, letters, and words used apart from their meaning.

    Loop the *9* more distinctly, cross the *t,* omit *very.*

Quotation Marks

1. Quotation marks are used before and after a direct quotation. For details see pages 206-208.

    The instructions say, "The operating range is from 20 C to 90 C."

2. Quotation marks enclose each part of the quotation when it is divided.

    "Optimum performance," the instructions continue, "is achieved from 75 C to 80 C."

3. Quotation marks set off the title of a work that ordinarily is not a separate publication, such as a magazine article, the chapter in a book, or a short story.

    The fourth chapter is entitled "Centrifugal Pumps."

4. Quotation marks should enclose a word or a phrase that amounts to slang in the given context.

    Two of the tanks have been "decrugged" already.

    We seem to be finally "on the beam" in locating the trouble.

Note: "On the beam" would not be slang and therefore would not need quotation marks if it were used purely in its nautical, radio, or aeronautical sense.

5. Quotation marks may be used to denote numbers, letters, words, and phrases used apart from their meaning.

    Loop the "9" more distinctly, cross the "t," omit "very."

    Change "most of the year" to "eight months of the year."

6. In formal practice commas and periods are put inside the quotation marks regardless of their logical function, colons and semicolons

outside, question marks and exclamation points inside or outside according to their function.

The tanks have already been "decrugged."

The next step is to apply the "hypo"; this is the fixing agent.

The title of the article is "To Utopia or Annihilation?"

Have you read "The Scientist and Society"?

Capitals

1. The first word in a sentence is capitalized, as here.
2. The first word in a direct quotation is capitalized unless the quotation is made part of the construction preceding it.

The report concludes, "Most of the trouble is due to the faulty timer. It should be replaced."

The report concludes that the malfunctioning "is due to the faulty timer. It should be replaced."

Note: When the quotation is interrupted, the second part does not begin with a capital unless the interruption occurs between sentences.

"Most of the trouble," the report concludes, "is due to the faulty timer. It should be replaced."

"Most of the trouble is due to the faulty timer," the report concludes. "It should be replaced."

3. Proper nouns are capitalized.

A proper noun names a specific person, place, or thing.

Charles P. Steinmetz	Mesta Machine Company
Rice Institute	Atomic Age
Monongahela River	Wednesday
Rocky Mountains	October
Grand Coulee Dam	Easter

a. When common nouns, such as *river* and *company,* are part of the name, they are capitalized.

b. Common nouns are capitalized when they are used with a number or a letter to designate a specific thing.

at Plant 7	in Laboratory D
shown in Table 4	explained in Section B
from No. 8 to No. 12	including Nos. 8-12

c. Ordinarily, the names of the seasons are not capitalized.

Consumption is lowest during the fall and winter.

4. Proper adjectives are capitalized.

A proper adjective is either a modified form of a proper noun or is the noun itself modifying a noun after it.

Newtonian theory	Wheatstone bridge
British thermal unit	Otto cycle
Copernican system	India ink

Note: Some proper adjectives are no longer capitalized, and others are in the transitional state between being capitalized and not being. If there is any doubt about the status of a word, the safest procedure is to check it in a dictionary.

a china bowl	a Diesel engine
a cashmere sweater	a diesel engine

5. *North, south, east, west,* and their combinations are not capitalized when they indicate mere direction.

    The prevailing wind is from the north.

    The stream runs from the southwest to the east.

    a. Such terms are capitalized when they designate geographical areas.

        We have three branch offices in the Northeast.

    b. Adjectives follow the same principle as the nouns: they are capitalized only when they refer to specific areas.

        along the western boundary line

        in the large Western cities

6. Studies in a curriculum are capitalized only if they are languages, have a proper adjective as part of their name, or represent a specific course.

    This semester I am taking German, American history, Economics 51, physics, and calculus.

7. In literary titles the first and the last word are capitalized regardless of what they are, and all others are capitalized except the articles (*a, an, the*) and conjunctions and prepositions having fewer than five letters.

    The Return of the Native

    Of Human Bondage

    The Red and the Black

    Engineers Within Their Society

Note: In the names of newspapers and magazines the introductory *the* is not capitalized even though it may be part of the title.

    a copy of the *Engineering Journal*

8. Titles preceding a person's name are capitalized. Those that follow are capitalized only if the title is of considerable distinction, *Junior* and *Senior* being exceptions.

    Superintendent Evans

Evans, superintendent of Plant 2
Dean L.B. Ogden
L.B. Ogden, dean of the engineering school
Charles E. Hughes, Secretary of State
L.D. Bonelli, Jr.

Standard Abbreviations

1. A period follows an abbreviation unless it is composed of capital letters that stand for different words or parts of words.

the Holton Co.   Washington, D.C.   No. 23
TVA   FCC   ICBM   GHQ   DEW

2. *Mr., Mrs.,* and *Dr.* are preferable to the full word when they are used as a title before a person's name. Other titles are better written out. *Miss* is not an abbreviation.

Mrs. Grant   Dr. Clemmons   Superintendent Evans
Captain Hines   Professor Spearman   Miss Dudley

3. Abbreviations pluralize by adding *s.*

Nos. 8 and 9   Drs. Wynne, Clemmons, and Rossilimo

Note: Two common exceptions are *Messrs.* (plural of *Mr.*) and *Mmes.* (plural of *Mrs.*).

4. The names of cities and states should not be abbreviated in the text. *D.C.*, however, is preferable to the full form.

5. *Etc.* should not be used in formal writing. A more precise summarizing phrase should be used instead.

Loose: in London, Paris, Rome, etc.
Better: in London, Paris, Rome, and other European capitals
Loose: the use of coal, wood, gasoline, etc.
Better: the use of coal, wood, gasoline, and other fuels

6. *For example, that is,* and *namely* are preferable to their Latin abbreviations: *e.g., i.e.,* and *viz.*

7. When an abbreviation ends a declarative sentence, one period suffices for the abbreviation and the sentence.

Trains leave daily at 4:30 a.m. and 2 p.m.

Abbreviation of Technical Terms

Abbreviations are used much more widely in technical writing than in writing in other fields. Their use is particularly encouraged in reports, both formal and informal. Many company publications and technical magazines also use them freely.

1. Abbreviate a unit of measurement when it follows a figure. Most,

but not all, extremely short terms (four letters or fewer) are exceptions to this rule. Other than *a-c* and *d-c* when used as adjectives, no term should be abbreviated unless a figure precedes it.

rated at 200 hp
the horsepower of the motor
weighs 50 tons
drove 15 miles
a charge of 30 v

2. Use the singular form for all abbreviations.
   rotates at 2500 rpm
   weighs 20 lb and holds 10 gal

3. Do not put a period after the abbreviation unless it can be confused with a word.

   12 ft   10 in.
   1200 psi   300 sq miles

4. Use no signs in the text. There are only four permissible exceptions: $, ¢, % and the degree sign to show angular measurement but not temperature. Even the use of *x* in giving measurements is avoided in the text; the word *by* is used instead. In illustrations, however, where clear space is desirable, signs are good.
   measures 3 ft by 2 ft by 8 in.

5. Show temperature only by a capital letter that indicates the scale.
   35 C   200 F   150 K

6. Do not capitalize an abbreviation unless the full form has a capital. Several exceptions to this rule are included in the list on pages 321-325.

7. Hyphen the abbreviation of a unit of measurement and the figure preceding it when they are used as a single adjective before a noun.
   a 15-ft rise   a 30-lb increase
   But: a rise of 15 ft   an increase of 30 lb

8. Consult the list of abbreviations in the appendix (pages 321-325) for the proper form. It was compiled by the American Standards Association and is generally regarded as official. In addition to units of measurement and temperature scales, it includes many other terms.

Numbers

The following principles simplify the expression of numbers in technical writing.

1. Use a figure for any number above nine; write out any number lower than 10. This is the basic rule and covers all situations except

those noted below, where figures are generally used regardless of whether the number consists of a single figure or more.

2. Use a figure before a unit of measurement whether it is above nine or not.

    3 in.   8 lb   5 v   20 w
But: five automobiles   nine gaskets

3. Use figures for every item in a series, even when all of them are below 10.

    6 hammers, 2 saws, 5 screw drivers, 1 ax

4. Use figures after terms of specific designation.

    page 8   Plant No. 2
    Order No. 4   Vat 7

5. Use figures in dates and for time when *a.m.* or *p.m.* follows.

    June 18, 1946   18 June 1946
    5 a.m.   4:30 p.m.
But: five o'clock in the morning
        half past four in the afternoon

6. Use figures for sums of money. For sums less than one dollar place zero before the decimal or use *cents, ¢,* or *c.*

    $1800 $748.32 $1.85
    $0.67   67 cents   67¢   67c

7. Use figures for addresses.

    1803 Princess Street   Box 831, Route 8
        847 Hill Building

8. Use figures to show percentage.

    5 percent   5 per cent   5%

9. Use figures for decimals. Values of less than one have a zero before the decimal point.

    1.8 million   15.9 ft   0.87 ft

10. Use figures for fractions that appear with a whole number and for the number too. Write out fractions that appear alone. Use a hyphen only if the word *of* does not follow the fraction.

    a gain of 4½ lb
    a gain of three fourths of a pound
    a gain of one-half pound
    is two-thirds completed

11. Write out numbers that must come at the beginning of a sentence. As long as the reading is smooth, however, it is better to recast the sentence so that the number is not at the beginning.

    Twenty-seven men have reported.
    Of the grand total $517 is unaccounted for.

12. Write out approximations. This is advisable because figures suggest
exactness.

> about forty-five hundred dollars
> for the next twenty-five years or longer

a. When the approximation is within specific limits, the basic rule
applies.

> We have 10-15 applicants per day.
> We have from 10 to 15 applicants per day.
> We have from five to eight applicants per day.

b. It is a violation of idiom to write "from 10-15 applicants."
Either use both prepositions *from* and *to* and omit the hyphen,
or omit both prepositions and use the hyphen.

13. When numbers designating two different things come together,
write out one and use figures for the other, observing rules 1 and 2
insofar as it is practical.

> 20 six-foot girders or twenty 6-ft girders
> six 20-ft girders
> twenty 50-w bulbs or 20 fifty-watt bulbs
> three 5-w bulbs

14. Hyphen two numbers when they combine to form one number.

> Twenty-five units will be needed.
> sixty-three 75-ton cars

15. Hyphen a number and a unit of measurement when they modify
a noun that *follows* them.

> a 50-ton hoist
> a 5-ohm resistance
> The capacity of the hoist is 50 tons.
> a resistance of 5 ohms

RHETORIC

Rhetoric goes beyond correctness in writing, which involves grammar, spelling, and punctuation. Rhetoric is the body of principles that make for effectiveness in writing, the principles that enable us to show the relationship between ideas more clearly and quickly.

Parallelism

RULE

Two or more ideas that deserve the same emphasis should be stated in the same kind of grammatical construction. In other words, ideas parallel in value should be parallel in structure.

EXAMPLES

Faulty: All of the water pipes have been installed. Half of the sewers have been laid, and work will begin on the steam lines next week.

(The last two points should be separate sentences to parallel the first one, or all three ideas should be independent clauses in a single sentence.)

Faulty: We trade with Hadley and Merrick because of the big discount they give us and their stock is complete.

Correct: We trade with Hadley and Merrick because they give us a big discount and their stock is complete.

Correct: We trade with Hadley and Merrick because of the big discount they give us and the completeness of their stock.

Faulty: We give the new men the opportunity to go through the entire training program and then choosing the special field they prefer.

Correct: We give the new men the opportunity to go through the entire training program and then choose (or to choose) the special field they prefer.

Correct: We give the new men the opportunity of going through the entire training program and then choosing the special field they prefer.

Faulty: He showed me how to disassemble the machine, check for worn parts, lubricate it, and to reassemble it. (Either *to* should be a part of all four infinitives, or the first *to* should control all four.

In the latter case the parallel elements will be the infinitive stems: *disassemble, check, lubricate,* and *reassemble.*)

Faulty: I have found the new method a time-saver and that it requires fewer men. (*And that, and which,* and *and who* are incorrect unless a *that, which,* or *who* clause precedes them respectively.)

Correct: I have found that the new method saves time and that it requires fewer men. (Or the second *that* may be omitted.)

Correct: I have found that the new method saves time and requires fewer men.

Note: The material that follows the second correlative conjunction should be parallel to the material that follows the first one. The correlative conjunctions are those conjunctions that are used in pairs: *either-or, neither-nor, not only-but* (*also*), *both-and.*

Faulty: She is prepared for a job as either a secretary or keeping books.

Correct: She is prepared for a job as either a secretary or a bookkeeper.

Faulty: We found trouble both in the rotor and stator.

Correct: We found trouble both in the rotor and in the stator.

Correct: We found trouble in both the rotor and the stator.

Subordination

RULE

When we do not wish to give two ideas the same emphasis, we make an independent clause of the one we want to stress, and put the other one in a dependent clause or a phrase.

In sentences having more than two ideas the principle of subordination is the same.

EXAMPLES

Faulty: He called the department managers to his office and explained the new credit system to them.

Correct: After he called the department managers to his office, he explained the new credit system to them.

Correct: After calling the department managers to his office, he explained the new credit system to them.

Faulty: Your order was directed to the wrong plant; that is why it could not be filled at once.

Correct: Because your order was directed to the wrong plant, it could not be filled at once.

Faulty: He has an excellent knowledge of the language; nevertheless, he does not get along well with the native labor.

Correct: Although he has an excellent knowledge of the language, he does not get along well with the native labor.

Faulty: Perkins is the guard at Gate 5, and he sent in the alarm.

Correct: Perkins, who is the guard at Gate 5, sent in the alarm.

Correct: Perkins, the guard at Gate 5, sent in the alarm.

Faulty: Claudia wants to study engineering, but her father believes that a woman has little chance of succeeding as an engineer, and he will probably refuse to let her enter the field.

Correct: Although Claudia wants to study engineering, her father will probably refuse to let her because he believes that a woman has little chance of succeeding in that field.

Note: Sometimes a sentence can be faulty not because it lacks subordination but because the subordination is reversed; that is, the idea that deserves the emphasis is in the dependent construction.

Faulty: They had to spend an extra month on the foundation, thus forfeiting the $10,000 bonus for completing the project on schedule.

Correct: Because they had to spend an extra month on the foundation, they forfeited the $10,000 bonus for completing the project on schedule.

Viewpoint

RULE

Needless shifts in viewpoint should be avoided.

EXAMPLES

1. Shift in Subject

Faulty: The *regulations* require each man to wear a uniform; *he* must also cover his mouth and nose with a gauze mask before entering the laboratory.

Correct: The *regulations* require each man to wear a uniform; *they* also require him to cover his mouth and nose with a gauze mask before entering the laboratory.

Correct: *Each man* must wear a uniform; *he* must also cover his mouth and nose with a gauze mask before entering the laboratory.

2. Shift in Person

Faulty: If the *employees* want a clubhouse, let them petition for it. (Understood subject of *let* is *you*.)

Correct: If the *employees* want a clubhouse, *they* should petition for it.

(This is also another example of an unnecessary shift in subject.)

3. Shift in Tense

Faulty: I *pushed* the switch and then *check* the ammeter.

Correct: I *pushed* the switch and then *checked* the ammeter.

Correct: I *push* the switch and then *check* the ammeter. (This last sentence, using the present tense, would be undesirable except in describing a routine procedure.)

4. Shift in Mood

Faulty: They *would* save almost $500 if they *can* re-use the containers.

Correct: They *would* save almost $500 if they *could* re-use the containers.

Correct: They *will* save almost $500 if they *can* re-use the containers.

5. Shift in Voice

Faulty: He *lists* his objections to the plan, but its good points *are* not *mentioned.*

Correct: He *lists* his objections to the plan, but he *does* not *mention* its good points.

Consistent, but questionable use of the passive: His objections to the plan *are listed,* but its good points *are* not *mentioned.*

Dangling Modifiers

RULE

A word, phrase, or clause should be placed as near the element it modifies as smooth reading will permit.

EXAMPLES

1. Dangling adverb

Faulty: We *only* plan to work one shift next week.

Correct: We plan to work only one shift next week.

2. Dangling prepositional phrase

Faulty: *Without extra help* the job will require two months.

Correct: Without extra help we shall need two months for the job.

3. Dangling infinitive phrase

Faulty: *To refill the grease cups,* the cylinder head has to be removed.

Correct: To refill the grease cups, the operator has to remove the cylinder head.

Correct: Before the grease cups can be refilled, the cylinder head must be removed.

4. Dangling participial phrase

Faulty: *Having two conveyer belts,* the danger of overloading is minimized.

Correct: Having two conveyer belts, the company has minimized the danger of overloading.

Correct: Because two conveyer belts are used, the danger of overloading
is minimized.

5. Dangling gerund phrase

Faulty: *By reducing our overhead* it has not been necessary to raise our
prices.

Correct: By reducing our overhead we have not had to raise our prices.

Correct: Because we have reduced our overhead, it has not been necessary to raise our prices.

6. Dangling clause

Faulty: The gauge on the outside of the boiler, *which was repaired last
week,* is working satisfactorily.

Correct: The gauge, which is on the outside of the boiler and which was
repaired last week, is working satisfactorily.

Correct: The boiler, which was repaired last week, has a gauge on the
outside; it is working satisfactorily.

Correct: The outside of the boiler was repaired last week, and the gauge
on it is working satisfactorily.

7. Dangling elliptical clause

Faulty: *Although tested the day before,* he could not start the auxiliary
engine when the main power supply failed.

Correct: Although tested the day before, the auxiliary engine would not
start when the main power supply failed.

Correct: Although it had been tested the day before, he could not start
the auxiliary engine when the main power supply failed.

Note: A phrase is not regarded as dangling when it gives the basis of
the speaker's thinking and qualifies all of the idea that follows.

EXAMPLES

To judge by our past experience, transportation will be the chief cost.
Considering the excellence of the ore, this price is reasonable.

Mixed Constructions

RULE

Two different constructions should not be fused to state a single idea.

EXAMPLES

Faulty: We are recommending *what* procedure *that* you should follow.

Correct: We are recommending the procedure that you should follow.

Correct: We are recommending what you should do.

Faulty: The new fan will be installed in *such* a place *so that* the whole area will be cooled.

Correct: The new fan will be installed in such a place as to cool the whole area.

Correct: The new fan will be installed in such a place that the whole area will be cooled.

Correct: The new fan will be installed where it will cool the whole area.

Faulty: They have *asked us would we* submit an estimate.

Correct: They have asked us to submit an estimate.

Correct: They have asked whether we would submit an estimate.

Faulty: He is a man *of* whom the company expects much *of*.

Correct: He is a man of whom the company expects much.

Correct: He is a man whom the company expects much of.

Faulty: "Overlapped *valves" is when* the exhaust and the intake valves are open simultaneously for an instant.

Correct: "Overlapped valves" occurs when the exhaust and the intake valves are open simultaneously for an instant.

Correct: "Overlapped valves" is the brief simultaneous opening of the exhaust and the intake valves.

Incomplete Constructions

RULE

Words should not be omitted if any ambiguity will result.

EXAMPLES

Faulty: We shall appreciate any suggestions that you make and are ready to answer further questions if you have them.

Correct: We shall appreciate any suggestions that you make, and we are ready to answer further questions if you have them.

Faulty: This model tractor should fill your needs.

Correct: This model of tractor should fill your needs.

Note: Particular care should be taken not to omit necessary words in comparisons.

Faulty: Coke has proved to be more efficient than any fuel we have tried. (This sounds as if coke is not a fuel.)

Correct: Coke has proved to be more efficient than any other fuel we have tried.

Faulty: The boiling point of the solution is higher than any of its separate components. (The comparison is illogical because it is between unlike things.)

Correct: The boiling point of the solution is higher than that of any of its separate components.

Faulty: We get more reports from the Combustion Division than the Aerodynamics Division. (Two interpretations are possible.)

Correct: We get more reports from the Combustion Division than from the Aerodynamics Division.

Correct: We get more reports from the Combustion Division than the Aerodynamics Division does.

Split Constructions

RULE

Related elements should be kept together insofar as the natural order of ideas permits.

EXAMPLES

Faulty: I *have,* as you requested in your letter of July 8, *investigated* the possibilities of enlarging our parking lot.

Correct: As you requested in your letter of July 8, I have investigated the possibilities of enlarging our parking lot.

Correct: I have investigated the possibilities of enlarging our parking lot, as you requested in your letter of July 8.

Faulty: The *hopper,* unless it is scraped frequently, *becomes* caked with slag.

Correct: Unless the hopper is scraped frequently, it becomes caked with slag.

Correct: The hopper becomes caked with slag unless it is scraped frequently.

Faulty: The older men showed me how *to* quickly *make* the changes.

Correct: The older men showed me how to make the changes quickly.

Note: Although the general practice is not to split an infinitive, there are times when putting an adverb between the *to* and the stem gives the clearest reading.

EXAMPLE

We are planning to rapidly improve working conditions in the old part of the building and in the machine shop.

SPELLING

The business world puts great stress on spelling. There are several reasons why it does. One is that most businessmen regard misspelling as a sign of innate carelessness and feel, whether rightly or wrongly, that a man who is careless about his spelling is likely to be careless about more important matters. Another reason is that misspelling can be construed as the writer's assuming that the reader is also ignorant or indifferent on the subject. And a third reason is that no other error in writing is more quickly spotted or more readily contemned than a spelling error.

This being the case, a writer is only deceiving himself when he tries to shrug off his poor spelling with the excuse "I've never been able to spell" or the equally fatuous remark "My secretary will check the spelling for me." After all, part of the process of education is learning to do what we could not do before, and as for the secretary, there is no guarantee that she will be able to spell either.

The problem of spelling correctly is not nearly so complicated as some students assume it to be. Even if you are a weak speller, you can eliminate 90 percent or more of your errors by following the procedure given below.

A. When reading through a letter, a report, or an article that you have written, have a dictionary beside you and check the spelling of every word you have any doubt about.

B. Keep a list of the words that give you the most trouble—the words that you regularly misspell or spell on a hit-or-miss basis—and have the list before you as you write the original draft and as you reread it.

C. Learn the five rules that cover the most recurrent difficulties. There are exceptions—and sometimes very important exceptions—to most of these rules; still, a knowledge of them will minimize the necessity of consulting a dictionary.
   1. The first rule governs the doubling of a final consonant when a suffix is added to a word. This is probably the most useful of all spelling rules because it applies to the past tense and the participles of verbs, and because the exceptions to it are few and rather obvious. Perhaps the best way to learn and apply it is by steps, *every one* of which must be fulfilled.

Double the final consonant of a word if

  a. The suffix begins with a vowel,
  b. The final consonant is preceded by a vowel, not another consonant,
  c. That vowel is preceded by a consonant, not another vowel,
  d. And the accent is on the last syllable of the word and remains on the *same* syllable after the suffix is added. This condition, of course, is true of all monosyllables.

The following words are examples of the positive working of the rule; that is, the consonant is doubled.

fit + ed = fitted	allot + ed = allotted
hot + er = hotter	begin + ing = beginning
plan + ed = planned	control + ing = controlling
rid + ance = riddance	forget + ing = forgetting
run + ing = running	occur + ed = occurred
set + ing = setting	occur + ing = occurring
stem + ed = stemmed	occur + ence = occurrence
stem + ing = stemming	refer + ed = referred

The words listed below illustrate the negative working of the rule; that is, the consonant is not doubled

  a. because the suffix does not begin with a vowel
       hot + ly = hotly   allot + ment = allotment
  b. because the final consonant is preceded by another consonant
       award + ed = awarded   spend + ing = spending
  c. because the vowel is preceded by another vowel
       clear + ance = clearance   appear + ed = appeared
       cool + ed = cooled   detain + ing = detaining
  d. because the accent is not on the last syllable of the word or because it shifts from that syllable when the suffix is added
       offer + ed = offered   prefer + able = preferable
       solder + ing = soldering   refer + ence = reference

The most important exceptions to this rule involve words that end in *w* or *y* (the consonant does not double) and words in which the vowel is preceded by *qu*. In the latter instances *qu*, for orthographic purposes, is the equivalent of *kw* and the consonant doubles if all the other conditions are satisfied.

draw + ing = drawing	quit + ing = quitting
glow + ed = glowed	quiz + es = quizzes

renew + able = renewable   equip + ed = equipped
key + ed = keyed   equip + ing = equipping
employ + ing = employing   But: equip + ment = equipment
relay + ed = relayed   (suffix begins with a consonant)

2. Prefixes have no effect on the spelling of a word. That is, the word is unchanged except for the addition of the prefix.

dis + connect = disconnect
mis + spend = misspend
pre + pay = prepay
non + productive = nonproductive
re + unite = reunite
un + necessary = unnecessary

Note: Sometimes a hyphen between the prefix and the stem is desirable to prevent confusion with another word or to facilitate pronunciation.

re-cover vs. recover   co-own
re-creation vs. recreation   pre-exist
re-form vs. reform   re-enter

3. The vowel combinations *ei* and *ie* can be bothersome. The following jingle is helpful in choosing between them:

Write *i* before *e*
Except after *c*
And when sounded as ā
As in *neighbor* and *weigh*

EXAMPLES

a. The combination does not follow *c* or have the sound of ā— therefore, *i* before *e*

believe   field   relief
chief   grievance   yield

b. The combination follows *c*—therefore, *e* before *i*

ceiling   conceive   receipt
conceit   deceive   receive

c. The combination is pronounced ā—therefore, *e* before *i*

feint   reign   skein
neighbor   seine   weigh

Helpful as the rule is, there are several important exceptions—words that do not meet any of the conditions.

conscience   leisure   seize
either   neither   seizure
financier   science   species
foreign   scientist   weird

4.a. Words ending in silent *e* retain the *e* before a suffix beginning with a consonant.

> complete + ness = completeness
> large + ly = largely
> replace + ment = replacement
> use + ful = useful

The most common exceptions to this rule are *argument, awful, duly, truly,* and the preferred forms of *acknowledgment* and *judgment.*

b. Words ending in silent *e* drop the *e* before a suffix beginning with a vowel.

> come + ing = coming   situate + ion = situation
> guide + ance = guidance   use + age = usage

There are three general groups of exceptions:

1. Words in which the *e* is retained to distinguish the word from a similar one; *dyeing-dying* and *singeing-singing* are conspicuous examples.

2. Words ending in *ce* or *ge* when the suffix begins with *a* or *o.* The *e* is retained to preserve the soft sound of the *c* or *g.*

> notice + able = noticeable
> replace + able = replaceable
> advantage + ous = advantageous
> manage + able = manageable

3. Words that have two accepted forms with the suffix *able,* in one of which the *e* remains.

> likeable or likable   saleable or salable
> moveable or movable   useable or usable

Analogous to this group is *mileage-milage.*

5.a. Words ending in *y* preceded by a consonant change the *y* to *i* before any suffix except one beginning with *i.* (For the pluralizing of nouns that end in *y* see pages 257-258.)

> carry + ed = carried   supply + ed = supplied
> carry + ing = carrying   supply + er = supplier
> foggy + er = foggier   supply + ing = supplying
> foggy + est = foggiest   worry + some = worrisome

b. Words ending in *y* preceded by a vowel retain the *y* before a suffix.

> annoy + ance = annoyance   employ + ed = employed
> survey + or = surveyor   employ + ee = employee
> display + ed = displayed   employ + er = employer

Common exceptions are *daily* (*day*) and the verb forms *laid* (*lay*), *paid* (*pay*), and *said* (*say*).

D. Learn the distinction in spelling and meaning between words that have the same or nearly the same pronunciation. Some of those used most frequently are listed below. An asterisk indicates those words that are differentiated in the Glossary (pages 299-312).

accept, except*
advice, advise
affect, effect*
already, all ready
altogether, all together
brake, break
censor, censure
cite, sight, site
coarse, course
complement, compliment
credible, creditable
dual, duel
eminent, imminent
faze, phase, phrase

formally, formerly
its, it's*
lead, led
loose, lose
passed, past
personal, personnel
perspective, prospective
precede, proceed
principal, principle*
respectably, respectfully, respectively
stationary, stationery
statue, stature, statute

E. In the following list, made up of words which are frequently misspelled and to which the rules given under C do not apply, check those you are uncertain of and then memorize them. The italics show where error is most liable to occur.

accident*a*lly
accomm*o*date
an*n*ual
any time (two words)
appear*a*nce
appro*p*riate
ath*l*etic
auxi*li*ary
benef*i*ted
calend*a*r
carbure*t*or
com*m*it*t*ee
compar*a*tive
conv*e*nient
defin*i*te
depend*e*nt
d*e*scribe
develop (preferred form)

development (preferred form)
di*a*phra*g*m
effic*i*ent
embar*r*ass
envir*o*nment
excell*e*nt
ex*h*aust
exist*e*nce
extracurricula*r* (solid word)
famil*i*ar
feas*i*ble
fin*a*lly
flu*o*re*s*cent
gover*n*ment
heig*h*t
hind*r*ance
hydra*u*lic
immedi*a*tely

indispensable
interest
laboratory
maintenance
manual
mathematics
miniature
necessary
occasion
old-fashioned
oscillate
pamphlet
partner

permissible
practically
prejudice
procedure
quantity
recommend
repetition
representative
separate
similar
structural
thorough
tragedy

GLOSSARY OF USAGE

The following comments on troublesome words and phrases are intended only as a general guide and not as inviolable rules. Many of the expressions are in the transitional stage between being unacceptable and being acceptable, and the avoidance of them or the use of them often rests on the occasion and the level of writing or speaking that is suitable to it.

A, AN

The choice between these words is governed by the introductory *sound* of the word that immediately follows—*a* if the sound is consonant and *an* if it is vowel.

a hectic situation	a union
a humble man	an understanding
an hour	a one-story house
an honorable man	an olive

ABLE, CAPABLE

It is dubious practice to use either word to describe something without animal life since they mean, respectively, "having ability" and "having capability." Thus: "The machine can do the work of five men" rather than "The machine is able to do (or is capable of doing) the work of five men."

Note also the idiomatic construction each calls for: *able* is followed by an infinitive, *capable* by *of* and a gerund.

He was *able to* help us.

He is *capable of* doing the work.

ABOVE

There is still a good deal of opposition to using this word as an adjective or a noun: "the above figures show," "the above shows." As an adverb and a preposition, of course, it is perfectly legitimate: "the figures above show," "the ceiling above the desk."

ACCEPT, EXCEPT

The verb *accept* means "to receive" or "to agree to." As a verb *except* means "to omit"; as a preposition it means "omitting" or "but."

AFFECT, EFFECT

Affect is a verb whose chief business meaning is "to influence, to have an effect on." *Effect* is used primarily as a noun meaning "the result," but it can also be a verb meaning "to bring about, to cause."

> Sickness has *affected* production.
> The warning had little *effect*.
> The arbitrator hopes to *effect* a compromise.

ALRIGHT

A spelling that is considered substandard. Prefer *all right*.

ALSO

A weak connective with which to introduce a sentence. Stronger are *further, furthermore, in addition,* and *moreover.*

AMONG, BETWEEN

Among is used when three or more units are concerned; *between* when only two are.

> found it *among* the papers in his file
> found it *between* two books

AMOUNT, NUMBER

Amount is preferred if the thing involved is a single unit even though collective in its implication. *Number* is used if more than a single unit is involved. Often the distinction is the same as that between *much* and *many.*

> A large *amount* of (much) traffic uses the road.
> A large *number* of (many) trucks use the road.
> In terms of labor the *amount* is not great.
> In terms of men the *number* is not great.

See also *Number.*

AND/OR

Despite its convenience and economy this expression is widely censured as indefinite. Safer is the use of the phrase *or both* to indicate the third alternative.

> Questionable: We shall use rubber *and/or* a plastic.
> Accepted: We shall use rubber or a plastic *or both.*

ANYPLACE

Not recognized as a word. Prefer *anywhere*.

AS

The best practice is to avoid using this word altogether to introduce a clause giving a reason. *Because* and *since* are less subject to misinterpretation.

Ambiguous: The workmen should be warned *as* the job becomes more dangerous each day.

Clear: The workmen should be warned *because* the job becomes more dangerous each day.

AS PER

In questionable taste as a substitute for *according to*.

BALANCE

Except in connection with money the word is better replaced by *rest* or *remainder*.

BECAUSE OF, DUE TO

The distinction between these phrases is not commonly observed today, though it does exist: *because of* introduces an adverbial construction that explains a verb, an adverb, or a predicate adjective; *due to* introduces an adjectival construction that explains a noun.

He was *promoted because of* his excellent record.

The work has progressed *slowly because of* bad weather.

The work has been *slow because of* bad weather.

His *promotion* was *due to* his excellent record.

On the basis of this distinction, then, *due to* should not begin a sentence, for the phrase it introduces modifies a verb, an adverb, or a predicate adjective.

Open to criticism: *Due to* the increase in costs we *must raise* prices.

More acceptable: *Because of* the increase in costs we *must raise* prices.

BEING THAT

A loose, clumsy phrase with which to introduce a reason. *Because* or *since* is much better.

Awkward: *Being that* the thermostat was broken, they had to control the furnace manually.

BESIDE, BESIDES

Beside means "by the side of." *Besides* means "furthermore" or "in addition to."

BETWEEN

See *Among*.

CANNOT HELP BUT

A redundancy. "Cannot help" is sufficient.
Redundant: I *cannot help but* object to the change.
Correct: I *cannot help* objecting to the change.

CAPABLE

See *Able*.

CAUSING

A word to be used with care in introducing the last part of a sentence. Often it is modifying a whole idea instead of a single word and is therefore a dangling modifier. At other times—not infrequently, at the same time—it represents a case of upside-down subordination (emphasis on the less important idea preceding it).

Dangling modifier: The shipment was sent to the wrong destination, *causing* the delay.

Upside-down subordination: Two bulkheads gave way, thus *causing* the cargo to shift and the boat to capsize.

Correct: The delay was caused by the shipment being sent to the wrong destination.

Correct: Because two bulkheads gave way, the cargo shifted and the boat capsized.

CONTACT

Although the use of this word in the sense of "get in touch with" is rather general in the business world, it is still of questionable status and offensive to many people.

CONTINUAL, CONTINUOUS

These words do not mean quite the same thing. *Continual* implies close but separate occurrences, as "continual oversights." *Continuous* implies no interruption, as "continuous improvement." Of course, an oversight would be continuous if it went uncorrected for a long time, and improvement would be continual if it was by stages.

DATA

This is the plural form of *datum* and accordingly requires a plural modifier, verb, and pronoun. The present trend to regard it as singular when it refers to a body of facts considered as a whole seems, so far, not to have the support of most careful writers and speakers.

DIFFERENT FROM, DIFFERENT THAN

The older expression is *different from,* and it is still preferable when a word or a phrase follows. When a clause follows, either expression is good.

The winters here are *different from* those in Montana.

The response has been *different from* what I expected.

Or: The response has been *different than* I expected.

DISINTERESTED, UNINTERESTED

Disinterested means "without self-interest," "impartial," "unbiased." *Uninterested* means "without any interest," "indifferent." A disinterested person can be completely absorbed in the subject but his attitude is uncolored by personal considerations.

DUE TO

See *Because of.*

EFFECT

See *Affect.*

ELECTRIC, ELECTRICAL

According to American Standards Definitions of Electrical Terms, the general distinction between these words is that *electric* describes anything that carries or is composed of, charged with, or operated by electricity and *electrical* describes that which pertains to electricity in any other way.

electric conductor, current, equipment, motor, surge, welding

electrical capacity, insulation, measurements, rates

ENABLE

Since this verb means "to make able," the word receiving its action should not name an inanimate object.

Faulty: The larger hopper *enables the cars* to be loaded more quickly.

Correct: The larger hopper *makes it possible* to load the cars more quickly.

Correct: The larger hopper *enables the men* to load the cars more quickly.

EQUALLY AS GOOD, EQUALLY AS WELL

In both expressions the *as* is superfluous.

ETC.

An abbreviation of *et cetera,* meaning "and others." Hence an *and* before it is redundant. But the expression itself is weak and often vague. A noun that summarizes the preceding series is more precise.

Weak: from Bentley, Whittier, Moore, etc.
Better: from Bentley, Whittier, Moore, and the other chemists
Weak: with brick, concrete, granite, etc.
Better: with brick, concrete, granite, and similar materials

EXCEPT

See *Accept.*

FACT, FACTOR

A *fact* is something that exists or occurs or has existed or has occurred. A *factor* is a fact that combines with one or more others to bring about a condition or result.

His letter omits some important *facts.*
One *factor* in his success has been perseverance.

FARTHER, FURTHER

Farther is better in speaking of actual distance; *further* is better in the sense of "furthermore" or "additional."

It should be built *farther* from the river than the plans call for.
Supplies will be scarce. *Further,* there is the question of manpower.
A *further* advantage is its speed.

FEWER, LESS

Fewer is to be preferred when the noun that follows is plural; *less* when the noun is singular.

fewer dollars, less money
fewer parts, less equipment
fewer orders, less business

IF

This is the correct word with which to introduce a condition or supposition, but it is weak as a substitute for *whether* in introducing an indirect question or indicating an alternative.

Correct: *If* we get the contract, we must hire more men.

Correct: I would change the regulation *if* I were manager.

Correct: He asks *whether* our present facilities are adequate.

Correct: We must start the excavation Monday *whether* the weather clears or not.

Note: The use of *or not* after *whether* is optional, and it may follow immediately or, as in the last example, come at the end of the clause.

IMPLY, INFER

These words are often used as though they were synonyms, the use of *infer* in the sense of *imply* being especially common. In discriminating usage, however, they mean two opposite processes: *imply* is to give information indirectly, to suggest; *infer* is to receive information indirectly, to deduce. A listener infers what a speaker implies.

His letter *implies* that we should assume the cost.

I *infer* that he thinks we should assume the cost.

IN, INTO

In general, *in* is used to indicate movement or position within one place and *into* to show movement from one place to a different one.

He walked *in* the room (moved about inside it).

He is *in* his office (position).

He walked *into* the room (entered it).

Nevertheless, a few verbs denoting movement from one place to another are idiomatic exceptions to the rule. *Put* and *place* are probably the most common of these exceptions.

We *put* money *in* the bank.

The rinsing tanks will be *placed in* the basement.

INCREMENT

Strictly speaking, an increment is an increase, usually the amount added in a series of additions. Though the practice of using the same word to denote the opposite—a decrease—is fairly common, the more precise word in this latter sense is *decrement*.

INFER, IMPLY

See *Imply*

IRREGARDLESS

An erroneous form of *regardless*.

ITS, IT'S

Its is the possessive form of *it*. The apostrophe indicates the contracted form of *it is*.

KIND OF

In formal expression the two words are correct when used as a noun followed by a preposition but incorrect when used as an adverb. Even in the first sense the two words do not require an *a* or *an* after them.

Correct: He is used to working with this *kind of* material.
Incorrect: The job is going to be *kind of* costly.
Correct: The job is going to be *somewhat* costly.

LAY, LIE

Lay (laid, laid, laying) is used when the meaning is "to put"; *lie* (lay, lain, lying) when the meaning is "to rest" or "to be in position."

After *laying* the sample on the table he began to study it.
The debris *lies* where the wrecking crew left it.
Exeter *lies* west of here.

LESS, FEWER

See *Fewer*.

LIE, LAY

See *Lay*.

LIKE

The best practice is not to use this word to introduce clauses but to prefer *as, as if,* or *as though*.

They plan to make no changes but to do it exactly *as* they always have.
It looks now *as if* (or: *as though*) there will be no shortage.
The men resumed their work *as if* (or: *as though*) nothing had happened.

LOT OF, LOTS OF

In the sense of "many" or "much" both expressions are too casual for business writing.

Undesirable: He interviewed a *lot of* applicants.
We expect *lots of* criticism at first.
Better: He interviewed *many* applicants.
He interviewed *a large number* of applicants.
We expect *much* criticism at first.
We expect *a great deal* of criticism at first.

MAXIMUM, OPTIMUM

Though closely associated, these words do not mean quite the same thing. *Maximum* refers to the limit possible or permissible. *Optimum* refers to the most favorable circumstances or highest degree.

We can attain *maximum* output only under *optimum* conditions.
Optimum efficiency is achieved in warm weather.

MOST

A colloquialism when used for *almost*.
Colloquial: The speech pleased *most* everybody.
They have used *most* all of the reserve supply.
Better: The speech pleased *almost* everybody.
They have used *almost* all of the reserve supply.
They have used *most* of the reserve supply.

NO PLACE

Incorrect in the sense of "nowhere."

NUMBER

When used before a figure, this word is better abbreviated; the abbreviation is capitalized and followed by a period to differentiate it from the word *no*.

the No. 3 mill   order No. A-3121

When not used attributively, the word should be spelled out.

A large *number* of men are absent today.
He could not tell us the exact *number*.

When *number* is the subject of a verb, the verb is singular when *number* is modified by *the*, plural when it is modified by *a*.

The number of accounts still open is small.
A small *number* of accounts are still open.

See also *Amount*.

OF

Redundant after the prepositions *inside, outside,* and *off*. But when *inside* and *outside* are used as nouns, the *of* is correct.

They went *inside* the boiler.
They examined *the inside of* the boiler.

OPTIMUM

See *Maximum.*

PER

See *As per.*

PER CENT, PERCENTAGE

Per cent is used after the actual figures. *Percentage* is used when no figure precedes. *Per cent* may also be spelled *percent*, but one should be consistent throughout a paper.

Production declined 8 *per cent* during May.
May brought an 8-*percent* decline in production.
The *percentage* of rejected caps is small.

PRACTICABLE, PRACTICAL

The best way to distinguish between these words is to remember that *practicable* usually means "workable" or "possible" and *practical,* when not applied to persons, usually means "demonstrable" or "useful."

Before Bell the transmitting of voices over a wire was not considered *practicable,* but because of his work and the subsequent improvements the telephone has proved to be a thoroughly *practical* instrument.

PRESENTLY

The established definition of this word is "in a short time, soon." The current tendency to use it for *now* or *at present* is questionable.

Correct: He will join us *presently*.
Doubtful: We are *presently* using the Baker system.
Correct: We are *now* using the Baker system.
Correct: *At present* we are using the Baker system.

PRINCIPAL, PRINCIPLE

Principal, which is used as both noun and adjective, has the meaning of "chief person, chief amount," or as an adjective, simply "chief." *Principle,* which should never be used to modify a noun after it, means "the underlying idea."

They have paid back about half of the *principal.*
The high cost of upkeep is my *principal* objection.
He explained the *principle* of its operation.

REASON IS (WAS) BECAUSE

There is still a good deal of opposition to this construction. It is based on the ground that *because* should introduce only an adverb clause and that what follows here has the function of a subjective complement and is therefore a noun clause. Such being the case, *that* is preferable to *because*.

> Questionable: One reason for their success *is because* they offer attractive credit terms.
>
> Better: One reason for their success *is that* they offer attractive credit terms.

SELDOM EVER

Ever is redundant.

SERVE, SERVICE

Although these words are often used interchangeably, it is probably better to use *serve* in the sense of "render service" and *service,* when a verb, in the sense of "make or keep ready for service."

> The power plant *serves* most of the valley.
>
> The machine is *serviced* every two months.

SET, SIT

Apart from a few idiomatic uses, *set* means "to put." *Sit* means "to rest."

> They used a 2-ton pulley to *set* the compressor on its base.
>
> The compressor *sits* on a concrete base.

SEWAGE, SEWER, SEWERAGE

Sewage is the waste products themselves. A *sewer* is a pipe that carries off water and sewage. *Sewerage* is a system of such pipes.

SHALL, WILL

The original distinction between these words is still generally observed.

To indicate simple expectation, *shall* is used when the subject is *I* or *we; will* when the subject is any other word.

To indicate determination or an order, the usage is reversed: *will* is used when the subject is *I* or *we; shall* when the subject is any other word.

> Barring an accident, *we shall* finish by the end of the month.
>
> *You will* find that the company is a progressive one.
>
> *Trucks will* be used to haul the gravel.

We will not tolerate habitual absenteeism.

You shall report any violation immediately.

Employees shall not transact personal business on company time.

SHAPE

The use of this word in the sense of "condition" or "state" is always colloquial and sometimes ambiguous.

SIT

See *Set.*

SOME

Some is acceptable as an adverb only with the meaning of "approximately." It should not be substituted for *somewhat.*

Correct: We are short *some* 30 men.

Unacceptable: Sales are *some* better this month.

Correct: Sales are *somewhat* better this month.

SOMEPLACE

Not recognized as a word. *Somewhere* is the proper form.

SORT OF

Correct when used as a noun followed by a preposition but incorrect when used as an adverb. The article *a* or *an* is unnecessary after the *of.*

Correct: This *sort of* weather is unsuitable for outdoor work.

Incorrect: He was *sort of* surprised by the information.

Correct: He was *rather* (or: *somewhat*) surprised by the information.

THERE

For a discussion of *there* used as the subject of a clause, see pages 11-12.

THUS CAUSING

See *Causing.*

THUSLY

Thus is an adverb; hence, *ly* is superfluous.

TRY AND, TRY TO

The older idiom is *try to,* and though *try and* is widely used, many people regard it as a colloquialism.

Open to question: They will *try and* reach a decision next week.

Accepted: They will *try to* reach a decision next week.

TYPE

As it stands, this word is a noun or a verb and not an adjective. Accordingly, it should not modify another noun, which is the case when *of* is omitted between it and a following noun.

Questionable: We plan to use a new *type* cooler.

Correct: We plan to use a new *type of* cooler.

Type should not be used indiscriminately; often *kind, sort, variety, species,* or *class* expresses the meaning better.

No *a* or *an* is needed after *of.*

Type is sometimes the second component in a compound word, and in this form it can be used as an adjective.

The vibration is absorbed by a *coil-type* spring.

UNINTERESTED, DISINTERESTED

See *Disinterested.*

UPCOMING

A needless intensive of *coming.*

Questionable: We are ready for the *upcoming* tests.

Acceptable: We are ready for the *coming* tests.

We are ready for the *approaching* tests.

We are ready for *next week's* tests.

USAGE, USE

Though *usage* does mean "use," the best practice is to reserve it to describe long-established use.

Correct: I do not recommend the *use* of acids.

Correct: The machine has had little *use.*

Correct: The machine broke down because of hard *usage.*

USE, UTILIZE

Use is "to employ for a given purpose." *Utilize* is more restricted in meaning: "to put a thing to profitable service, usually by developing its latent possibilities."

Oil will be *used* as the lubricant.

We are searching for a way to *utilize* the sawdust.

VERY

A badly overworked word. It should not be carelessly used to intensify an adjective or adverb that either is forceful in itself or has a stronger synonym.

Superfluous: He considers the proposal *very* ridiculous.
Superfluous: He has done a *very* excellent job.
Poor diction: The wheels turned *very* fast.
Better: The wheels turned *rapidly*.

WHILE

A weak and sometimes ambiguous substitute for *although, and, but,* or *whereas.*

Questionable: *While* we are working around the clock, we shall not make up all the lost time.
Correct: *Although* we are working around the clock, we shall not make up all the lost time.
Questionable: The walls are green *while* the ceiling is white.
Correct: The walls are green *and* the ceiling is white.
Questionable: The shop closes at four o'clock *while* the office works until five.
Correct: The shop closes at four o'clock *but* (or: *whereas*) the office works until five.

WILL, SHALL

See *Shall.*

WITH

This preposition should not be used to introduce a second idea that merits as much attention as the one preceding it.

Incorrect: The heat is increased gradually *with* a corresponding rise in pressure.
Correct: The heat is increased gradually, *and there is* a corresponding rise in pressure.

GRAMMATICAL TERMS

The terms listed here are used in the preceding text. In some cases they are defined there; in others, they are not.

Adjective. A word that describes or limits a substantive. See pages 267-269.

Adjective clause. See Clause.

Adverb. A word that describes or limits a verb, an adjective, another adverb, a clause or a phrase used like an adverb, or a sentence. See pages 267-269.

Adverb clause. See Clause.

Antecedent. The noun for which a pronoun substitutes or which an appositive renames.

> The *men* have done *their* work well. (*Men* is the antecedent of the pronoun *their.*)
> The two *foremen, Wells and Petersen,* are not in agreement. (*Foremen* is the antecedent of the appositive *Wells and Petersen.*)

Appositive. A substantive, together with its modifiers, that follows and renames another substantive without the two being connected by a verb. In effect, an appositive is a condensed clause.

> The site is near Brigadoon Forest, *a new housing development.* (As a clause: The site is near Brigadoon Forest, which is a new housing development.)
> The wall was built during the reign of William *the Conqueror.* (As a clause: The wall was built during the reign of William who was called the Conqueror.)

Auxiliary verb. A verb that helps form the tense, voice, or mood of other verbs. Examples are *be, can, do, have, must, shall, will.*

> The plans *have been* drawn.

Case. The relationship of a noun, pronoun, or adjective to other words as shown by its form or its position. See pages 259-262.

Clause. A group of words having both a verb and a subject of that verb.

> An *independent,* or main, *clause* makes sense alone. It is literally independent in that no other element is needed for it to be a sentence.

The western entrance of the tunnel will be at Seventh Street.

A *dependent,* or subordinate, *clause* does not make sense alone. It has both a verb and a subject, but an independent clause must be in the sentence for it to depend on.

We must run more tests *because our present data are inconclusive.*

Dependent clauses are subject to further classification according to their use.

An *adjective clause* functions like an adjective by modifying a substantive.

Britton, *who has been with the company 35 years,* will retire on June 30.

An *adverb clause* functions like an adverb by modifying a verb, an adjective, or another adverb.

The forms should not be removed *until the concrete has set.*

A *noun clause* functions like a noun by serving as the subject or the object of a verb or the object of a preposition.

At the very beginning we realized *that we had underestimated the cost.*

In an *elliptical clause* the subject and the verb, or part of the verb if it is compound, are omitted.

Although ill, he continued to work.

We damaged the timer *while removing the shield.*

Complement. An element that in its normal position follows the verb and completes the statement.

An *objective complement* may be either an adjective that follows and modifies the direct object or a noun that follows and means the same thing as the direct object.

Adjective: The results have left us *uncertain.*

Noun: He has made wages the first *subject* for discussion.

A *subjective complement,* also called a predicate adjective or a predicate noun, is either an adjective that follows the verb and modifies the subject or a noun that follows the verb and means the same thing as the subject.

Adjective: An auxiliary pump will be *necessary.*

Noun: Tulsa is an oil-producing *center.*

See also Direct object and Indirect object, both of which are complements.

Conjunction. A word that joins words, phrases, or clauses. Coordinating conjunctions give equal value to the elements they connect.

Subordinating conjunctions introduce a dependent clause and show its relationship to an independent clause.

Co-ordinating conjunctions: and, but, for, or, nor. There is an increasing tendency to include *so, yet,* and *whereas* in the group.

Subordinating conjunctions (partial list): *although, as, because, before, if, since, when, whether, while.*

Conjunctive adverb. An adverb used as a conjunction to show the relationship between two ideas. The principal ones are *accordingly, consequently, furthermore, hence, however, moreover, nevertheless, still* (when it means "nevertheless"), and *then* (when it means "therefore").

Dependent clause. See Clause.

Direct object. A word, phrase, or clause that receives the action of a verb.

He roundly criticized the *suggestion.*

Elliptical clause. See Clause.

Gender. The classification of a noun or a pronoun with regard to sex or the lack of it.

Masculine: man, host, he, his, him
Feminine: woman, hostess, she, hers, her
Neuter: mountain, industry, slide rule, it, its

Gerund. The *ing* form of a verb used as a noun.

Building the caisson is our first job.

Also see Phrase.

Idiom. An accepted grammatical construction that has been established through usage rather than on the basis of grammar or logic.

He is *opposed to* the plan.

Not: He is *opposed against* the plan.

They *took steps* immediately to eliminate the trouble.

Not: They *made steps* immediately to eliminate the trouble.

Independent clause. See Clause.

Indirect object. A word or clause that receives a direct object but is not connected to it by a preposition.

They have made *me* a good offer.

Infinitive. The form of the verb that is used after *to* and the *to* when it is present, though in modern English the *to* is often omitted.

He asked us *to return* the drawings.

We shall *return* the drawings tomorrow if our draftsmen can *finish* the copies by then.

Also see Phrase.

Modifier.   A word, phrase, or clause that limits the meaning of another word, phrase, or clause.

The *storage* tank *together with the piping* will cost $12,000 *if it is built of aluminum.*

Storage is an adjective modifying *tank. Together with the piping* is a prepositional phrase modifying *tank. If it is built of aluminum* is an adverb clause modifying *cost.*

Mood.   The form of a verb that shows whether the action or state it denotes is a fact, a possibility, or a command.

Indicative (denoting a fact): The demand *is* greater than the supply.

Subjunctive (denoting a possibility): If the demand *were* greater than the supply, the price *would be* higher.

Imperative (denoting command): *Close* the switch and *record* the readings.

Nonrestrictive material.   See page 272.

Noun.   A word that names something, such as a person, a place, an object, an emotion, or a color.

Noun clause.   See Clause.

Number.   The distinction in form that shows whether a word refers to one thing or more.

Singular number refers to only one.

The *man understands* what *he is* to do in *this room.*

Plural number is used for two or more.

The *men understand* what *they are* to do in *these rooms.*

Object.   The object of a preposition is a word, phrase, or clause that follows the preposition and the preposition joins to another word.

He gave most of his *time* to *auditing the books.*

Also see Direct object and Indirect object.

Objective complement.   See Complement.

Participle.   The verb form that functions partially or wholly as an adjective.

The *present participle* ends in *ing*.

> He is *speaking* at a banquet tonight.
> He has a *speaking* engagement tonight.

The *past participle* is the form that follows the auxiliary verb *have* and sometimes *be*.

> The cables have *broken*.
> The cables are *broken*.
> The *broken* cables will cause a delay.

Also see Phrase.

Person. The distinction in a pronoun and a verb that shows whether the subject of discussion is the speaker (writer), the listener (reader), or somebody else or some thing.

First person is the speaker and, if plural, those grouped with him: I am, we are.

Second person is the listener and, if plural, those grouped with him: you are, you are.

Third person is who or what is being spoken about if it is not the speaker or the listener: he is, she is, it is, they are.

Phrase. A group of words lacking either a subject or a verb or both.

A *gerund phrase* consists of a gerund and the words related to it, such as its subject, object, and modifiers.

> *Your notifying us ahead of time* will be helpful.

An *infinitive phrase* is an infinitive and the words related to it, such as its subject, object, and modifiers.

> We asked *him to read the paragraph again*.

A *participial phrase* is a participle and the words related to it, such as its object and modifiers. The phrase functions as an adjective to describe a noun or a pronoun.

> *Examining the thermocouple more closely,* I discovered that it was cracked.

A *prepositional phrase* is a preposition and its object plus any modifiers of the object.

> We proceeded *to the nitrate house*.

Predicate. The part of a clause having the verb, its complement, and their modifiers.

> If we *hire a consultant,* we *shall probably save time*.

Preposition. A word that connects a noun, a pronoun, or a noun clause to another element.

> They sent catalogues *to* whoever wrote *for* them.

Also see Phrase.

Pronoun.   A word used as a substitute for a noun. See pages 260-264.

Restrictive material.   See pages 272-273.

Stem.   The root word to which a prefix or a suffix is added or, with infinitives, before which the *to* is placed.

    re*build*   *build*ing   to *build*

Subject.   The word or group of words that name the topic which a verb or a verbal concerns.

                Subject of a verb: *They* found that the *trouble* was in the fan belt.

            Subject of a gerund: I appreciate *your* giving us first choice.

          Subject of an infinitive: He told the *men* to wait.

When the subject is *you,* it is frequently left to inference.

    (*You*) Make out an invoice for each lot.

Subjective complement.   See Complement.

Substantive.   A noun or any other element that functions like a noun. Such an element can be a pronoun, a gerund, an infinitive, or a noun clause.

Tense.   The time indicated by the form of a verb. See pages 266-267.

Verb.   A word that asserts action or indicates a state of existence.

    He *reports* that the situation *is* good.

Verbal.   A verb form that, even when it has a subject, cannot assert a complete action or state of existence. English has three verbals: infinitive, gerund, and participle.

Voice.   The form of a verb that shows the relationship between the verb and its subject.

    The *active voice* is used when the subject does the acting.

    A donkey engine *lifts* the bucket to the deck.

    The *passive voice* is used when the subject receives the action.

    The bucket *is lifted* to the deck by a donkey engine.

Appendix

APPENDIX

Abbreviations for Scientific and Engineering Terms

The American Standards Association has compiled the following list in an attempt to standardize the abbreviation of scientific and engineering terms.[1] The extent to which a writer draws on it should be governed by his readers' familiarity with the terms.

absolute.................. abs
acre................. spell out
acre-foot............... acre-ft
air horsepower...........air hp
alternating-current (as
    adjective)............... a-c
ampere.................. amp
ampere-hour........... amp-hr
amplitude, an elliptic function.. am.
Angstrom unit...............A
antilogarithm............ antilog
atmosphere............... atm
atomic weight.............at. wt
average.................. avg
avoirdupois.............. avdp
azimuth............... az or a

barometer................ bar.
barrel.................... bbl
Baumé................... Bé
board feet (feet board
    measure)............... fbm
boiler pressure.........spell out
boiling point............... bp
brake horsepower.......... bhp

brake horsepower-hour.... bhp-hr
Brinell hardness number..... Bhn
British thermal unit...... Btu or B
bushel.................... bu

calorie.................... cal
candle.................... c
candle-hour............... c-hr
candlepower............... cp
cent.................... c or ¢
center to center...........c to c
centigram................. cg
centiliter................. cl
centimeter................ cm
centimeter-gram-second
    (system)................ cgs
chemical................. chem
chemically pure............. cp
circular................... cir
circular mils.............cir mils
coefficient................ coef
cologarithm.............. colog
concentrate.............. conc
conductivity.............. cond

---

[1] Extracted from American Standards Association, Abbreviations for Scientific and Engineering Terms, Z10. 1—1941 with the permission of the publisher, The American Society of Mechanical Engineers.

constant................. const
continental horsepower....cont hp
cord..................... cd
cosecant................. csc
cosine................... cos
cosine of the amplitude, an
    elliptic function............ cn
cost, insurance, and freight.... cif
cotangent................. cot
coulomb...............spell out
counter electromotive force.. cemf
cubic..................... cu
cubic centimeter......cu cm, cm³
    (liquid, meaning milliliter, ml)
cubic foot................ cu ft
cubic feet per minute........ cfm
cubic feet per second......... cfs
cubic inch............... cu in.
cubic meter.......... cu m or m³
cubic micron..cu μ or cu mu or μ³
cubic millimeter...cu mm or mm³
cubic yard............... cu yd
current density..........spell out
cycles per second....spell out or c
cylinder................. cyl

day................. spell out
decibel.................... db
degree............... deg or °
degree centigrade............ C
degree Fahrenheit............ F
degree Kelvin................ K
degree Réaumur............. R
delta amplitude, an elliptic
    function................. dn
diameter................ diam
direct-current (as adjective)...d-c
dollar..................... $
dozen.................... doz
dram..................... dr

efficiency.................. eff
electric................... elec
electromotive force......... emf
elevation................... el
equation................... eq
external................... ext

farad............. spell out or f
feet board measure (board
    feet).................. fbm
feet per minute........... fpm
feet per second............. fps
fluid....................... fl
foot....................... ft
foot-candle............... ft-c
foot-Lambert.............. ft-L
foot-pound............... ft-lb
foot-pound-second (system)... fps
foot-second (see cubic feet per
    second)
franc..................... fr
free aboard ship........ spell out
free alongside ship...... spell out
free on board.............. fob
freezing point.............. fp
frequency............. spell out
fusion point............... fnp

gallon..................... gal
gallons per minute.......... gpm
gallons per second.......... gps
grain................. spell out
gram....................... g
gram-calorie.............. g-cal
greatest common divisor...... gcd

haversine.................. hav
hectare.................... ha
henry....................... h
high-pressure (adjective)..... h-p
hogshead.................. hhd

horsepower................ hp
horsepower-hour.......... hp-hr
hour...................... hr
hour (in astronomical tables)....h
hundred................... C
hundredweight (112 lb)...... cwt
hyperbolic cosine.......... cosh
hyperbolic sine............ sinh
hyperbolic tangent......... tanh

inch...................... in.
inch-pound............... in-lb
inches per second........... ips
indicated horsepower....... ihp
indicated horsepower-hour.. ihp-hr
inside diameter............. ID
intermediate-pressure
   (adjective)............... i-p
internal................... int

joule...................... j

kilocalorie............... kcal
kilocycles per second........ kc
kilogram.................. kg
kilogram-calorie.......... kg-cal
kilogram-meter............ kg-m
kilograms per cubic meter..kg per
   cu m or kg/m³
kilograms per second....... kgps
kiloliter................... kl
kilometer................. km
kilometers per second...... kmps
kilovolt................... kv
kilovolt-ampere............ kva
kilowatt.................. kw
kilowatthour............. kwhr

lambert................... L
latitude................ lat or φ
least common multiple...... lcm

linear foot............... lin ft
liquid.................... liq
lira.................. spell out
liter....................... l
logarithm (common)........ log
logarithm (natural).... log. or ln
longitude.............long. or λ
low-pressure (as adjective).... l-p
lumen...................... l
lumen-hour................ l-hr
lumens per watt............ lpw

mass.................. spell out
mathematics (ical)......... math
maximum................. max
mean effective pressure...... mep
mean horizontal candle-
   power................ mhcp
megacycle............. spell out
megohm.............. spell out
melting point............... mp
meter...................... m
meter-kilogram............ m-kg
mho.................. spell out
microampere........ μa or mu a
microfarad.................. μf
microinch................. μin.
micromicrofarad............ μμf
micromicron....... μμ or mu mu
micron............... μ or mu
microvolt.................. μv
microwatt......... μw or mu w
mile.................. spell out
miles per hour............. mph
miles per hour per second.. mphps
milliampere................ ma
milligram................. mg
millihenry................. mh
millilambert............... mL
milliliter.................. ml
millimeter................. mm

millimicron......... mμ or m mu
million.............. spell out
million gallons per day...... mgd
millivolt................... mv
minimum................ min
minute................. min
minute (angular measure)...... ′
minute (time) (in astronomical
   tables)................... m
mole................ spell out
molecular weight........ mol. wt
month............... spell out

National Electrical Code.... NEC

ohm.............. spell out or Ω
ohm-centimeter......... ohm-cm
ounce..................... oz
ounce-foot............... oz-ft
ounce-inch............... oz-in.
outside diameter........... OD

parts per million.......... ppm
peck.................... pk
penny (pence)............... d
pennyweight.............. dwt
peso................. spell out
pint..................... pt
potential............. spell out
potential difference...... spell out
pound.................... lb
pound-foot................ lb-ft
pound-inch.............. lb-in.
pound sterling............... £
pounds per brake horse-
   power-hour...... lb per bhp-hr
pounds per cubic foot.. lb per cu ft
pounds per square foot....... psf
pounds per square inch....... psi
pounds per square inch

absolute................ psia
power factor...... spell out or pf

quart..................... qt

radian................ spell out
reactive kilovolt-ampere.... kvar
reactive volt-ampere......... var
revolutions per minute...... rpm
revolutions per second........ rps
rod................. spell out
root mean square........... rms

secant.................... sec
second................... sec
second (angular measure)..... ″
second-foot (see cubic feet per
   second)
second (time) (in astronomical
   tables)................... s
shaft horsepower........... shp
shilling..................... s
sine..................... sin
sine of the amplitude, an
   elliptic function........... sn
specific gravity........... sp gr
specific heat............. sp ht
spherical candle power...... scp
square.................... sq
square centimeter... sq cm or cm^2
square foot.............. sq ft
square inch.............. sq in.
square kilometer.... sq km or km^2
square meter......... sq m or m^2
square micron..sq μ or sq mu or μ^2
square millimeter..sq mm or mm^2
square root of mean square.. rms
standard.................. std
stere..................... s

tangent	tan	volt-ampere	va
temperature	temp	volt-coulomb	spell out
tensile strength	ts		
thousand	M	watt	w
thousand foot-pounds	kip-ft	watthour	whr
thousand pound	kip	watts per candle	wpc
ton	spell out	week	spell out
ton-mile	spell out	weight	wt
versed sine	vers	yard	yd
volt	v	year	yr

Index